The Mammals of Essex

This book is dedicated to all those people whose observations have contributed to a better understanding of the status and distribution of the mammals of Essex

Badger Earth in Epping Forest.

Frontispiece. An illustration from Laver's 1898 book *The Mammals, Reptiles and Fishes of Essex*. Just over a century later, the present book traces the changing fortunes of the mammals of Essex. The signs of this badger sett are still visible in Epping Forest but the last badgers were seen there in the 1960s. Today in many areas of Essex, badgers are more common than in Laver's time.

The Mammals of Essex

by

John Dobson

Published by Lopinga Books
Tye Green House, Wimbish, GB-Essex, CB10 2XE

In association with, and in support of the work of, the
Essex Field Club and Essex Wildlife Trust

With financial support from the Corporation of the City of London,
Environment Agency, English Nature,
Essex & Suffolk Water Company and GlaxoWellcome UK

First published 1999

ISBN 0-9530362-1-9

British Library Cataloguing-in-Publication Data
A catalogue record for this book is available from the British Library

Printed by Healeys Printers Ltd,
Unit 10, The Sterling Complex, Farthing Road, Ipswich IP1 5AP

The *Nature of Essex Series* No. 2

Contents

Foreword

As a young mammalogist in Essex, I relied heavily on Henry Laver's 1898 monograph on *The Mammals, Reptiles and Fishes of Essex*. This was still the most comprehensive and up-to-date account of the mammals of Essex, and was an invaluable source of information. In particular, Laver made me appreciate the great changes that can occur in our mammal fauna, often in a very short period of time. Laver, for instance, reported that badgers were so scarce that most people only knew of them from hearsay from a previous generation, pine martens were still occasionally seen in Epping Forest, polecats had been common but were becoming rare, water voles were very common, and so on.

Having relied so heavily on Laver's work, it is a great pleasure to write a foreword to John Dobson's *The Mammals of Essex*. Without the efforts of people like Henry Laver and John Dobson, significant changes in the biodiversity of Essex would go either unnoticed or unrecorded. Quantifying and understanding change is important because it is the foundation of conservation; we can only implement effective conservation measures once we know what changes are occurring, and why they are occurring.

Comparing Henry Laver's and John Dobson's reviews makes fascinating reading. There are more species of mammal in Essex today than in Laver's time. Laver did not record some bats and there are several new species of invasive aliens. Understanding their impact on the local ecology will be a key aim for Essex mammalogists over the next few years. As John Dobson says, "*Essex mammals matter*". More than any other group, changes in mammal populations have a big impact on the overall biodiversity of an area. Changes in the numbers of deer and rabbits matter because they have a big impact on the local flora, as is all too obvious in some woodlands in north Essex. Changes in small mammal abundance matter because this affects both the numbers and breeding success of many predatory birds. Changes in the numbers of predators such as foxes matter because this can have a big impact on the breeding success of rare ground-nesting birds.

Yet we should also remember that mammals have great intrinsic value. For instance, Essex is one of the most heavily urbanised counties in Britain. For many urban residents, the appearance of foxes in their gardens in the post-war period was a major source of enjoyment. Similarly, south-east Essex is famous for its urban badger population, and these have featured in many films and magazine articles. With ever-greater urbanisation throughout Britain, the changes seen in the Essex mammal fauna will be repeated in many counties in years to come.

In the century since Laver's monograph, there have been great advances in our knowledge about mammals. Collating all this new information has been a massive undertaking; John Dobson has done an outstanding job and *The Mammals of Essex* will be a standard reference for many years to come. Besides documenting the current distribution of each species and providing a comprehensive overview of the status of Essex mammals, there is an extensive discussion of the factors leading to the observed population changes and detailed plans for the conservation of Biodiversity Action Plan species. In recent years, The Mammal Society has been encouraging local mammal recording and the production of county mammal reports. John Dobson has set a standard that will be hard to follow. Let's hope that he achieves one of his key goals, to stimulate more mammal work in Essex, so that we do not have to wait another hundred years before the next update.

Professor Stephen Harris
Chairman, The Mammal Society
15 Cloisters House, 8 Battersea Park Road, London, SW8 4BG

Acknowledgements

A large number of people and organisations have contributed to this atlas and I am grateful to them for their support.

I am especially indebted to Gerald Lucy for contributing an excellent article on fossil mammals.

The illustrations for this book were drawn by Richard Allen, George Brown, John Cox, Alan Harris and Richard Hull – an exceptionally talented team to whom I am particularly grateful.

Many historical records were obtained from the Essex Biological Records Centres based at the county's museums. John Skinner and Roger Payne at Southend, Jerry Heath at Colchester and Dr Tony Walentowicz at Chelmsford all gave up their time to assist this project.

Clive Herbert, the mammal recorder for the London Natural History Society exchanged records for metropolitan Essex where the recording boundary overlaps between Essex and Greater London. Jeff Martin, the mammal recorder for Suffolk, provided records for north-east Essex and the Suffolk border

Thanks are also due to Dr Jeremy Dagley and Amanda Samuels, ecologists with the Corporation of London for supplying records and historical data for Epping Forest.

Many records of small mammals were obtained from the analysis of owl pellets. Since 1994, R. Alasdair Love has analysed more than 8,000 barn owl pellets from Essex, three-quarters of which have been collected by Robert Harvey. My thanks go to both for this important source of records.

Dr Derek Yalden kindly supplied archaeological records of Essex mammals from his recently-published *The History of British Mammals.*

I am grateful for the guidance of experts who commented on early drafts of the species accounts. Martin Sheldrick (cetaceans), Tony Hutson (bats), Dr Chris Mason (mink and otter), Dr Tony Mitchell-Jones (small mammals), Norma Chapman (deer) and Dr Chris Gibson (other species and introductory chapters) all gave their time (and patience) freely, which is greatly appreciated. In addition, Martin Sheldrick generously gave me access to his records of stranded cetaceans; Dr Chris Mason provided many records of otter and mink gained through his survey work in Essex.

Janet Spencer and Gillian Thompson of the Essex Wildlife Trust made records from the Trust's reserves available and also shared the results of both the Essex Water Vole Survey of 1998 and the ongoing survey of dormice in ancient woodland.

All records were entered onto the RECORDIT database, devised by Mike Weideli. The maps were generated using the DMAP software package created by Dr Alan

Morton. Both offered advice during this project that is gratefully acknowledged. The Essex county boundary used for the distribution maps was compiled by Peter Harvey.

Finally I should like to thank my family for their assistance and patience during the five years of this project; in particular, Richard Dobson, who corrected many 'first drafts'. Without their support, this atlas would not have been completed.

List of observers

The Mammals of Essex is the result of the observations of many people but I would particularly like to thank Geoff Gibbs, Julian and Susie Torino, Sue Ward and Alf Gudgion for their commitment to this project. I apologise to any observer whose name I have inadvertently omitted from this list.

M. Allen
S. Anthony
R. Arthur
G. Bailey
J. Balaam
C-A. Banwell
I. Beech
E. Benton
K. Biggins
I. Black
J. Bowdrey
D. Bradshaw
J. Bucknell
N. Chapman
D. Clark
Alan Cook
Andrew Cook
D. Corke
E. Corke
R. Cottrill
J. Cox
A. Dally
B. Dawson
M. Dennis
M. Drake
A. Duffield
G. Duncan
B. Eastcott
G. Ekins
S. Flanders
J. Flowerdew
P. Fontaine
V. Forbes
A. Ford
L. Forsyth
P. Fox
S. Fox
J. Gamble
K. Gash
R.G. Gibbs
C. Gibson
P. Giddings
D. Gomer
W. Gray
J. Greenwood
M. Gregory
A. Gudgion
T. Gunton
C. Hall
R. Hart
M. Harvey
N. Harvey
R. Harvey
R. Hawes
A. Heath
J. Heath
R. Heathfield
C. Herbert
R. Hills
K. Hine
S. Hudgell
D. Hunford
J. Ireland
J. Jarmy
S. Jiggins
J. Jopling
J. Kaye
J. Keeliher
M. Lake
S. Leatherdale
R. Leavett
J. Little
P. Luke
S. Macdonald
R. Marsh
J. Martin
C. Mason
S. Massey
P. Massini
B. McGhie
J. McKenna
F. Mundy
D. Nicholls
R. Payne
J. Pepper
S. Perry
C. Plant
E. Potter
H. Ransom
C. Rawlings
J. Ridgewell
M. Robinson
J. Rostron
M. Rowley
J. Ruffell
R. Ruffell
A. Sadgrove
A. Sapsford
P. Saunders
R. Seago
J. Skinner
G. Smith
J. Smith
P. Smith
R. Smith
J. Spencer
C. Swan
K. Swan
R. Tabor
C. Taylor
W. Thomas
G. Thompson
C. Thurlow
J. Torino
S. Torino
B. Turnpenny
C. Tyas
S. Ward
C. Watson
L. Watts
L. Wells
S. White
P. Wilson
N. Wood
R. Wood
D. Wright
J. Wright
M. Wright.

Records were also obtained from the following organisations:

Bradwell Bird Observatory
Epping Forest Conservation Centre
Epping Forest Conservators
Essex Badger Protection Group
Essex Wildlife Trust
Hainault Forest Country Park
Highwoods Country Park
London Bat Group
London Natural History Society
London Wildlife Trust
North-East Essex Badger Group
Old Hall Marshes RSPB Reserve
South Woodham Ferrers Natural History Society
Stour Wood RSPB Reserve.

Sponsors

I am grateful to the organisations that provided financial support for this project:

The Corporation of London is the local authority for the City of London, the financial and commercial heart of Britain. However, its responsibilities extend far beyond the City boundaries and it provides a host of additional facilities for the benefit of the nation. Included amongst these is its protection of open spaces in and around London, such as Hampstead Heath, Ashtead Common, Burnham Beeches and, the largest of all, Epping Forest, straddling the borders of Essex and London. The Corporation saved Epping Forest from destruction by developments and the resulting Epping Forest Act of 1878 constituted the Corporation of London members as Conservators of Epping Forest and invested the Corporation with legal powers and duties as the owner of and managing body for the Forest. Today, the Corporation, through its Epping Forest and Open Spaces Committee, oversees the management of all the open spaces, details of which are set out in comprehensive published management plans for each area.

English Nature is the statutory adviser to Government on nature conservation in England and promotes the conservation of England's wildlife and natural features. Its work includes selecting, establishing and managing National Nature Reserves; identifying, notifying and protecting Sites of Special Scientific Interest; providing advice and information about nature conservation, and supporting and carrying out research relevant to these functions. A major part of English Nature's work is devoted to developing and implementing Biodiversity Action Plans, at the national and local level. English Nature leads on the action plans for 59 of the 116 species identified as threatened and declining in the UK, and works to safeguard these populations and enhance the habitats which support them.

The Environment Agency has a wide range of duties and powers relating to environmental management and improvement in the quality of air, land and water.

Part of this responsibility is to encourage the conservation of natural resources, animals and plants. As part of the government's UK Biodiversity Action Plan, the Agency is the contact point for 12 species of aquatic animal and plant including the otter and water vole. In Essex, we have undertaken collaborative surveys of these species to determine their extent in the county.

Essex & Suffolk Water is committed to conducting the business of water supply in a sustainable manner throughout, what is, the driest region in the UK. There is an

intense competition between environmental needs and social demands for water, so to balance these criteria, Essex & Suffolk Water works in close liaison with local wildlife trusts, the Environment Agency and English Nature in all its projects. These include the development of a 100 acre reserve and the building of a visitor centre in partnership with Essex Wildlife Trust at Hanningfield Reservoir which opens in 2000, and the successful management of key habitats at sites like Lound, Abberton Reservoir and Ormesby Broad.

GlaxoWellcome is a research-based company whose people are committed to fighting disease by bringing innovative medicines and services to patients

GlaxoWellcome

throughout the world and to the healthcare providers who serve them.

As one of Britain's largest companies GlaxoWellcome also believes that it has a responsibility to the communities in which it operates. The company has a long tradition of supporting education, the arts and the environment on a national and local level, and its support for this book is part of its programme of responsible corporate citizenship.

I began this project at 7.30am on the 1st January 1994. An annual event to record as many bird species as possible on New Year's Day started in Tollesbury; the walk out to Shinglehead Point produced not only the usual birds but also rabbit, brown hare, field vole, fox and weasel. Grey squirrel and common rat were seen later in the day and, more surprisingly, a pipistrelle flying in daylight at Thorpe-le-Soken. I took notes of all the birds observed during the day, but who would be interested in the mammals? Since mammal recording in Essex had faltered some years previously, I decided to write down the details – species, 6-figure grid reference, date and circumstance – hoping that the records would be of value in the future. As more species of mammal were recorded during subsequent days, I decided to begin a mammal atlas and visited the distant corners of the county. Fields were scanned with binoculars and road casualties examined, methods that soon provided provisional maps of mainly the most visible species such as mole, rabbit, brown hare, grey squirrel and deer. It soon became apparent that a county-wide survey would need as much support as possible, and friends were coaxed and cajoled to record mammals while birdwatching or walking in the countryside. After three years, 6,000 records had been obtained and the success of the project was guaranteed. Further fieldwork, concentrating on gaps in the distribution of several species, took place until the middle of 1999 and the compilation of this volume began.

For the last hundred years, Essex mammals have been neglected. Although the latter part of the 20th century has seen the publication of a county flora and avifauna, breeding bird atlas and, most recently, atlases of butterflies and grasshoppers, it was in 1898 that Henry Laver wrote *The Mammals, Fishes and Reptiles of Essex.* For mammals, this remains the most recent definitive work. Since Laver's time, the level of interest in mammals has varied. The Essex Field Club (the premier society of county naturalists) has always had an appointed mammal recorder and reports of Essex mammals have appeared in its publications since 1880, with additional records held in the archives of the county's museums.

Perhaps the most productive decade for the study of Essex mammals was the 1970s, when reviews of badgers, deer, squirrels and small mammals in Essex were all published (Cowlin, 1972; Chapman, 1977; Harris, 1973/74 and Corke & Harris, 1972). In the 1980s, specialist groups such as the Essex Bat Group and three badger groups (covering all areas of the county) were formed to look after the conservation needs of these species; the status and distribution of bats has been published annually in the *Essex Bat Group Report.* For the other species, Essex Field Club recorders have ensured that county records have contributed to provisional atlases of British mammals produced by the Institute of Terrestrial Ecology in 1978 and 1984, as well as the latest *Atlas of Mammals in Britain* published in 1993 by the Natural Environment Research Council.

The first county mammal atlas was published in 1986 (Hughes, 1986), in collaboration with the three Essex Biological Records Centres based at Southend, Colchester and Passmore Edwards Museums. The purpose of this 1986 provisional atlas was to present distribution maps and to act as a catalyst for further recording, leading to the publication of a more comprehensive review. Thirteen years later, the second aim has been achieved.

The objectives of this latest volume are threefold. Firstly, it details those mammals that have occurred in the county (from pre-history to the present day), including distribution maps and comment on all species that have been recorded in Essex during the last 200 years. Secondly, the status and distribution of several species has changed since Laver wrote his account; the current situation is contrasted with that of one hundred years ago. (In addition, much of the historical information recorded by Laver is peppered with anecdotes that deserve to be perpetuated – many are included herein). Lastly, it is hoped that this book will be a stimulus for yet more mammal recording, thereby adding to our knowledge of the mammals of Essex as we enter a new millennium. By the time you read these lines, this atlas will already be out of date. The Essex countryside is changing at an alarming rate and the need to monitor our mammals (and other wildlife) has never been greater.

Methodology

For the current survey, the majority of records were collected between 1994 and the middle of 1999 and mapped at a tetrad (2km × 2km square) level. A fuller description of those species for which historical records have been included occurs in the introduction to the species accounts. As the project progressed, it became apparent that four groups of species were emerging, separated by the nature of their recording – a phenomenon that has been reported elsewhere (Groupe Mammalogique Normand, 1988). The groups were:

- 'visible species': hedgehog, mole, rabbit, brown hare, squirrels, rats, all the carnivores and deer. Records of these species originated from road casualties, molehills, dreys, tracks, smell (fox), droppings and sightings of live animals
- 'small mammals': shrews, voles and mice; most records came from the analysis of owl pellets and Longworth trapping. A 'What the cat brought in' initiative, launched in the Essex Wildlife Trust journal and on BBC Essex, also generated a number of valuable reports
- 'bats', which were identified at night using a bat detector, in the hand (often following the discovery of an injured specimen) and from visits to both summer roosts and hibernation sites
- 'marine mammals', for which records included details of stranded cetaceans and sightings of live animals at sea.

Table 1.1 **Number of tetrads from which terrestrial mammal species have been recorded in Essex (Total number of tetrads = 1,074)**

Rank (national)	*Species*	*Number of tetrads*	*Rank (national)*	*Species*	*Number of tetrads*
1 (12)	grey squirrel	869	22= (42)	noctule	76
2 (1)	rabbit	742	22= (20)	pygmy shrew	76
3 (5)	fox	521	24 (23)	house mouse	75
4 (2)	mole	486	25 (47)	serotine	74
5 (3)	hedgehog	402	26 (40)	yellow-necked mouse	71
6 (7)	brown hare	366	27 (38)	Daubenton's bat	49
7 (13)	pipistrelle	350	28 (21)	mink	42
8 (4)	badger	334	29 (25)	water shrew	40
9 (15)	brown rat	329	30 (35)	common seal	35
10 (19)	water vole	235	31 (53)	Leisler's bat	33
11 (26)	harvest mouse	212	32 (37)	Natterer's bat	27
12 (14)	wood mouse	200	33 (36)	dormouse	25
13 (10)	weasel	191	34= (28)	grey seal	15
14 (8)	stoat	182	34= (17)	roe deer	16
15 (29)	brown long-eared bat	178	36 (24)	red deer	7
16 (11)	common shrew	164	37 (44)	ferret	4
17 (31)	muntjac	150	38 (61=)	parti-coloured bat	2
18 (18)	bank vole	141	39= (49)	ship rat	1
19 (27)	fallow deer	125	39= (39)	whiskered bat	1
20 (16)	field vole	121	39= (61=)	Nathusius' pipistrelle	1
21 (6)	otter	111	39= (51)	barbastelle	1

Although it is a measure of the relative difficulty in recording various species, this type of segmentation does not reflect the populations present in the county. Mice, voles and shrews are the most numerous species, but are seldom recorded due to their nocturnal and subterranean lifestyles. In contrast, a relatively comprehensive coverage has been achieved for many of the 'visible species' – more than 70% of all tetrad records have come from species in this group. This disparity can be demonstrated by a ranking list, tabling all the terrestrial species recorded during 1994–99 in descending order of the number of tetrads from which they have been recorded. The national ranking, based on the number of 10km squares from which a species has been recorded (Arnold, 1993), is also included – of the ten most frequently recorded mammal species in Essex, six are also in the top ten of the national list. 'Visible species' comprise eight of the top ten in the county, yet the most populous mammals – house mouse, common rat, pygmy shrew, bank vole, mole, rabbit, wood mouse, common shrew and field vole – are all estimated to have national pre-breeding populations in excess of 5,000,000 (Harris *et al.*, 1995). Only the common rat, mole and rabbit occur among the most frequently recorded species in Essex.

The high placings for water vole, harvest mouse and otter are the result of species-specific surveys – the low ranking of several small mammals is a measure of the difficulties of recording this group.

Species accounts

The chapters 5–11 record the status and distribution of all those mammals that have been recorded in the wild in Essex during the last 200 years. After some deliberation, species extinct in historical time were included in this section, rather than elsewhere in the volume, as the status of some has been subject to considerable change. Roe deer and otters were both extinct in Essex for part of the 20th century, yet are now recolonising the county: sadly, however, the larger bat species are now recorded less frequently than was the case fifteen years ago and may cease to be present during the next decades. The coypu and pine marten have, presumably, gone forever but the polecat, with recent records from Northamptonshire and Oxfordshire, would seem to be heading our way!

Each mammal is presented in a similar way – a brief biology of the species being followed by a historical review and details of the results of the current survey. The distribution maps include all records received between 1994 and mid-1999 with three exceptions. Bats have been recorded by the Essex Bat Group since 1981 and all sightings since that date are included. The account for the water vole includes observations made during a Breeding Bird Survey conducted by the National Rivers Authority (now Environment Agency) in 1991–92 and the successful findings of the Great Nut Hunt of 1993 have been included in the text for common dormouse.

For some species, historical as well as recent records, are mapped. This has been done for those species with few records (barbastelle, ship rat, cetaceans and red deer); for others where the status has changed (coypu, mink, otter and roe deer); and for the water shrew, so that the results of a county-wide bottle survey conducted in the 1970s might be included.

The taxonomic order, English and scientific names are after Corbet and Harris (1991). The recording unit is the 2km × 2km square (tetrad) based on the 10km square system of the Ordnance Survey's National Grid.

Results

Recent fieldwork and records from earlier literature have revealed that 61 species – 48 terrestrial and 13 cetaceans – have been recorded in Essex during the last 200 years. Of these, 51 species have occurred since 1980; many of the records have been collected since 1994. In comparison, 47 were recorded by Laver (1898) and 90 were recorded for the whole of the British Isles (excluding the Channel Islands) by Corbet and Harris (1991).

Table 1.2 **The numbers of mammal species recorded in Essex by Laver (1898), in Essex during the last 200 years and in the British Isles**

Order	*Laver (1898)*	*This volume (covering the last 200 years)*	*British Isles (excluding Channel Islands) Corbet & Harris (1991)*
insectivores	5	5	6
bats	8	12	17
lagomorphs	2	2	3
rodents	10	13	15
cetaceans	9	13	25
carnivores	7	9	10
seals	3	3	7
even-toed ungulates	3	4	7
Total	**47**	**61**	**90**

Changes since 1898

Some of the species that have been added to the Essex list during the last century have been introduced; others, particularly the bats, have been discovered following the development of improved identification skills, methods and criteria. The Leisler's bat was confirmed as an Essex species in 1949 and two migratory species – Nathusius' pipistrelle and parti-coloured bat – were recently added when greater awareness of their possible occurrence grew amongst bat workers. The fourth new species of bat was the result of the separation of the pipistrelle into two phonotypes as a result of ultrasound studies and DNA analysis.

Of the rodents, the yellow-necked mouse was discovered in Essex shortly after the publication of Laver's book and has now been found to be present in all but the built-up areas of the south-east and south-west of the county. The grey squirrel successfully colonised Essex following its first appearance in Gaynes Park in 1921 and the coypu was introduced (and subsequently eradicated) during the second half of the century. Sadly, the red squirrel was last recorded in 1972 – its decline coinciding with the spread of its larger American cousin.

The presence of cetaceans in the southern North Sea has become increasingly rare since Laver's time and, today, most records refer to stranded individuals that have reached Essex under the influence of offshore winds and currents. Of the new additions, the stranding of a narwhal at Rainham in 1949 was perhaps the most unexpected; the sighting of a humpback whale at Harwich in 1995 was the most intriguing. There have also been recent strandings of Sowerby's beaked whale and common dolphin; however, the sei whale has not been recorded during the last 50 years and the only record of Risso's dolphin is of one found stranded at Creeksea in 1885.

Two carnivores, the ferret and the mink, have recently been added to the county list. Whether the ferret is present as a self-sustaining feral population is uncertain; in contrast, the mink, although seldom seen, has now been recorded on most Essex rivers and is here to stay. A brief programme of trapping (with a view to eradicating the species) was conducted by MAFF during the 1960s; it was abandoned in 1970 when it became apparent that further spread was inevitable (Thompson, 1968).

The second most successful colonist (after the grey squirrel) is the muntjac. This small deer has achieved pest status in some Essex woodlands a mere 50 years after it was first recorded; it is now to be found in all but some coastal regions of the county.

It is interesting to speculate – but difficult to predict – which species will be recorded for the first time during the next few years. Perhaps the most likely are two species of bat. Brandt's bat (*Myotis brandtii*) is rarely recorded in south-east England, but there are recent reports from both Dartford (only one mile away!) and Hertfordshire. The second – Savi's pipistrelle (*Pipistrellus savii*) – is a migratory species that has been recorded in England on several occasions in recent years.

Changes in status

It has become apparent during the current study that much more information is required on the distribution of some species in order to make an informed comment regarding their status in the county. Stoats and weasels are rarely observed; water shrews and house mice seldom trapped; some larger species, such as roe deer, are under-recorded as a result of their secretive lifestyles. Species-specific surveys (often conducted by a small number of people) can make a substantial difference to our knowledge of the distribution of some species: the current status of the otter, for example, is largely based on the research of Drs C.F. Mason and S.M. MacDonald of the University of Essex. In the summer of 1998, a survey organised by the Environment Agency and the Essex Wildlife Trust produced many new records of water voles along the river catchments in the north of the county. Finally, a more random approach by the author, which involved searching suitable habitats for nests of the harvest mouse, identified 106 new sites during the autumn and early winter of 1998. Future projects could include a bottle survey for small mammals (water shrew in particular) and searching for the nests of dormice in ancient woodland.

***Table 1.3* Subjective estimates of the status of mammals in Essex based on recent changes in the countryside**

Increasing	*Stable*	*Declining*
rabbit	mole	hedgehog
grey squirrel	common shrew	Natterer's bat
fox	pygmy shrew	serotine
mink	water shrew	noctule
badger	Daubenton's bat	Leisler's bat
otter	brown long-eared bat	pipistrelle
common seal	brown hare	field vole
grey seal	bank vole	water vole
fallow deer	wood mouse	harvest mouse
roe deer	yellow-necked mouse	house mouse
muntjac	common rat	ship rat
red deer	common dormouse	stoat
		weasel

Of those species that are increasing in number, four – otter, common seal, grey seal and roe deer – may have a total population of fewer than 100 individuals. The rabbit, grey squirrel and fox have adapted well to life in urban areas with the badger, fallow deer and muntjac present in both the deeper countryside and the wooded outskirts of some of our larger towns. The mink – a recent colonist like the muntjac – is still extending its range in the county.

Where species are declining, it is almost always a result of changes in agricultural practice. The removal of hedgerows in order to achieve larger fields producing higher yields has removed both the cover required for small mammals and mustelids and the linear corridors used by feeding bats and juvenile animals dispersing in search of new territories. The larger bat species are declining along with their prey: the use of newer worming agents for grazing animals has hastened the disappearance of dung beetles, particularly favoured by the serotine. Rough grassland, inhabited by field voles and harvest mice, is often lost to urban development; where this habitat occurs as roadside verges, it is 'tidied up' by the over-zealous cutting regimes of local authorities. If the decline in some of our mammals is to be halted in the next century, a greater commitment to conservation will be required from those organisations that have the greatest impact on the countryside. A key aim of the Essex Biodiversity Action Plan, published in March 1999, is to achieve just that.

In the first half of the 19th century, before the invention of Portland cement, the town of Harwich was the centre of an industry making 'Roman cement', a product then popular for the rendering of buildings. The cement was made by breaking up the hard nodules known as 'cement stones' that commonly occurred in the London Clay cliffs. During the course of extracting these nodules the workmen were used to finding fossils and these were often sold to passing collectors; but in 1856 a workman found something that nobody had seen before. On breaking open a 30cm diameter nodule he noticed, on the fracture surface, the faint outline of a skull. This discovery was to be of scientific importance in the history of fossil mammals.

The skull was similar in size and shape to that of a fox and there were also other bones visible. In fact, close inspection revealed that the greater part of the skeleton was present, around which the nodule had been formed. The specimen came into the possession of a local collector of fossils, who passed it on to the British Museum (Natural History), where it was examined by Britain's most famous palaeontologist, Sir Richard Owen.

What had been discovered was the earliest ancestor of the horse *Hyracotherium*, also known as *Eohippus* or 'Dawn Horse'. It was the second time bones of *Hyracotherium* had been found (the first record was only a fragment of skull, with teeth, from the London Clay of Herne Bay, Kent in 1839) but no other specimens were then known. From subsequent discoveries in North America it became clear that this tiny horse had toes instead of hooves and was adapted to living on lush forest vegetation. So how did its remains end up in the London Clay that was originally laid down as mud on a sea floor?

The London Clay underlies most of Essex and was formed on the floor of a shallow sea that covered south-east England during the Eocene epoch, some 50 million years ago. Although almost all of the fossils present in the clay are of marine creatures there are also fruits, seeds and pieces of fossil wood which proves that the coastline was not far away and consisted of a dense subtropical rainforest similar to present day Indonesia and Malaysia. Mud brought into the London Clay sea by rivers must also have carried large floating masses of vegetation, together with the carcasses of animals such as *Hyracotherium*, that lived on the river banks.

Another mammal whose remains found their way into the London Clay was *Coryphodon*, a large rhinoceros-like plant eater, the first discovery of which was a fragment of jaw, with teeth, dredged up between Harwich and St Osyth in 1845. Complete skeletons of this animal have since been found in North America. Many other fossil mammals have also been found in the London Clay and also in the sands and shell beds beneath it known as the Lower London Tertiaries. Most are small shrew-like creatures identified only by their teeth but there are also many larger herbivores and carnivores. These fossils enable geologists to piece together the rapid evolution of mammals following the Cretaceous/Tertiary extinction, some 65 million years ago; a time when probably half of all the world's living species (including the dinosaurs) died out, providing the opportunity for mammals to dominate the world.

In Essex, there is a great gap in the geological record between the Eocene epoch and the present Ice Age, and the evolution of Essex mammals must be inferred from fossils that have been found elsewhere. However, there is some fragmentary evidence in the cliffs of Walton-on-the-Naze, where, at the base of a two-million-year-old shelly sand called the Red Crag, there is a layer containing rolled whale teeth, pieces of whale bone and the rare bones of terrestrial mammals such as deer and early elephant. These fossils have probably been recycled several times before being incorporated into the Red Crag and may even be of Miocene age (some 10 to 25 million years old).

The Ice Age has provided Essex with a rich diversity of deposits left behind by glaciers, lakes and rivers. Until about 450,000 years ago the River Thames flowed through central Essex and the River Medway flowed north across Essex to join this early course of the Thames. The Thames was diverted to its present course by the great Anglian ice sheet which reached as far south as Hornchurch and Hanningfield. After diversion the Thames adopted the route we know today but in the Southend area it joined the Medway and flowed north along the old Medway valley as a combined Thames/Medway river. Most of the sites in Essex that have produced Ice Age fossil mammals are situated on former flood plains, or terraces, of the Thames or the Thames/Medway rivers.

Table 2.1 **Geological time scale of the Ice Age (not to scale) showing the major fossil mammal sites (reproduced from *Essex Rock – a look beneath the Essex landscape* by Gerald Lucy)**

Epoch	*Age in years*	*Stage*	*Climate in Essex*	*Geology/fossil mammal sites*	*Archaeology*
Holocene	0 10,000	Flandrian	Present interglacial	Alluvium, peat beds and recent coastal deposits	Neolithic Mesolithic
Pleistocene	20,000 80,000	Devensian	Glacial	Cold climate fauna of the Lea valley and Great Totham	Palaeolithic
	120,000	Ipswichian	Temperate	East Mersea, Wrabness etc.	
	200,000	Wolstonian	Glacial/ interglacial sequence	Ilford and Aveley	
	400,000	Hoxnian	Temperate	Thames/Medway gravels at East Mersea and Clacton-on-Sea	First evidence of man in Essex (Clacton)
	450,000	Anglian	Glacial	Thames diverted	
	500,000 1.6 million	Early Pleistocene stages	Climate of early stages uncertain	Sand and gravels laid down in central Essex by pre-diversion Thames and in east Essex by River Medway	First evidence of man in Britain Sussex)
Pliocene				Red Crag at Walton-on-the-Naze	

An ice age consists of alternating cold (glacial) and temperate (interglacial) stages. Nothing much is known about our Ice Age mammals prior to the Anglian glacial stage, due to lack of suitable deposits with fossils but the subsequent Hoxnian interglacial (about 400,000 years ago) is represented by sediments in the former cliffs at Clacton. This site has yielded the bones of mammals that were living on the banks of the former Thames/Medway river and include straight-tusked elephant (*Palaeoloxodon antiquus*), lion (*Panthera leo*), rhinoceros (*Dicerorhinus* sp.), giant deer (*Megaloceros giganteus*), horse (*Equus* sp.), beaver (*Castor fiber*) and aurochs (*Bos primigenius*). Also present are worked flint tools which represent the earliest evidence of human occupation in Essex. Sediments in the cliffs at Cudmore Grove, East Mersea have produced a similar fauna including wolf (*Canis lupus*), bear (*Ursus* sp.) monkey (*Macaca* sp.) and an extensive range of small mammals such as voles and shrews.

The period following the Hoxnian was formerly known as the Wolstonian glaciation but it is now thought to have consisted of three cold stages separated by two temperate stages. Laid down during this time were many of the terraces of the present Thames valley, and numerous sites such as Aveley and Ilford have produced remarkable mammalian fossils. Aveley received national publicity in 1964 with the discovery of two elephant skeletons, one lying almost on top of the other; the lower one a straight-tusked elephant and above it, a woolly mammoth (*Mammuthus primigenius*). Although they were separated by only 30cm, this may represent a considerable time interval. Associated with the elephants were horse (*Equus ferus*), red deer (*Cervus elaphus*), and ox (*Bos* sp.) or bison (*Bison* sp.). In 1997 the nearby road cutting for the A13 produced similar fossils from the same sediments including brown bear (*Ursus arctos*), lion and the first record in Britain of the jungle cat (*Felis chaus*), a species that today lives in Central Asia.

One of the most famous Ice Age sites in Britain is Ilford, where brick pits in the 1850s produced an astonishing number of mammal bones, mostly of woolly mammoth and woolly rhinoceros (*Coelodonta antiquitatis*). In 1863 the skull of the so-called 'Ilford mammoth' was unearthed which had tusks nearly three metres in length. It is still the largest complete mammoth skull to have been found in Britain. The fossils at Ilford and Aveley are very difficult to date but they are probably between 150,000 and 200,000 years old. Another of these Lower Thames sites that have produced fossil mammals is Grays where the brick pits yielded great numbers of bones to the workmen in the early 19th century.

The Ipswichian, or last interglacial, about 120,000 years ago, was a time when Britain was warmer than the present day. Several mammals are characteristic of the Ipswichian stage, one of which is hippopotamus (*Hippopotamus amphibius*) which does not appear to have been present in Britain at any other time. Also characteristic of this stage is the complete absence of horse. There are a number of Ipswichian sites in Essex such as Wrabness on the River Stour but the most important site is a channel beneath the beach at East Mersea which is thought to be associated with a former course of the River Blackwater. The East Mersea channel contains not only hippopotamus but also straight-tusked elephant, rhinoceros, bison, giant deer and spotted hyaena (*Crocuta crocuta*). This fauna is identical to that found at Britain's most famous Ipswichian site, Trafalgar Square in London, which was discovered during building excavations in the 1950s. No flint tools are known from Ipswichian deposits, indicating that humans were not present in Britain at this time.

Table 2.2 List of Ice Age fossil mammals found in Essex

Species	*Scientific name*	*Species*	*Scientific name*
common shrew	*Sorex araneus*	wolf	*Canis lupus*
pygmy shrew	*Sorex minutus*	brown bear	*Ursus arctos*
water shrew	*Neomys fodiens*	spotted hyaena	*Crocuta crocuta*
lesser white-toothed shrew	*Crocidura suaveolens*	lion	*Panthera leo*
bank vole	*Clethrionomys glareolus*	jungle cat	*Felis chaus*
extinct vole	*Mimomys savini*	woolly mammoth	*Mammuthus primigenius*
water vole	*Arvicola cantiana*	straight-tusked elephant	*Palaeoloxodon antiquus*
water vole	*Arvicola terrestris*	horse	*Equus ferus*
field vole	*Microtus agrestis*	narrow-nosed rhinoceros	*Dicerorhinus hemitoechus*
common vole	*Microtus arvalis*	Merck's rhinoceros	*Dicerorhinus kirchbergensis*
root vole	*Microtus oeconomus*	woolly rhinoceros	*Coelodonta antiquitatis*
narrow-headed vole	*Microtus gregalis*	wild boar	*Sus scrofa*
pine vole	*Pitymys gregaloides*	hippopotamus	*Hippopotamus amphibius*
wood mouse	*Apodemus sylvaticus*	red deer	*Cervus elaphus*
Barbary ape	*Macaca sylvanus*	fallow deer	*Dama dama*
red squirrel	*Sciurus vulgaris*	roe deer	*Capreolus capreolus*
beaver	*Castor fiber*	elk	*Alces alces*
giant beaver	*Trogontherium cuvieri*	early giant deer	*Megaloceros dawkinsi*
Arctic lemming	*Dicrostonyx torquatus*	early giant deer	*Megaloceros verticornis*
Norway lemming	*Lemmus lemmus*	giant deer	*Megaloceros giganteus*
barbastelle	*Barbastella barbastellus*	reindeer	*Rangifer tarandus*
serotine	*Eptesicus serotinus*	bison	*Bison priscus*
steppe pika	*Ochotona pusilla*		

As the ice sheets advanced and retreated sea level fell and rose again in response to the amount of water locked up in the ice. During many of the interglacials Britain was therefore isolated from the rest of Europe, thus explaining why some species are found to be absent during a whole interglacial stage.

During the last glacial stage, the Devensian, the ice sheet spread south as far as the north Norfolk coast and there are two major sites in Essex that belong to this extremely cold period: the well known terrace deposits of the River Lea (one of the few British records of the steppe pika, *Ochotona pusilla* is from Nazeing) and a gravel pit at Great Totham. Great Totham provided a typical cold climate mammalian fauna in a peat layer associated with a terrace of the River Blackwater. It consisted of woolly mammoth, woolly rhinoceros, reindeer (*Rangifer tarandus*), giant deer, horse, spotted hyaena and wolf.

The retreating of the ice sheets, some 10,000 years ago marked the end of the Devensian glaciation, bringing the world into the present interglacial (also known as the Flandrian stage or Holocene Epoch). As mammals recolonised the whole of Britain sea levels rose until, some 5,000 to 7,000 years ago, Britain became an island again.

Bibliography

Bridgland, D.R. (1994) *The Quaternary of the Thames.* Chapman and Hall

Bridgland, D.R., Allen, P. and Haggart, B.A. (eds) (1995) *The Quaternary of the Lower Reaches of the Thames: Field Guide.* Quaternary Research Association

Davies, W. (1874) *Catalogue of the Pleistocene Vertebrata from Ilford in the Collection of Sir Antonio Brady.* Private Publication

Gibbard, P.L. (1994) *Pleistocene History of the Lower Thames Valley.* Cambridge University Press

Lister, A. and Bahn, P. (1995) *Mammoths.* Boxtree

Lucy, G (1999) *Essex Rock: A look beneath the Essex landscape.* Essex Rock and Mineral Society

Stuart, A.J. (1982) *Pleistocene Vertebrates of the British Isles.* Longman

Sutcliffe, A.J. (1985) *On the Track of Ice Age Mammals.* Natural History Museum

Woodward, A.S. (1925) Primitive Mammals in the London Clay of Harwich. *Essex Naturalist* **21:** 97–103

Yalden, D.W. (1999) *The History of British Mammals.* T. & A.D. Poyser

Since 1852, the county boundaries used for biological recording comprise the two Watsonian vice-counties of North and South Essex. The dotted line on each map shows the boundary between these vice-counties. Together, these two units coincide with the geographical county (the administrative county plus the London boroughs of Barking, Havering, Newham, Redbridge and Waltham Forest) except for the extreme north-west where the parishes of Heydon and Great and Little Chishill are included. The total area is around 4,000km^2, making Essex one of the larger English counties. It is also one of the most densely populated, the 1991 census recording a population of 2,552,171 residents living at a density of 638 people per km^2 – a level which, if Essex had retained its status as a 'kingdom', would make it the most densely populated country in Western Europe! In the last fifteen years, development has continued at an increasing rate, particularly in the south; the current county structure plan requires a further 250,000 homes to be built. However, a rich variety of habitats are to be found and it is still possible to observe mammals in the Essex countryside without being disturbed by the human population.

The late Sir John Betjeman described Essex as a large square with two sides water. This, however, is an under-estimation: as the map reveals, it is only between Bishop's Stortford in the west and Wixoe in the north that the county boundary is not formed by a river or the North Sea. A feature of the tidal boundary is its many creeks and inlets; the sea walls of Essex, from the Stour estuary to Bow Creek, total around 500km in length.

The geology of the county has only a limited influence on its mammals. The chalk 'surface' of Essex, laid down many millions of years ago, has since been covered with later deposits of London Clay and gravels in the south and east (with chalky boulder clay predominant north of Danbury Ridge), and it is only in the north-west and the Grays area that exposed chalk is apparent. Near Chafford Hundred, a small tunnel cut into the cliff face of a chalk quarry has held hibernating bats and further east, at Hangman's Wood, where the chalk is covered by about fifteen metres of Thanet Sand, the medieval mining of deneholes has created chalk caves used in winter by up to 98 bats of three species. In much of south Essex, London Clay is dominant and where it is overlain with sand (the Claygate and Bagshot Beds), badgers have thrived in soil that has proved easy to excavate.

Essex is correctly regarded as a flat county, with much of the coastal region in the east of the county at or below sea level. Inland, the countryside becomes more undulating, with around one-third of the land surface more than 60m above sea level. The highest ground occurs in the extreme north-west, near Saffron Walden, where chalk slopes reach over 120m. Further south, ridges of ground above 90m occur in Epping Forest, the Langdon Hills and Danbury Ridge. It is in the gravelly, unproductive soils of these two latter areas that badgers are most common.

Coastal habitats

The estuaries, sea walls and coastal grazing marshes of Essex support a rich variety of mammals and, for the smaller mammals, an equally rich variety of both terrestrial and avian predators. However, it is only the seals and cetaceans that are present in our inshore waters, occasionally being recorded well upstream from the open sea. Common seals are more frequently recorded than the grey, having been sighted at South Woodham Ferrers on the River Crouch and off Northey Island in the Blackwater. Small breeding colonies are present on Buxey Sands in the Thames Estuary and also in the Walton backwaters and, despite the increase in leisure craft, numbers seem to be increasing. Of the cetaceans, there have been just six sightings of live animals – these comprised three species (humpback whale, minke whale and porpoise) – in the last thirteen years and all species are now rare in the southern North Sea.

The freshwater grazing marshes behind the sea walls were created from saltings many years ago. Fields are divided by dykes and fleets, most of which are lined by rough grass and *Phragmites*. It is in these habitats that small mammals are plentiful. The Essex population of barn owls is mainly confined to the coastal strip: analysis of their regurgitated pellets reveals the presence of all three species of shrew, field vole and bank vole, wood mouse, house mouse and harvest mouse. Larger species, such as water vole and juvenile common rats were also taken. The largest area of this habitat that now remains is behind the northern shores of the Blackwater. Similar areas are also present along the Thames and the now-threatened Rainham Marshes have recently been found to hold the largest population of water voles in the Greater London area.

Carnivores are also present – the mink has been recorded from East Tilbury, Bradwell and Tollesbury, and the otter from Holland Haven and Hamford Water. Stoats and weasels can be seen along sea walls, and the fox is widespread, preying on the field voles and rabbits that shelter in the bramble scrub and dyke walls. However, where winter cereals are grown inside the sea wall, it is the brown hare that is most visible, particularly during the winter months.

Freshwater

The inland rivers and streams, reservoirs and lakes, flooded gravel pits and irrigation reservoirs are attractive feeding areas for a number of mammal species but their high productivity of insects makes them especially favoured by bats. The large reservoirs such as Abberton (500ha), Hanningfield (350ha), the fourteen reservoirs of the Lea Valley totalling 460ha and Ardleigh (55ha) have all been surveyed, with the noctule often the first to appear on a summer evening. The presence of Daubenton's bat, a riparian species, has proved more difficult to detect on these larger bodies of water. Where woodland and water are in close proximity however, such as in Country Parks at Thorndon, Hainault, South Weald and Danbury, then this bat is commonly found and has been proven to be widespread throughout the county. Perhaps the best stretch of water on which to observe this distinctive species is the Chelmer and Blackwater Navigation Canal, where surveys conducted in 1997 and 1998 have shown it to occur commonly from Boreham to Maldon. Other species to be found feeding along the edge of lakes and rivers are both species of pipistrelle and, until recently, the serotine.

Of other mammals associated with freshwater, the water shrew is apparently widespread (though seldom recorded apart from in owl pellets) and the water vole has been the subject of a recent survey conducted by the Environment Agency and the Essex Wildlife Trust. The recent decline of this species, as a result of habitat mismanagement (and perhaps the arrival of the mink), is to be addressed by the implementation of an Essex Biodiversity Action Plan designed to increase the distribution and quality of water vole habitats throughout the county.

The otter is another species for which it is hoped that positive intervention will allow to return to its former status in Essex. Widely recorded in the 1950s, the otter became extinct in Essex some twenty years later and it is only now that a gradual recolonisation (assisted by a programme of releases throughout East Anglia) is taking place. During the last twenty years the coypu has been eradicated and the mink has become established. Evidence of the latter has come from the Stour, Colne, Blackwater and Chelmer and, although rarely observed, it is likely that the mink is now present on all our inland rivers.

Where recreational use such as angling and boating is permitted, the common rat is common, feeding on discarded bait and food. It is, however, the rank vegetation of stream and river valleys that is one of the last strongholds for the harvest mouse. Invisible until the autumn, when the abandoned breeding nests become apparent amongst dying grasses, this enigmatic species has been found to be widespread in such habitats during the present survey.

Farmland

Agricultural land covers more than 70% of Essex and the majority of it is intensively farmed for arable crops. In 1994, tilled land (i.e. crops or fallow) totalled 179,521ha with a further 33,226ha of set-aside (Essex County Council, 1996). The larger fields of today's modern farms have been created by the grubbing out of miles of hedgerow and the loss of the elm through Dutch elm disease. The decline in the diversity of the farmed countryside has had a deleterious effect on a number of species, particularly small mammals (which require vegetation for cover) and the mustelids that prey upon them. Today the typical species of the arable prairies is the brown hare, good numbers of which can still be seen on winter cereals in the north and east of the county. However, despite the introduction of set-aside schemes, the national population has continued to decline; the brown hare is the subject of an Essex Biodiversity Action Plan, designed to reverse the decline of past decades.

The mole is also most noticeable during the winter months, emerging from the shelter of hedgerows after the harvest to create new molehills in the edge of newly-sown fields. Other species, such as deer, rabbits and badgers, pass the day in adjoining woodland before foraging in farmland as the light fades. A major predator of farmland (as in urban surroundings) is the domestic cat. During 1998, two Wimbish cats accounted for 210 small mammals of seven species, 80% of which were field voles! (K. Swan, pers. comm.). Where rough grassland remains, field voles and harvest mice are still to be found. This habitat is declining however, either through being lost to development or as a result of changes to roadside cutting regimes. Minor changes can be beneficial to small mammals and the retention of field headlands, or uncut areas of roadside verge that border onto arable land, would provide a much-needed refuge for both species.

Woodland

From a period in prehistoric times when perhaps 85% of Essex was covered by wildwood, woodland comprises just 5.7% of the surface of our modern-day county. The principal areas occur south of a line between Colchester and Bishop's Stortford via Dunmow, of which Epping Forest (2,430ha) is the largest. Hatfield Forest (375ha), with its deer, cattle and coppices, is of unique interest as "*the only place where one can step back into the Middle Ages to see, with only a small effort of the imagination, what a forest looked like in use*" (Rackham, 1986). Those woodlands that remain are, however, rich and varied, with hornbeam predominating in the south (with some beech in Epping Forest), ash-maple-hazel woods on the chalky clays, limewoods in mid-north Essex and chestnut woods in the east. More recently, plantations of willows, poplars and conifers have added further variety although have had limited impact upon the mammal fauna. The Forestry Commission's coniferisation of Essex (particularly in the north of the county), that took place during the 1960s and 1970s has stopped; today, where conifers are thinned or felled, they are replaced with native broad-leaved trees. The most recent review of existing ancient woodland of over two hectares in Essex (Nature Conservancy Council, 1992) showed that 8,618ha remained, much of it 'coppice with standards'. It was the decline of coppicing for economic reasons during the early years of the 20th century that was a major factor in the decline of the dormouse. Today, although suitable woodland is now being re-established through sympathetic management, it will remain inaccessible to dormice unless hedgerow corridors are replaced, enabling the species to extend its range from those woods where it is present, to these newer, managed woodlands.

Woodland is important for many species of mammal. Bats will feed along the rides and amongst the trees, with several species also roosting in holes and crevices – and occasionally, bat boxes. Small mammals are to be found among the ground litter (with both the wood mouse and the yellow-necked mouse having been recorded in boxes erected for birds, bats or dormice); the peak populations of voles and mice coincide with the autumn seed crop. Other species such as deer, badger, fox, rabbit and hedgehog, will use woodland as cover before emerging to feed on adjacent fields. Many woodlands are now used for game-rearing – the associated control of predators allowing rats to thrive on the supplementary seed provided at feeding stations. In the newer plantations, harvest mice have been found nesting in the tubes protecting new trees, with field voles colonising the new areas of grassland.

In its vision for the 21st century, the Essex Wildlife Trust seeks to increase the amount of woodland in the county by 18,000ha, covering 10% of Essex. Much of this could occur at Thames Chase Community Forest, a 9,800ha area in south-west Essex where the long-term aspiration is to have 30% of land use as woodland by 2050. Here, the Forest Enterprise is committed to planting up to 426ha during a ten-year period, with an additional 25ha of woodland being created by the Woodland Trust. Elsewhere, it is hoped that existing Woodland Grant and Farm Woodland schemes will see the re-instatement of woodlands on agricultural land that has been taken out of production. The continuity of Epping Forest and its ancient pollards has been assured at Hainault, where a new management scheme will see the re-pollarding of 6,000 trees, together with the creation of 100 new pollards a year during the next twenty years.

Urban

The urban areas of Essex form over 20% of the county – a habitat second only in size to agricultural land. Buildings of all ages offer a variety of roost sites for bats, with five species having been recorded roosting in buildings such as medieval churches and modern homes on housing estates. Other man-made roosting sites have included a school, a telephone exchange and factory premises, with bats emerging to feed in parks and suburban gardens. Even in the more densely-populated London boroughs, pipistrelles are still present, taking advantage of open spaces such as parkland and cemeteries for feeding. Amongst the predators, the fox has adapted well to town life and thrived on the increasing tolerance shown to it by the human population. However, the fox as a hunter and opportunist, is greatly outnumbered by the domestic cat. If one assumes that the national cat population of

7.6 million animals is evenly distributed, then, Essex has over 300,000 cats – a figure in excess of the estimated national population of the fox! These cats, presumably, will compete with the fox for prey, taking an enormous toll, not only of commensal rodents such as house mice and young rats, but also of other small mammals such as field mice and voles caught in gardens, on undeveloped sites and along railway embankments. Of the other carnivores, only the badger has been regularly recorded from suburban areas: particularly in the south of the county, where it is actively encouraged by many householders. The hedgehog also takes advantage of the cover provided in gardens for feeding and breeding; in many cases eventually succumbing to the traffic that speeds through these built-up areas.

Urban growth is set to continue well into the next century. Between 1991 and 1995, around 22,700 dwellings were built; by April 1995, some 47,500 further sites had been identified in outer Essex for residential dwellings and nearly 75% of these had already received planning permission (Essex County Council, 1996). Most of these new properties will be constructed on sites that currently support several species of mammals – in 1998, a badger sett in central Chelmsford was threatened by a new housing development – yet the new, small gardens and limited landscaping of sites will make them unsuitable for mammals for many years. Although established gardens and open spaces will continue to hold a surprising variety of species, the new developments offer a bleak future to our mammal fauna.

Essex mammals matter. The sight of a herd of deer, a badger crossing the road or a seal swimming offshore is a source of pleasure; however, the study and recording of mammals in the county has been neglected during the last three decades. In contrast, through winter wildfowl counts and the monitoring of breeding birds since 1962 by the Common Birds Census, our knowledge of the county's avifauna is far greater than that of our mammals. Yet it is during the same period that almost 60% of our terrestrial mammals have received statutory protection (Deer Act 1963, Conservation of Seals Act 1970, Badgers Act 1973 and the Wildlife and Countryside Act 1981), in most cases as a result of a decline in the national population. In 1998, the latest Quinquennial Review of the Wildlife and Countryside Act, conferred protection on the bankside habitat used as 'dwelling places' by water voles – a measure that will have implications for the management of this habitat by the Environment Agency. As a result of this legislation (and a number of national surveys organised by the Mammal Society), there is now a greater awareness of the conservation needs of many species. In Essex, the formation of specialist groups has provided the expertise required to ensure that the welfare of bats and badgers is promoted among, not only the public, but also planners and developers. It seems likely that a further group of volunteers, in conjunction with the Essex Wildlife Trust, will take ownership of dormouse conservation: protecting those sites where dormice are known to be present and also taking part in county-wide surveys to establish the actual distribution of this elusive mammal.

The Essex Bat Group was formed in 1984 and has been successful at conserving bats with a programme of lectures and 'bat walks' (where up to 140 people have been involved in seeing bats as they feed after sunset). Perhaps more important has been the advice offered to householders after a bat colony has been discovered – in most cases, the bats are allowed to continue to visit and breed in the following years. In addition, two hibernation sites have been monitored and adapted: one at Grays has been so successful that it is the only Site of Special Scientific Interest in Essex to be created because of its importance for mammals.

Three badger groups, representing north-east, north-west and south Essex, have been actively involved in badger conservation. As evidence of badger digging became apparent after sett surveys during the 1970s, regular monitoring of active setts was initiated. In this way the security of setts could be enhanced and, through co-operation with the network of Wildlife Liaison Officers of the Essex Police Force, several successful prosecutions have taken place. Today, with added protection from an amended Wildlife and Countryside Act, badger digging is less of a threat than was the case twenty years ago. The badger groups also monitor road casualties, have been involved with the relocation of badgers at two sites in north Essex and have advised on the location of badger tunnels that have been constructed under many of our new roads.

Active management programmes for mammals have also been a high priority for the Essex Wildlife Trust. At the end of 1998, 23 reserves had been provided with nestboxes for dormice, and bat bricks (special house bricks made with six crevices that encourage hibernating bats) have been installed in a Second World War pillbox at Daws Hall Reserve on the River Stour. If the latter project is successful – a few droppings were present in the summer of 1998 – it will be extended to other reserves.

The re-colonisation of north Essex by otters has seen the provision of artificial holts at two sites on the Stort with a third due for construction on the Chelmer. A problem for returning otters, however, is the high volume of traffic along main roads – three road casualties have been recently recorded in the county – and, in two instances, the otter had left the safety of a river to cross a carriageway. In a new project along the Colne Valley, sprainting points and dry areas are being provided where the river passes under a road – a technique that has proved successful elsewhere in the country. Of other conservation projects, grassland management for hares is being undertaken at Fobbing Marshes, Tollesbury and the new Blue House Farm Reserve. At the Alexander Reserve, near Thorrington, a water level management scheme to attract and retain water voles has commenced. Finally, in its publication *Essex Wildlife 2000*, the Trust has committed itself (with the support of other groups) to achieving land-use changes that will benefit all wildlife in the county.

The Rio Convention on Biological Diversity of 1992, signed by the then Prime Minister, John Major committed the United Kingdom to take action to conserve the wide variety of wildlife in this country. National Action Plans were formulated, identifying threatened species and habitats but clearly actions had to take place at a county level to achieve local benefits for wildlife. A recent initiative, co-ordinated by English Nature, Essex County Council and the Essex Wildlife Trust, has seen the appointment of a Biodiversity Project Officer based at the Trust, and the production of local Biodiversity Action Plans for those habitats and species requiring active conservation measures to safeguard their future. Six mammals (pipistrelle, brown hare, water vole, common dormouse, porpoise and otter) have been addressed so far. The Action Plans are included in Chapter 13 in the hope that a greater number of the human population will become familiar with the objectives of the Plans and support their hoped-for success.

In Havering, Local Action Plans are being formulated so that local people may become involved in conserving their wildlife and, most recently, a county Red Data Book has been proposed, in which all rare species in the county and their current status, will be recorded. If the objectives of these Biodiversity Action Plans are met, then the millennium should see an increase in the population of several species of Essex mammals.

Essex mammals and the law

The protection of mammals by law is the result of the increasing interest in the conservation of rare species and also the need to bring the United Kingdom's legislation into line with that of our European partners. More than 60% of the mammal species occurring in Essex receive some degree of protection under several Acts of Parliament.

Table 4.1 **Legal status of Essex mammals (after Harris *et al.*, 1995)**

Species	*W & C Act 1981 (Schedule)*	*EC Directive (Annex/es)*	*Bern Convention (Appendix)*
hedgehog	6		III
common shrew	6		III
pygmy shrew	6		III
water shrew	6		III
all bat species in Essex	5,6	IVa	II
except:			
pipistrelle	5,6	IVa	III
barbastelle	5,6	IIa, IVa	III
water vole	5,		
common dormouse	5,6	IVa	III
all cetaceans	5		
stoat			III
weasel			III
badger	6, Protection of Badgers Act 1992		III
otter	5,6	IIa, IVa	II
common seal	Seals Act 1970	IIa	III
grey seal	Seals Act 1970	IIa	III
red deer	Deer Act 1991		III
fallow deer	Deer Act 1991		III
roe deer	Deer Act 1991		III
muntjac	Deer Act 1991		III

The Wildlife and Countryside Act 1981 (as amended) has two sections relevant to mammals. Schedule 5 confers total protection not only to the species concerned but also to nesting and resting places. Species listed on Schedule 6 receive limited protection from capture. The Act is subject to a quinquennial review when additional species may be added to the list as occurred in 1998 when the water vole was included in the legislation.

With regard to European legislation, the United Kingdom is a signatory of the Bern Convention on the Conservation of European Wildlife and Natural Habitats: Appendix II confers strict protection for the species under review and Appendix III states that exploitation of that species should be subject to regulation. EC Directive 92/43/EEC on the conservation of natural habitats and wild flora and fauna provides for designated areas of protection for species (Annex II) and special protection for species listed in Annex IV, and also rules that the exploitation of species listed in Annex V is to be subject to management.

All cetaceans are protected under schedule 5 of the Wildlife and Countryside Act 1981. The Whaling Industry (Regulation) Act 1934 (as amended) prohibits whaling in United Kingdom waters. All species are protected by this legislation.

All badger legislation was combined in the Protection of Badgers Act 1992.

The Conservation of Seals Act 1970 provides separate close seasons for grey and common seals during the pupping season. The season can be extended (as happened recently during the phocine distemper outbreak in 1988) by the granting of a Section 3 order.

The Deer Act 1991 confers close season protection for all species of deer.

The insectivores are represented by five species in Essex: the hedgehog, mole and three species of shrew. Although very different in size and appearance, they have several features in common. These characteristics – including the small brain (with relatively large lobes that serve the keen sense of smell), plantigrade feet with five toes and continuous tooth rows with comparatively few pointed cusps – are all evidence that the insectivores are the most primitive order of mammals, having diverged little from their early ancestors. The species have varying lifestyles: the hedgehog is nocturnal and the sole hibernator whereas the mole and the shrews have a very high rate of metabolism, their lives being a never-ending search for food. The mole and shrews eat approximately their own bodyweight in food every day; the mole also creating food stores of earthworms in its burrows as a safeguard against times of scarcity.

During the present survey more than 90% of hedgehog reports were of animals found dead on the roads; for the mole, 99% of records were of molehills, with only one live individual sighted. Shrews, too, are rarely sighted and evidence of their presence comes from specific study methods for small mammals.

Small mammals will commonly enter discarded bottles in search of prey, only to become trapped and die. Shrews are particularly vulnerable because of their small size and may be attracted to the insects scavenging on an already dead occupant. 'Longworth' live-traps are the standard method of surveying populations of living mammals. Owl pellets and domestic cat prey provide samples of small mammals caught by these predators. A number of studies have been conducted in the county using these methods and the results are summarised in Table 5.1.

Despite the presence of musk glands, which deter many predators, shrews are particularly vulnerable to barn owls: they comprise 30% of the 25,488 mammalian prey items recorded at seventeen Essex nest sites. Shrews are important to barn owls, and if the much commoner tawny owls take prey in similar proportions, the total predation rate by owls must be a significant part of the over one million shrews born each year in Essex (birth-rate estimate based on data from Harris *et al.*, 1995).

Two bottle surveys demonstrated that shrews are susceptible to being trapped in this way, with the three species forming around 56% of the victims of bottles found along roadside verges. In the live-trapping survey covering many habitat types in the 1960s/70s, shrews represented 20% of the small mammals. The other (mainly woodland) surveys caught far fewer shrews.

Future surveys should include: a bottle hunt covering the whole of Essex (conducted before plastic bottles and ring-pull cans become even more widespread), the use of 'hair-tubes' and an analysis of droppings to detect the presence of the water shrew. Hair-tubes have sticky walls which collect identifiable hairs from exploring small mammals. Water shrew droppings are identified by the presence of the remains of aquatic crustaceans.

Table 5.1 **Number of small mammals identified from analysing barn owl pellets, a 'What the cat brought in' survey, bottle hunts and Longworth trapping. ([1]Love, 1998; [2]Corke & Harris, 1972; [3]A. Gudgion pers. comm.)**

	Common shrew	Pygmy shrew	Water shrew	Bank vole	Field vole	Water vole	Wood mouse	Yellow-necked mouse	Harvest mouse	House mouse	Common rat	Total
Barn owl pellets												
2,217 pellets from 10 Essex sites	1,348	1,174	38	254	3,016	27	2,015		236	158	87	8,353
4,733 pellets from the Dengie[1]	3,464	1,672	42	829	4,891	80	5,269		549	245	94	17,135
% 10 sites	*16.2*	*14.0*	*0.4*	*3.0*	*36.2*	*0.3*	*24.2*		*2.8*	*1.9*	*1.0*	*100.0*
% Dengie	*20.2*	*9.8*	*0.2*	*4.8*	*28.6*	*0.5*	*30.8*		*3.2*	*1.4*	*0.5*	*100.0*
What the cat brought in												
9 survey forms	24	35		18	176		51	2	1	25	8	340
% cat prey	*7.1*	*10.3*		*5.3*	*51.8*		*15.0*	*0.6*	*0.3*	*7.3*	*2.3*	*100.0*
Bottle surveys												
1960/70s[2]	526	38	32	254	22		154		1	4		1,031
1999	59		4	38	6		5					112
% 1960/70s	*51.0*	*3.7*	*3.1*	*24.5*	*2.1*		*15.1*		*0.1*	*0.4*		*100.0*
% 1999	*52.7*		*3.6*	*33.9*	*5.4*		*4.5*					*100.0*
Longworth traps												
general[2]	174	16	3	125	48		421	13	15	37		852
Coptfold estate[2]	65	5	2	531	1		1,041	318		2		1,965
Brickles Wood[3]	32	8		557			1,215	40				1,852
% general	*20.4*	*1.9*	*0.4*	*14.7*	*5.6*		*49.4*	*1.5*	*1.8*	*4.3*		*100.0*
% Coptfold	*3.3*	*0.3*	*0.1*	*27.0*	*0.1*		*53.0*	*16.1*		*0.1*		*100.0*
% Brickles Wood	*1.7*	*0.4*		*30.1*			*65.6*	*2.2*				*100.0*

Hedgehog

Erinaceus europaeus Linn., 1758

Status: Common, declining

Hedgehogs are to be found throughout Essex but are likely to have declined during the last twenty years as a result of changes in the countryside. They are commonest in woodland, scrub, hedgerows and gardens where suitable cover is available for nesting and a plentiful supply of invertebrate prey is present. As grassland and pasture have been converted to arable fields, so hedgehog feeding habitat has been lost and the move towards larger fields as a result of the grubbing out of hedgerows has reduced available nesting sites. In addition, the lack of rain in recent summers will have adversely affected the variety of invertebrates available to hedgehogs at a time when the young are achieving independence (Harris *et al.,* 1995).

Laver (1898) recorded that *"I should think there are very few places in Essex where this very common animal is not to be found"* and the same is true today. The majority of records are either of road casualties or of visitors to gardens where they are often encouraged because of their fondness for slugs, earwigs and beetles. During the present survey, the hedgehog was recorded in every month of the year. The sharp increase in observations in late spring is associated with increased hedgehog activity after emergence from hibernation (Brockie, 1960). Records in August often referred to juvenile hedgehogs that would have recently left the breeding nest (Lucas, 1997). Two factors influence the increase in road casualties which is observed in October; firstly the adults are actively feeding to gain body weight in preparation for hibernation and secondly, there is the dispersal of young born from second litters. A feature of the recent run of fine summers, has been the increase in the number of hedgehogs producing two litters during the breeding

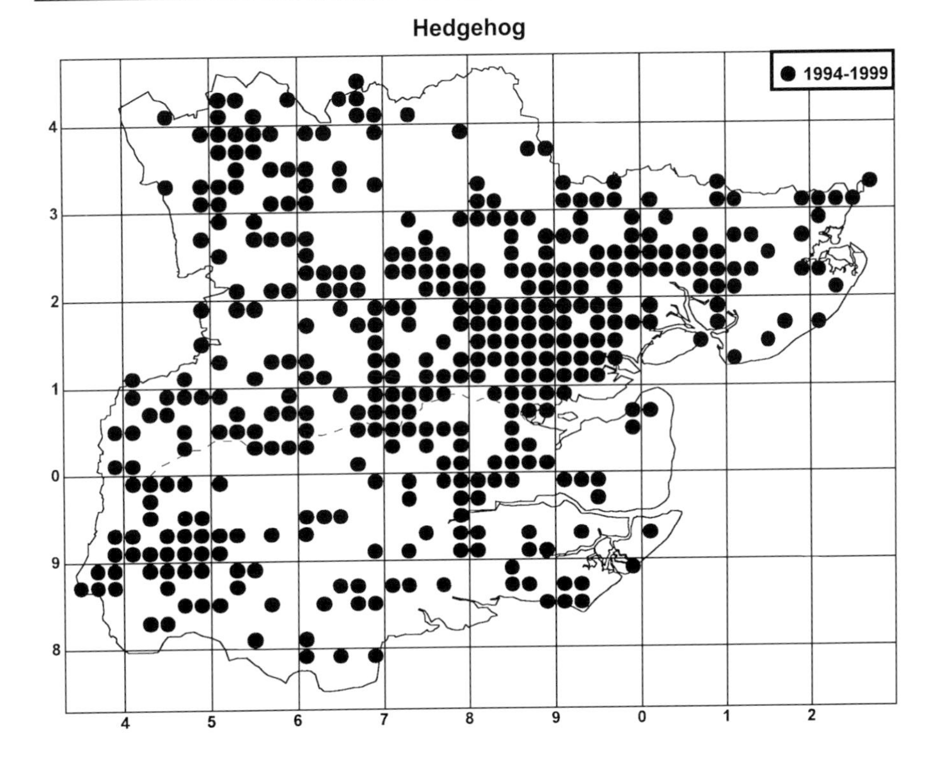

season and it has been shown that the majority of hedgehogs seen during the winter are young animals born late during the previous autumn. Most of these fail to survive their first winter and up to 65% of hedgehogs die during hibernation (Morris, 1983). Another risk faced by the hedgehog is that of drowning in garden ponds and several records have been received of hedgehogs that have suffered this fate, including an erythristic specimen from Colchester, now present in the local museum (J. Heath, pers. comm.).

The hedgehog is one of our most familiar mammals, regarded with affection by the human population. While the urban hedgehog will continue to be fed and encouraged, its rural cousin may need support with the provision of hedgerows and scrub as nesting cover, and field verges and headlands as feeding areas.

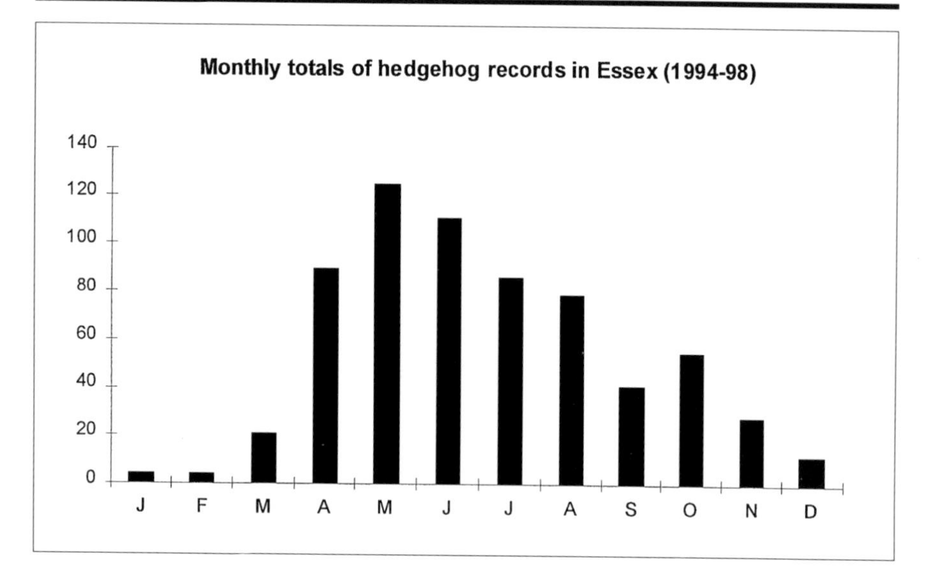
Monthly totals of hedgehog records in Essex (1994-98)
140
120
100
80
60
40
20
0
J
F
M
A
M
J
J
A
S
O
N
D

Mole

Talpa europaea Linn., 1758

Status: Abundant

The mole is supremely well adapted for its subterranean lifestyle. The head is set into the cylindrical body such that the animal appears to lack a proper neck and the eyes and ears are concealed by thick, black fur. The muzzle has short, sensitive hairs to assist in the detection of prey and the forelimbs are broad and flattened with strong claws to facilitate the digging of permanent tunnels. Although rarely seen above ground, except as a road casualty or when the juveniles are dispersing, the mole is unmistakeable (Stone & Gorman, 1991). Moles are highly adaptable and are found wherever the soil is deep enough to support their tunnels. In Essex, this includes deciduous woodland, agricultural land, pasture and gardens, moles being absent only from the wettest habitats and urban areas.

For most of the year, moles are solitary animals. However, during the breeding season, males tunnel over a large area seeking out receptive females and the single litter (occasionally there is a second) of three or four young is born in the spring. After six weeks, the young disperse and at this time they are most vulnerable to predation from stoats and cats (Gorman & Stone, 1990). Occasionally they are taken by barn owls and the distinctive humerus of the mole was found on eight occasions (amongst 17,352 prey items) in pellets collected over a two-year period on the Dengie (Love, 1998). The remains of moles have also been found in food pellets produced by herons and in one study of several hundred pellets, mole fur was found in 55% – making it the most frequently consumed mammal (Mellanby, 1971).

Mole

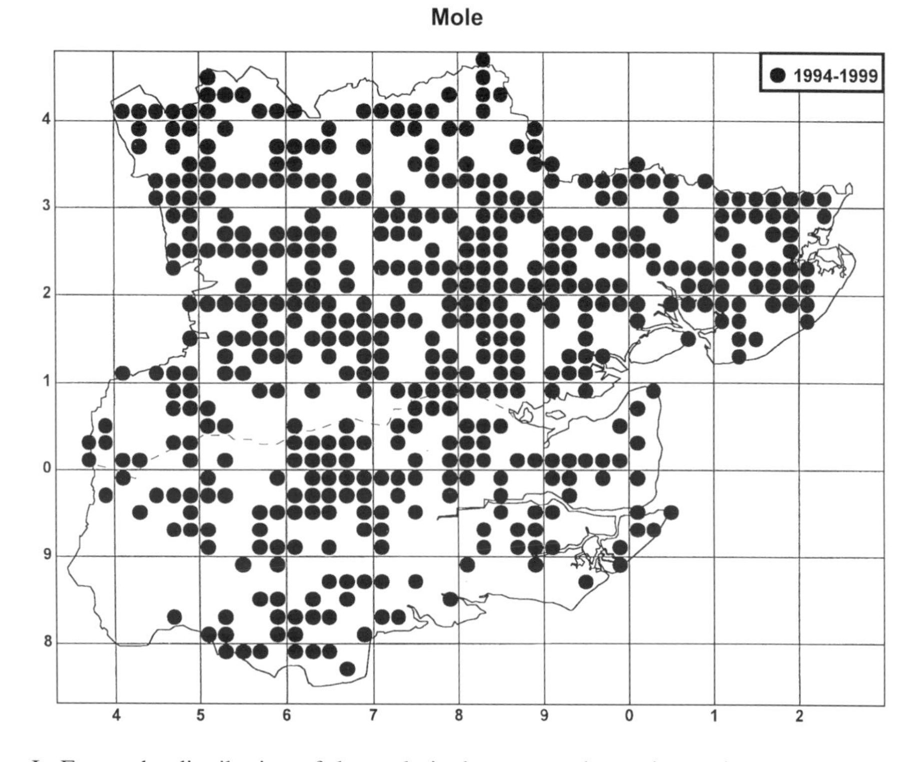

In Essex, the distribution of the mole is the same today as it was in Laver's time. Most of the records collected during the survey are of molehills and these are most obvious during the winter months when moles recolonise freshly cultivated ground from the field boundaries where they have spent the summer. The species is abundant in Essex: the apparent decline in Epping Forest which was reported in 1991 (Wheeler & May, 1992) is considered to have been an anomaly. In 1999, moles were regarded as common in the Forest (A. Samuels, pers. comm.). In winter, shallow surface tunnels are also found, which can cause damage to young plants. However, the most important problem caused by moles is the contamination of grass used to make silage. Soil from molehills causes poor fermentation and preservation of the silage which then lacks nutritional value as a food supply for grazing animals (Gorman & Stone, 1990).

Occasionally moles are found with abnormal fur colouration. An erythristic specimen, found in West Bergholt in July 1953 is in the collection at Colchester Museum and one *"the colour of a golden labrador"* was killed at Shoebury in 1966 (Hunford, 1967). Finally, an albino was found dead at North Shoebury in May 1974 (Hunford, 1976).

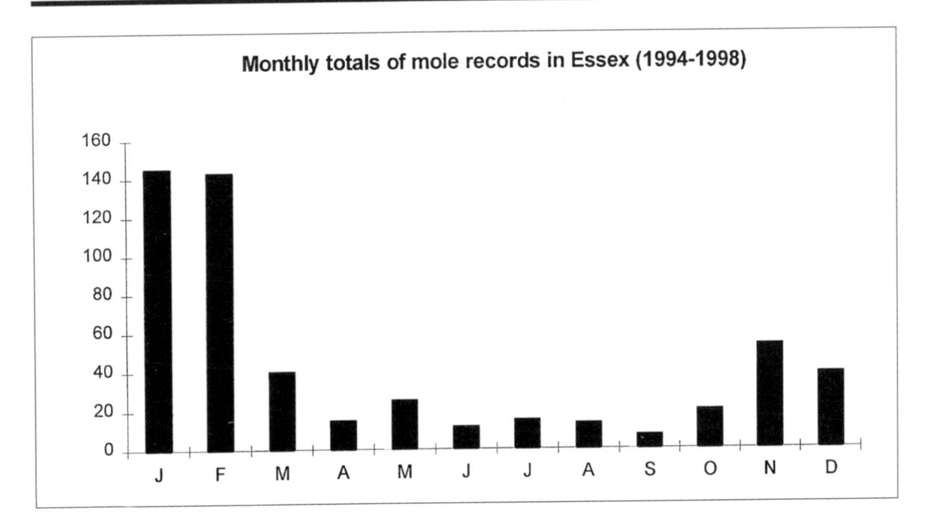

Monthly totals of mole records in Essex (1994-1998)
160
140
120
100
80
60
40
20
0
J
F
M
A
M
J
J
A
S
O
N
D

Common shrew

Sorex araneus Linn., 1758

Status: Abundant

Common shrews are found throughout Essex, preferring deciduous woodland, hedgerows, scrub and grassland. In favourable habitat, densities can exceed 50 per hectare with territories being vigorously (and noisily) defended. During the spring, male territories are abandoned as females are sought – the breeding season lasting from April to September with up to four litters of around six young raised during the summer. The young animals become independent at 25 days; however, they suffer high mortality as they establish home ranges, with only 20–30% surviving to breed in the following year. Common shrews are insectivorous and need to consume 80–90% of their body weight as food each day, particularly favouring beetles, earthworms, woodlice, slugs, snails, spiders and larvae (Churchfield, 1991a).

The status of the common shrew in Essex does not appear to have changed during the 20th century. Laver (1898) wrote: *"This animal occurs commonly in all parts of the county, although it is more frequently heard than seen. Like all the rest of the family, it is highly pugnacious and two rarely meet without engaging in a fight. Hedge and coppice, in consequence, frequently resound with their faint but shrill war-shrieks."* Corke and Harris (1972) considered that *"it is quite safe to say that this species is widespread and abundant throughout Essex."* In their review of small mammals in the county, the common shrew was the species most commonly found trapped in discarded bottles, comprising 51% of the 1,031 animals identified from this source.

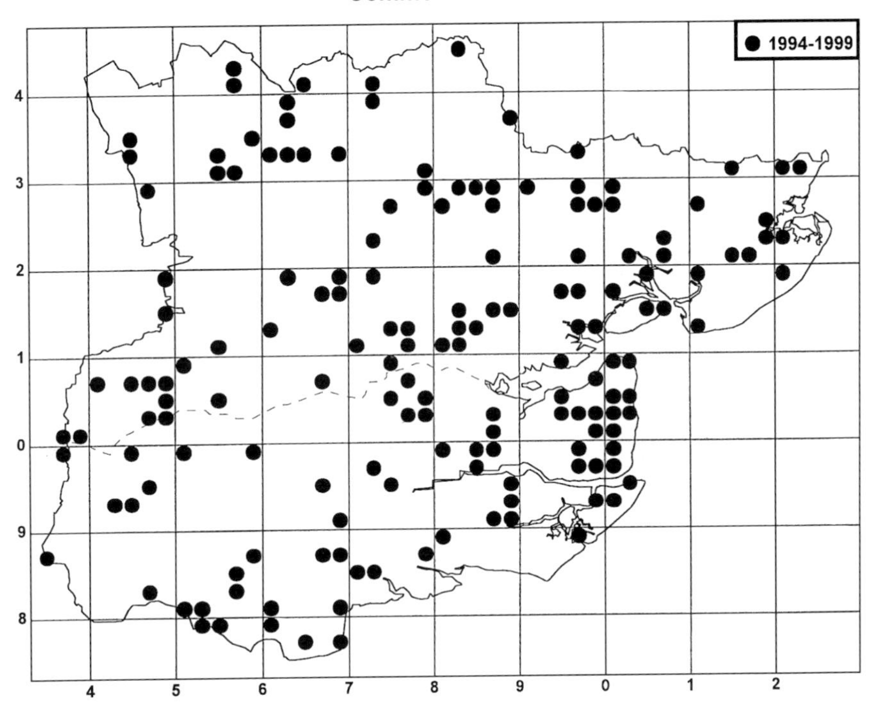

Records for the current distribution map have come from a variety of sources. Live-trapping produced a number of reports, as did the finding of dead specimens, particularly in autumn. These casualties occurred during the period of highest population density and could have been young animals vulnerable to predation while dispersing or older individuals, that were ousted from their territories by more aggressive, younger animals (Churchfield, 1990). Results from the 'What the cat brought in' survey added further records with the greatest number of common shrews coming from the analysis of barn owl pellets. In a two-year study at seven sites on the Dengie, 2,349 common shrews were identified in this way (R. Harvey, pers. comm.). Although light in weight and therefore less energy-efficient than larger prey items, the common shrew was preyed upon consistently throughout the year – the summer peaks coinciding with the height of the breeding season. Although not included on the map, three shrews, probably of this species, have been recorded from dormouse boxes in Tendring (R. Cottrill, pers. comm.).

The population of the common shrew in Essex is probably stable – losses of habitat due to agriculture and development being compensated for by the increase in long-

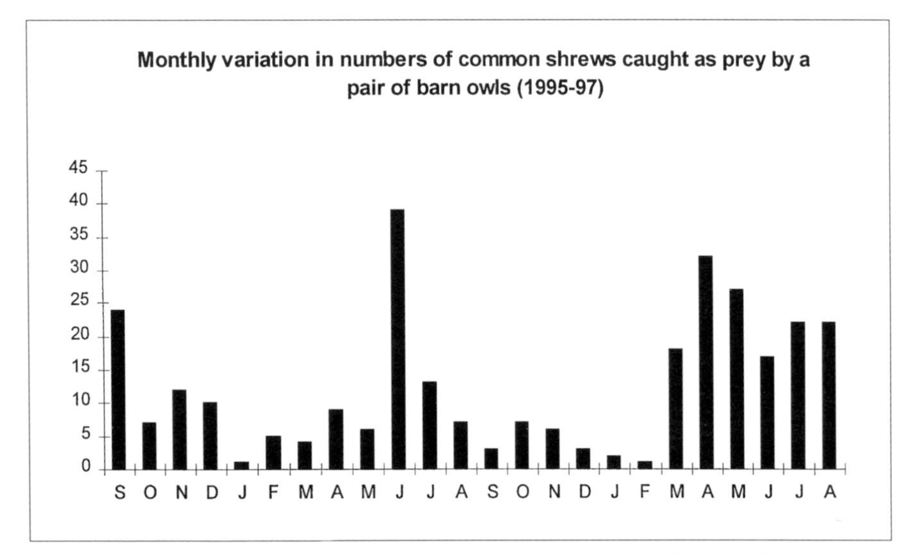

term set-aside and woodland planting schemes. The common shrew will continue to be one of our most abundant (albeit under-recorded) mammals.

Pygmy shrew

Sorex minutus Linn., 1766

Status: Common

Although fossil records from Europe date back around two million years to the Pleistocene period, the pygmy shrew (together with the common shrew) is thought to have become established in Britain about 10,000 years b.p. It is present throughout Essex; the apparent absence in the north-west is thought to reflect the lack of recorders in the area. Pygmy shrews can be found in all habitats where there is ground cover but grassland is generally preferred to woodland. The pygmy shrew can be separated from the common shrew by its smaller size, proportionately longer and thicker tail and more uniform coloration, lacking the contrast between the upper and under fur of its larger relative. As with the common shrew, territories are defended until sexual maturity in males, when they are abandoned in the search for mates, the breeding season peaking in June and July. The juveniles disperse and the overwintering population is made up of animals born the previous summer. The diet consists of a variety of invertebrates although earthworms are avoided (Churchfield, 1991b). The history of this species in Essex has been poorly recorded. Laver (1898) wrote *"I find Sorex vulgaris and Sorex minutus equally common, either as captured specimens or lying dead on the paths in autumn."* Corke and Harris (1972) recorded the pygmy shrew from 36 10km squares (identical with the present survey) but disagreed with Laver's view that both species were equally common. Studies have shown that the home range of the pygmy shrew is significantly larger than that of the common shrew reaching a maximum density of twelve per hectare (Pernetta, 1977) which, together with the results of live-trapping, bottle hunts and owl pellet analysis, suggest that the common shrew outnumbers the pygmy shrew by around 5:1. In Essex, the pygmy shrew's preference for grassland was evident in the results from barn owl pellets from the Dengie (Love, 1998) and Canewdon. Here, the higher relative abundance of pygmy shrews reduced the ratio to 2:1 and there was an excess of pygmy shrews over common shrews at both Tollesbury and Old Hall Marshes (author's data).

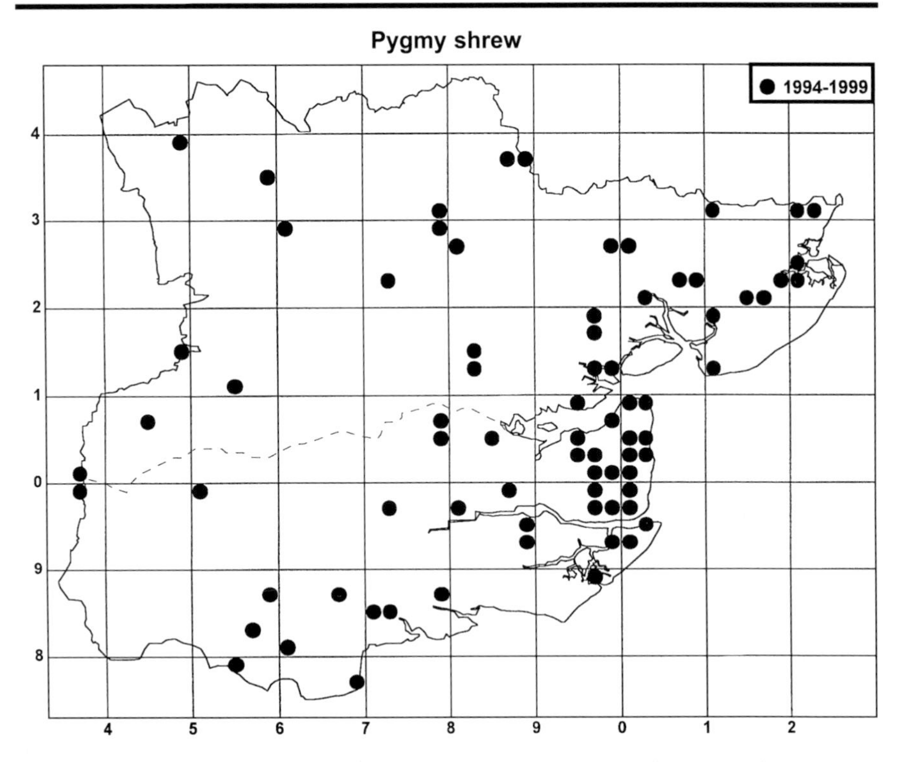

During the present survey, there were additional records of animals found dead, either found on footpaths or brought in by cats and a few live sightings from Longworth traps. The difficulty in finding this species and then separating it from the common shrew has led to a distribution map that is unrepresentative of the species status in the county. The challenge for the future will be to confirm the presence of the pygmy shrew in all areas of Essex.

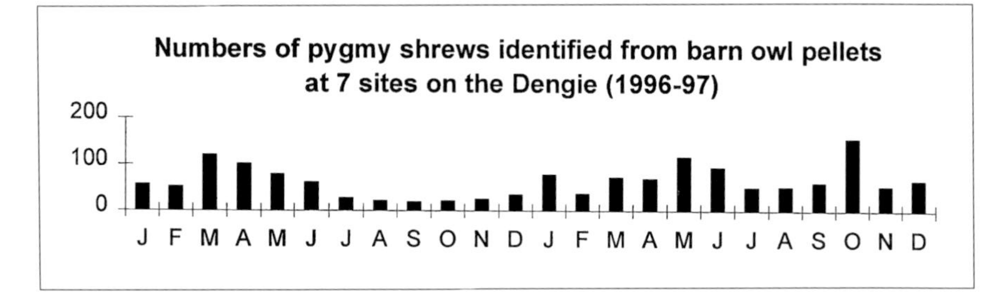

Water shrew

Neomys fodiens (Pennant, 1771)

Status: Fairly common

The water shrew can be distinguished from the previous two species by its large size, black dorsal fur sharply contrasting with white underfur and aquatic lifestyle. There is usually a tuft of white hairs on the ears and the keel of stiff hairs along the tail assists in swimming and diving. Water shrews prefer fast-flowing, unpolluted water systems but in Essex, have also been recorded from marshes, reed beds and gravel pits. Aquatic insects and crustaceans form around two-thirds of their prey, but they can be found up to three kilometres from water: it has been suggested that animals in well-populated areas disperse along hedgerows and through woodland to reach new territories (Shillito, 1963).

Of the water shrew, Laver (1898) commented that *"this interesting little animal occurs in all parts of the county, in suitable localities. It usually prefers shallow, stagnant pools to quick-running streams, but is occasionally found at some distance from water."* A century later, this species has proved difficult to find and most sightings have been made by naturalists who spend time in one particular area. In a telephone survey of Essex Wildlife Trust wardens, water shrews had been recorded from Maldon Wick, Sawbridgeworth Marsh, Cranham Marsh, Stanford Warren and Chigborough Lake, with additional observations from Cockaynes Wood, Alresford, Great Braxted and Earl's Colne. The only record obtained as a result of live-trapping was of an individual caught at Little Sampford in 1995.

The analysis of barn owl pellets has proved to be a major source of water shrew records, with 5 identified from a site at Canewdon, 13 from Tollesbury, 18 from two pairs of owls at Old Hall Marshes, 2 from Foulness (author's data) and 42 from 19 sites during a two-year study in the Dengie Hundred (Love, 1998).

Water shrew

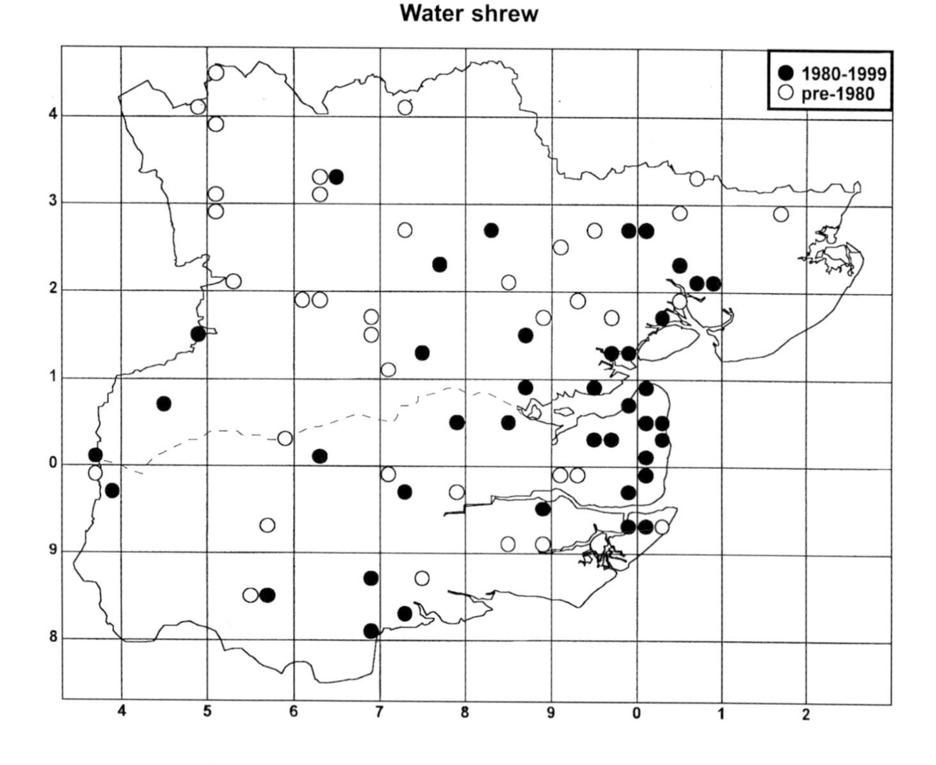

By comparing the incidence of the water shrew as a prey item with that of the common shrew, the relative abundance of both species can be calculated. In Essex, barn owls are predominantly found in coastal areas, hunting over grassland, sea walls, ditches and field edges. Of 6,934 pellets analysed from these habitats, it was found that common shrews outnumbered water shrews by 60:1 and 36:1 for pygmy shrew:water shrew. Bottle-hunting has proved the most successful for obtaining records of water shrews; perhaps because bottles are present when dispersing shrews explore non-breeding habitats (Corke & Harris, 1972).

As with the pygmy shrew, the distribution of the water shrew has proved difficult to monitor during the present survey. A technique recommending the use of blow fly pupae as bait under sheets of corrugated iron (the ensuing droppings can then be analysed for the remains of crustaceans, indicative of water shrews) has been recently suggested. Perhaps a project combining this method with a second bottle hunt would answer the question of the distribution of the water shrew in Essex.

"Epping Forest swarms with bats. They crowd by day into the hollow hornbeams, they creep into the faggot stacks, they hide in the piles of wood and in the roofs of cottages . . . Now if you wish for specimens, it is of no kind of use to shoot them on the wing, as some have attempted to do. I will not say that it is impossible to hit them, but it is impossible to find them; they fall into the thick brushwood, and are seen no more" (Newman, 1896).

As with many other counties, there are few historical records. However, Epping Forest was popular with Victorian naturalists and a list of bats was compiled by Doubleday in 1843. This was updated by Newman in 1896 and, two years later, Laver reviewed the status of bats in the county. At that time, eight species had been recorded in Essex and a ninth, the greater horseshoe (*Rhinolophus ferrumequinum*) was stated by Bell (1874) to be present at Colchester. In the 19th century, the species was described as abundant at Canterbury, was reported from Margate in 1874 and from Maidstone, Dover and Rochester Castle in the early 20th century (Heathcote & Heathcote, 1994). However, despite the proximity of Kent, no specimen was ever recorded from Essex and Laver chose to reject this species from his Essex list.

Table 6.1 **Status of bats in Essex at the end of the 19th and 20th centuries**

Species	*Present survey 1981-1999*	*Laver 1898*
Whiskered	rare	common
Natterer's	fairly common	common
Daubenton's	fairly common – under-recorded?	not rare
Parti-coloured	rare vagrant	unknown
Serotine	once common – declining	rare
Noctule	fairly common	common
Leisler's	fairly common	unknown
Pipistrelle	common	common
Nathusius' pipistrelle	rare vagrant	unknown
Barbastelle	rare	fairly common
Brown long-eared	common	common

That the distribution of bats is now better understood than ever before is due to the development of the 'bat detector' – specialist equipment that converts the ultrasound emitted by bats into a sound audible to the observer. With experience, different species of bats can be identified using a bat detector, in the same way that birds can be separated by their songs. This phenomenon has been enjoyed by several hundred people who have attended bat walks organised throughout Essex during the last decade. Partly as a result of studies involving bat detectors, it has recently been shown that there are in fact two species of pipistrelle present in Britain: one emitting ultrasound at 46kHz and the other at 55kHz (Barratt *et al.*, 1997), both are widespread in Essex. The twelve species of bat comprise 29% of the terrestrial mammal species of the county.

Another catalyst for the growth in knowledge of bats during the last twenty years has been the protection of all bats and their roosts by the Wildlife and Countryside Act 1981. To comply with this statute, action such as renovation, timber treatment or any other refurbishment that could potentially disturb a bat roost requires the authority of English Nature, the governmental advisor on conservation responsible for administering the Act. Additionally, any householder finding a summer roost of bats in their home will be referred to English Nature by their local Environmental Health Department and any bat found injured and reported to the RSPCA or other animal welfare group will also be referred for specialist assistance. In this way, details of many roosts and individual bats in Essex have been obtained. In 1984, the Essex Bat Group was formed to co-ordinate the conservation of bats and to deal with the enquiries and complaints arising from the presence of bats in buildings. The outcome, in most cases, is that roosts are conserved as home-owners are made aware of the lifestyle of their bats, and many grounded bats have been restored to full health.

In Essex, all species, except perhaps the Daubenton's bat, are thought to be in decline: as an example, the national population of the commonest species, the pipistrelle, fell by 70% between 1978 and 1993 (Harris *et al.*, 1995). The two main reasons for this decline are the loss of insect rich habitat such as pasture, deciduous woodland and hedgerows (changes that would also reduce roost availability) and the change in climate, with a move towards colder, wetter springs that reduce insect numbers as bats are emerging from hibernation.

Twenty years ago, one of the major problems for bats was the use of persistent, toxic chemicals such as lindane, used to kill wood-boring insects in roof spaces. Many bats were killed as a result, by direct contact with pesticide residues. Today, safer treatments based on permethrin, are widely used and at several houses, where permethrin has been sprayed, annual visits have been made to monitor the recolonisation by bats (Dobson, 1997). Two case histories are as follows:

- at a house in Frating, spraying took place in 1986 and the colony of brown long-eared bats returned the following year. Since then, the colony has numbered 25 bats and breeding occurs each year. A small group of pipistrelles has occupied the eaves during each summer since 1995
- at Broad's Green, the roof of a house was sprayed in October 1995; the colony of about 25 brown long-eared bats was present in the loft in July 1996 and a group of 40 adults and juveniles were counted the following summer.

Two further conservation projects are worthy of mention. The presence of bats in the Grays deneholes was first recorded by Newton (1884) and *"about twenty"* were present in 1962 (Chapman & Hammond, 1962). From 1985, access to the site was restricted to two visits per winter, and the shafts, that descend twenty metres into the underground cave system, were further protected by the provision of a new perimeter fence that excluded the assortment of household rubbish which had previously blocked access to the site for hibernating bats.

The deneholes are most important for hibernating bats during mild weather: during a severe winter, cold air rolls into the site and bats have a choice of suitable shelters above ground. However, if the weather relents, then the optimum conditions are underground and the number of bats recorded increases. In February 1998, during a spell of unseasonal weather with temperatures up to 16°C, the record number of 98 bats was achieved. As a result of the increased protection of the site and careful monitoring of the wintering population, the Grays deneholes are now one of the most important sites for hibernating bats in the country.

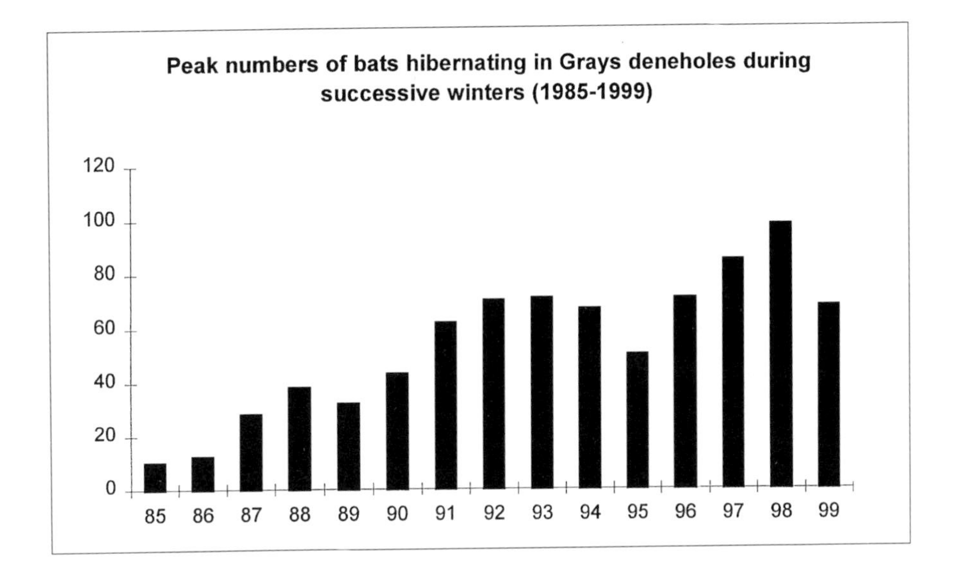

The second success concerns the conversion of several war-time bunkers into bat hibernacula in an area of mixed woodland near Coggeshall. This was achieved by the provision of 'bat bricks' (see page 21) and other artificial crevices, at a site that was previously unsuitable for hibernating bats. Today, just five years after completion of the scheme, up to 40 bats of three species have been counted during the winter period.

Despite the Wildlife and Countryside Act 1981, it is a bat, the serotine, that is in greatest danger of extinction in Essex. However, all species are vulnerable to the changes taking place in the countryside and the pace of development in the county. Roosts of rarer species such as Natterer's, although secure in churches, have been lost to barn conversions Other planning decisions, which have sacrificed feeding areas for new housing developments and roads, have also been detrimental. Whilst Epping Forest may no longer swarm with bats, it is hoped that in the future, co-operation between conservationists and planners can be enhanced to guarantee that future generations can continue to enjoy the sight of bats feeding throughout Essex. The current Biodiversity Action Plan process should highlight opportunities to assist in this.

Whiskered bat

Myotis mystacinus (Kuhl, 1819)

Status: One recent record

The whiskered bat is slightly larger than a pipistrelle but can be separated by its shaggy, dark brown fur, dark face and ears with long, pointed tragus and lack of a post-calcarial lobe. Newman (1896) described it as very rare in Epping, knowing of only two specimens, *"both of them, like our aged paupers, were found taking refuge in the union workhouse."* In contrast, Laver (1898) regarded this species as common throughout Essex saying, *"I have had no difficulty in finding all I have required for the purposes of study."*

Today whiskered bats are more common in the north and west of the country with just one recent record from Essex since 1980. In October 1987, an individual was found on the wall of a factory in Chelmsford, photographed and later released. A report of five, apparently identified in flight, at Ludgate Plain, Epping Forest in 1946 (Tucker, 1948) must now be considered doubtful due to the difficulty in identifying flying bats without a bat detector. In 1970, the whiskered bat was 'split' from the closely related and similar Brandt's bat (*Myotis brandtii*) and older records could refer to either species. Brandt's bat has frequently been recorded in Kent (Heathcote & Heathcote, 1994), notably at Dartford in 1995, and may well be found in Essex during the next century, although it is rarely recorded elsewhere in East Anglia.

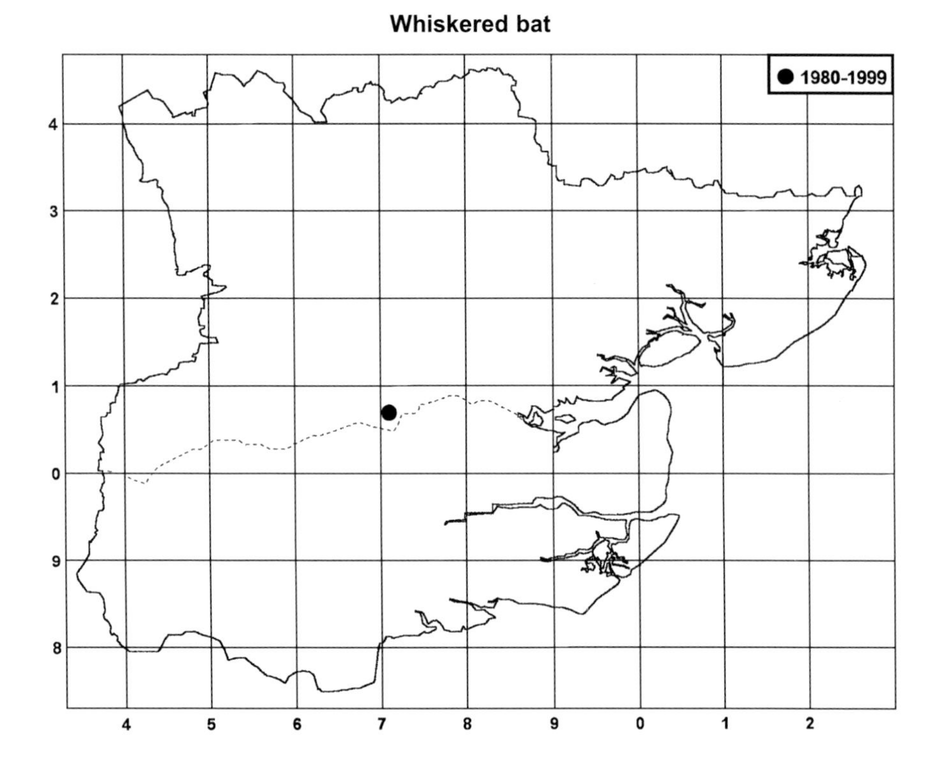
Whiskered bat
1980-1999
4
3
2
1
0
9
8
4
5
6
7
8
9
0
1
2

Natterer's bat

Myotis nattereri (Kuhl, 1818)

Status: Fairly common, declining

The Natterer's bat is widely distributed throughout Essex favouring deciduous woodland, parkland and riparian habitats where insect prey may be caught in flight or gleaned from foliage. It is identified by the bare pink muzzle, light brown ears that curve backwards at the tip and by the sharp contrast between the white underfur and grey-brown dorsal fur. The calcar is distinctively S-shaped, with a row of stiff hairs along the edge of the tail membrane between the tip of the calcar and the tail.

Laver (1898) records this bat as one of the commonest around Colchester. He found them regularly hibernating in the caverns under Colchester Castle, where they still occurred until the 1960s, and also believed the bat to *"hibernate in crevices in the brickwork of some of the deepest wells"* as several specimens were taken to him having been drawn to the surface in buckets. This species is difficult to survey using a bat detector as its ultrasound calls are quiet – typical of those species that fly in confined spaces amongst trees – and most records are of hibernating bats or summer roosts. Barns are particularly favoured for breeding and colonies have been found in the hollow mortise joints of tie beams at Great Totham, Great Henny, Stansted, Arkesden and Woodside Green. At this latter site and at Good Easter, colonies were lost when barns were converted to residential properties. Other roosts

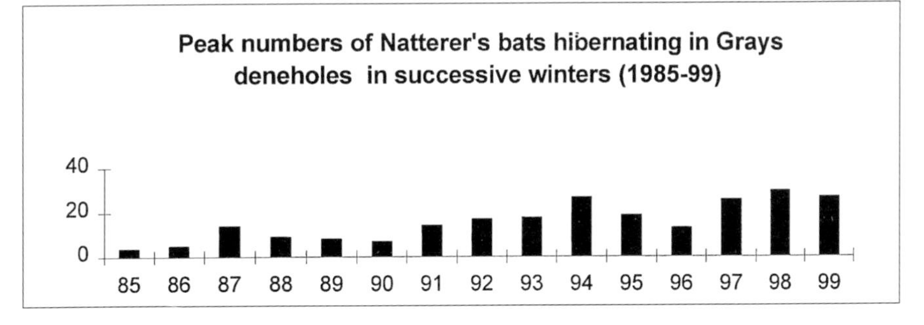

Peak numbers of Natterer's bats hibernating in Grays deneholes in successive winters (1985-99)

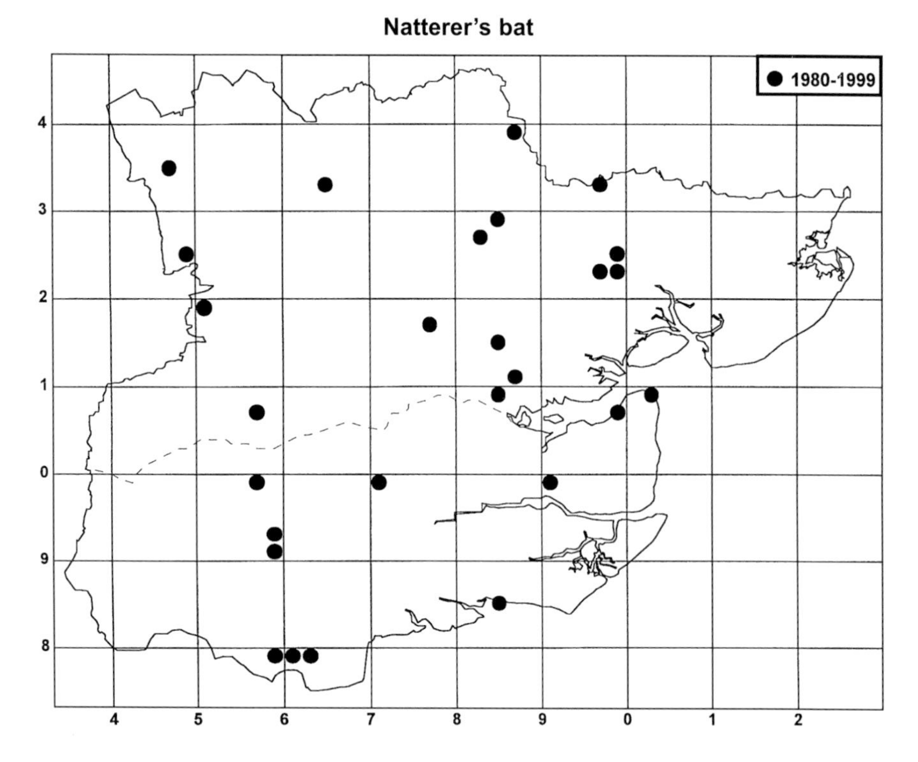

have been found in churches at Great Totham, Little Sampford and Great Horkesley, and also at Beeleigh Mill, where breeding was proved. Two roosts have been found in houses, with up to fifty observed in the loft of a house at Bradwell and droppings (larger than those of other medium-sized bats) recorded at Fairstead Hall.

The Natterer's bat is the most widespread species found in underground sites and is usually seen in crevices, often upside down or in other, apparently unnatural positions. The best counts are of 30 in the Grays deneholes in February 1998 and sixteen in adapted bunkers near Coggeshall. Hibernating bats have also been found in cellars at Warley and Leigh, an icehouse at Great Braxted and in an archway dividing a row of terraced houses at Earl's Colne.

As a woodland species, the Natterer's bat is rarely found by the public and there are few records of injured bats reported to the Essex Bat Group. The scattered records suggest that the species may be under-recorded and further records are likely to be of roosts or of bats found in hibernation. However, summer breeding colonies in older buildings are vulnerable to building conversion, which together with habitat fragmentation makes the future uncertain for this attractive species.

Daubenton's bat

Myotis daubentonii (Kuhl, 1819)

Status: Fairly common

Nationally, the Daubenton's bat is one of three species considered to be not threatened with extinction and may even be increasing in parts of its range. In the early 1900s, it was suggested that this bat was probably an abundant species in every part of England and Wales affording a suitable combination of water and woods (Barrett-Hamilton, 1910). Although probably true, there are very few Essex records to support this, with Laver (1898) reporting it as "*not rare*" in Colchester, but only offering additional records from Sudbury, Epping and Abridge.

Daubenton's bats use tree holes as summer roosts and although they will feed in woodland, they are easily identified with a bat detector as they feed low over the surface of the water gaffing insects such as caddis flies and mayflies with their feet. Most water bodies are suitable and they have been recorded from lakes at Gosfield, Fisher's Green, Weald and Thorndon Country Parks, canals at Spellbrook and Little Baddow, farm reservoirs at Wickham Bishops and Frating and gravel pits at Layer de la Haye and Tillingham. Roosts involving 30 bats have been found on two occasions, at Great Braxted and Beeleigh, and the only record of a bat in a house roof was from Baythorn End, on the River Stour. In August 1989, a female was found dying, caught on fishing line dangling from a riverside tree at Dedham.

A conservation success story involving this species has been the re-establishment of the Grays deneholes as a hibernation site. Bats were recorded here in 1880 (Christy, 1887), but by 1985 (Dobson, 1985) only six Daubenton's bats could be found; the low numbers due to regular disturbance of the site. Since then, following the erection of a new, secure perimeter fence, the numbers have increased to 68 in 1998, making the deneholes the eighth most important site in the country for hibernating *Myotis* bats. Additional winter records have come from Leigh, Great Braxted and Coggeshall. There are several autumn records of single bats in unusual locations. Three have been found in shops in Colchester High Street, two at Lakeside shopping centre, one at North Fambridge and one clinging to the wall of

Daubenton's bat

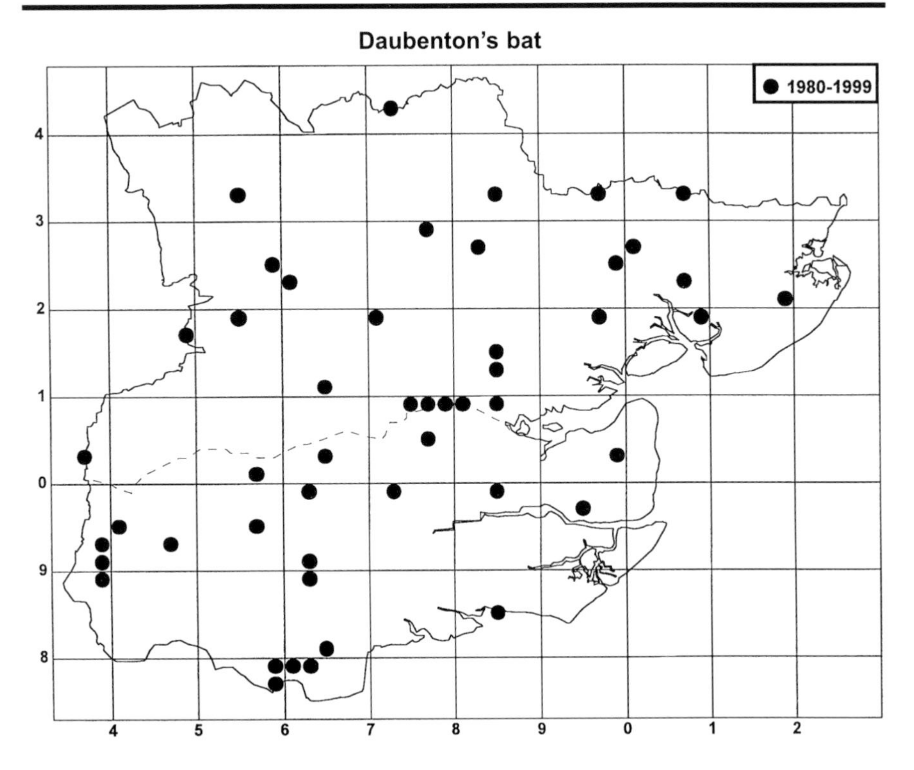

Orsett Fire Station. Could these displaced bats be migrants or young bats seeking out a hibernation site?

The improvement in water quality in our rivers, together with the flooding of worked-out gravel pits and creation of more farm reservoirs, will increase the productivity and number of feeding sites for Daubenton's bats. Of all the bat species in Essex, perhaps the Daubenton's bat has the best prospect of increasing its numbers in the 21st century.

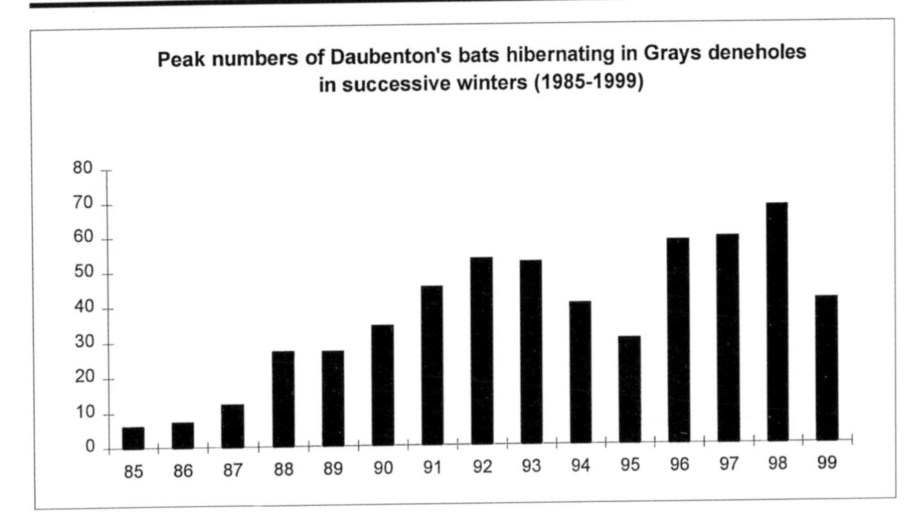
Peak numbers of Daubenton's bats hibernating in Grays deneholes
in successive winters (1985-1999)
80
70
60
50
40
30
20
10
0
85
86
87
88
89
90
91
92
93
94
95
96
97
98
99

Parti-coloured bat

Vespertilio murinus Linn., 1758

Status: Vagrant, two records

Newman (1874) wrote *"that many years ago, Doubleday shot at Epping, a bat which he believed to be of this species, after watching it on the wing for some time; but, unfortunately, the specimen, though searched for diligently at the place where it fell after being shot, could not be found."*

The parti-coloured bat is similar in size to the Leisler's bat but may be separated by its bicoloured dorsal fur. The upper fur is dark brown with silvery-white tips giving it a frosted appearance, contrasting sharply with the creamy white under fur. The dark brown ears are short, broad and rounded (Greenaway & Hutson, 1990). The parti-coloured bat is found in central and eastern Europe and southern Scandinavia, occurring as a vagrant in other European countries. It is a migratory species that has recorded movements of up to 1,440km (Roer, 1995) and has occurred in Britain on ten occasions including one record from a North Sea oil installation, 270km east of Berwick in June 1965 (Stansfield, 1966). The other records are from Plymouth and Yarmouth early in the 19th century; from Shetland in March 1927 (Ritchie), November 1981 and November 1984; from Cambridge in November 1985 and Brighton in March 1986 (Racey, 1991). The remaining two records both occurred in Essex.

On 22nd October 1994, a bat was collected from the fourth floor of a block of flats at Chadwell Heath and later confirmed as a female parti-coloured bat. It was in good condition (weight 19g, forearm 45.6mm), was photographed and released the following day (Dobson, 1994). The second occurrence was unusual in that it was found during the summer rather than the spring or autumn, more typical dates for a migrant species. On 5th June 1996, a teacher leading a field trip along the Roman River Valley near Colchester, found a bat on a bridge parapet that proved to be a male parti-coloured bat. This time the bat was in an emaciated condition, probably due to a torn wing membrane that would have prevented it from feeding, and

Parti-coloured bat

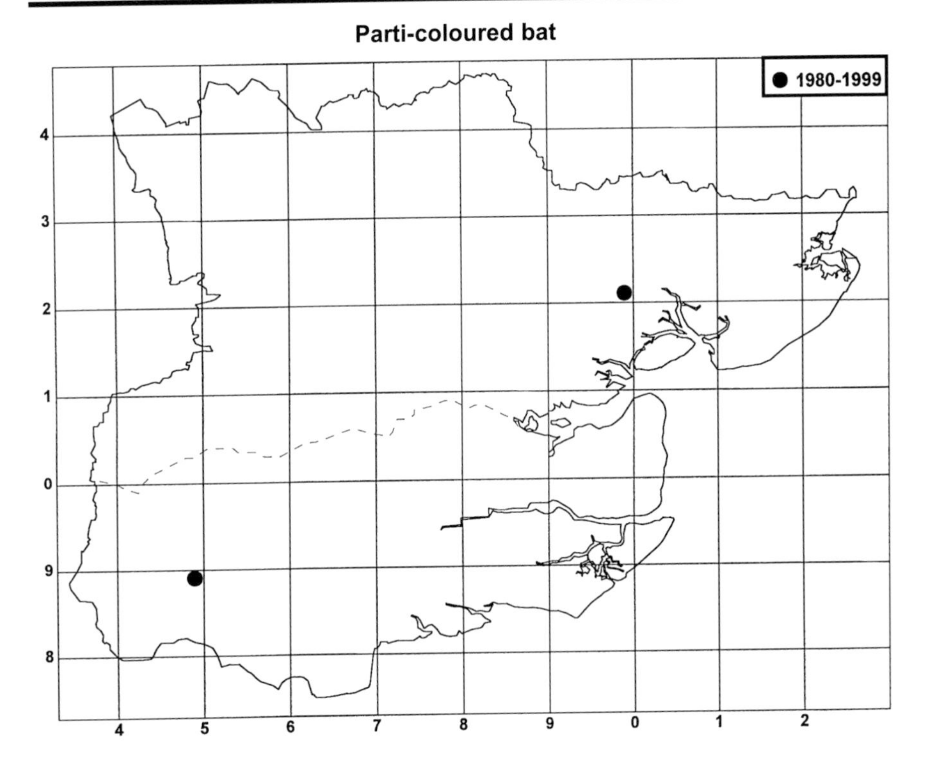

weighed only 7.5g (J. Greenwood, pers. comm.). It died later the same day. It is of interest to speculate whether this bat was injured and unable to migrate back to northern Europe, or perhaps part of an, as yet undiscovered, colony of parti-coloured bats present in north Essex.

The parti-coloured bat was likely to have originally been a bat of cliff habitats. Today, in its natural range it is often associated with tower blocks and in the autumn, the males perform a display flight, centred on a tall building. Significantly, two of the British records (Brighton and Chadwell Heath) are of bats found on the top floor of a high-rise building, suggesting that searching for this species in Essex town centres during September and October may produce additional records of this migrant bat.

Serotine

Eptesicus serotinus (Schreber, 1774)

Status: Rare, declining

Of all the mammal species found in Essex, the serotine has the dubious distinction of having shown the most marked decline in abundance during the last twenty years. Once regularly encountered feeding over pasture and along woodland edges, this bat is now a rare sight with only two new colonies having been found since 1994.

The serotine is a large species with a wingspan of over 30cm and long, dark brown upper fur, often with pale, golden-brown tips. The under fur is lighter brown and a distinctive feature is the 6mm extension of the tail beyond the tail membrane (Greenaway & Hutson, 1990). This species is dependent on buildings for its roosts and in Essex, two types have been preferred: firstly, houses built at the turn of the century, often with cavity walls and slate roofs; and secondly, more modern houses built on estates during the late 1960s. The serotine can also be identified from its large droppings and occasionally these have been found in churches, such as St James', Dengie, All Saints, Maldon and St Mary's, Salcott.

One hundred years ago, the serotine was very rare. Laver (1898) mentions just two records; the first shot at Pattiswick Hall, Coggeshall in around 1860 and the second captured at Pryors, Broomfield on 25th August 1894. With its large size, fondness for buildings, low flight and early emergence, the serotine would have been vulnerable to Victorian collectors. That there were so few records suggests that it was indeed uncommon and Laver commented that the two Essex records *"appear to be the most northerly ones recorded for the species."* There was a further report from Laindon Hills in 1900 (Hutton, 1903a) and the first colony was discovered at Loughton (Dent, 1907). From 1980, when the current bat survey in Essex commenced, the species was found in all but the extreme north-east and north-west of the county. The isolated record from Chrishall refers to a bat that had been radio-tracked from Chrishall Grange, some four kilometres away, as part of a study on serotines in south Cambridgeshire. After 1980, new colonies were often reported and the Essex Bat Group monitored several of these on an annual basis. The largest

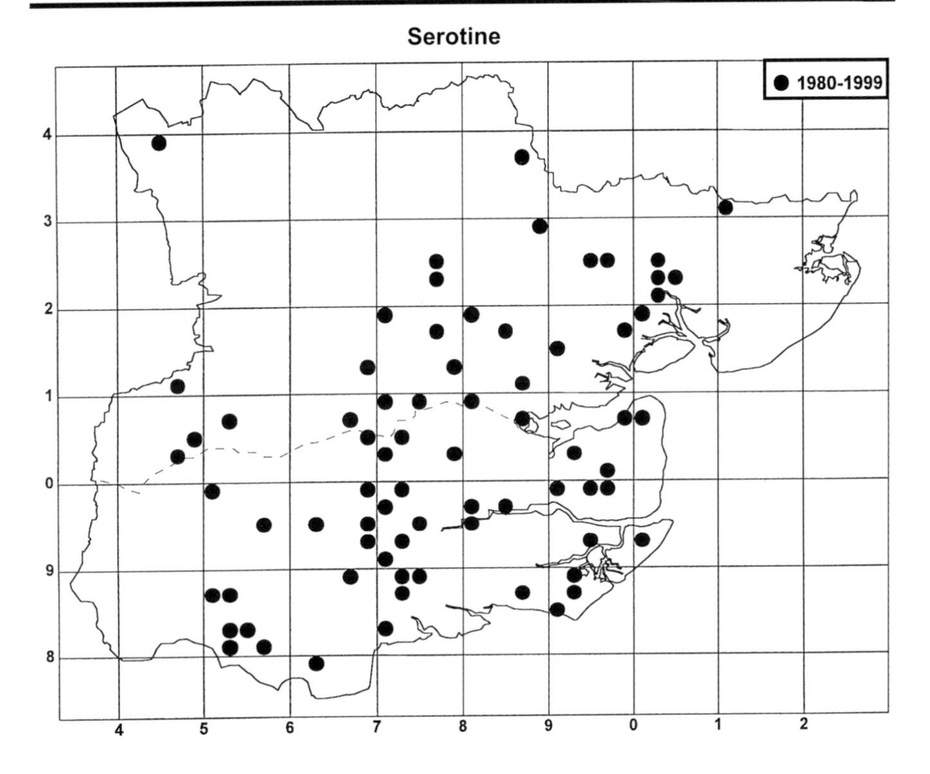

colony, at South Woodham Ferrers, numbered 45 bats in 1988 and used at least three houses on a modern estate. This group declined to seventeen by 1992, the last year it was recorded. Another colony of 26 bats, counted at Laindon, also in 1988, has since disappeared. The most recent colony to be monitored, at Vange comprised 25 bats in 1994. Three years later, in 1997, just eight bats emerged.

The main reason for this decline is thought to be the loss of feeding habitat, particularly pasture (Robinson & Stebbings, 1994). In early summer, serotines feed predominantly on chafers (*Amphimallon* spp. and *Melolontha* spp.) and during the autumn on dung beetles (*Aphodius* spp. and *Geotrupes stercorarius*) (Robinson & Stebbings, 1993). They will also take these insects from the ground by alighting with spread wings, before taking off with their prey (Dobson, 1985). The practice of keeping cattle indoors, with the fields being cut for silage, has led to a decline in the large insect prey favoured by serotines; the introduction of endectocides as worming agents for grazing animals has further reduced these insects as the chemical is still active after being excreted in the dung. The recent decline of the serotine has been mirrored in other south-eastern counties and it seems likely that this large bat will soon become extinct in Essex.

Noctule

Nyctalus noctula (Schreber, 1774)

Status: Scarce, declining

The noctule is a large bat that has been recorded from most areas of Essex. It is dependent on woodland throughout the year, usually roosting and hibernating in the cavities and woodpecker holes of both coniferous and deciduous trees. Roosts are changed regularly during the summer: one study, based in Yorkshire, found the mean number of roost changes for one group of noctules to be fourteen (Howes, 1979). During roost changes, the unweaned juveniles are carried by their mothers. The noctule can be identified by its sleek, golden brown fur and short, broad ears, characteristics that make it well adapted for fast flight in open areas. Of all the Essex bats, the noctule is perhaps the most easily observed. It is large, emerges before dusk – when it can often be seen hunting with hirundines – and feeds in the open over woodland, pasture and particularly reservoirs, where its high, straight flight is interspersed with steep dives to pursue its insect prey. As the evening temperature falls, noctules feed at lower heights and have been recorded around street lights.

The noctule was thought to be common throughout England at the end of the 19th century and Laver (1898) recorded that the species *"occurred commonly at Colchester as I believe it does throughout the county"*. However the number of records has declined in recent years and although still widespread, feeding groups have involved fewer bats than in the early 1980s. At that time, around 200 noctules were counted emerging from an ash tree near Colchester (A. Wake, pers. comm.) and up to 50 could be seen hunting high above Hanningfield Reservoir. A group of up to 30 was regularly recorded feeding over pasture at South Woodham Ferrers until the early 1990s but only smaller numbers have been observed recently. The sighting of a group of noctules is not indicative of a nearby roost, as radio-tracked individuals have been found to fly up to ten kilometres to a feeding area (Mitchell-Jones, 1990). In Essex, during the current survey, only five roosts have been found. Twenty-one bats emerged from an ash tree in Little Baddow, 15 from a sweet

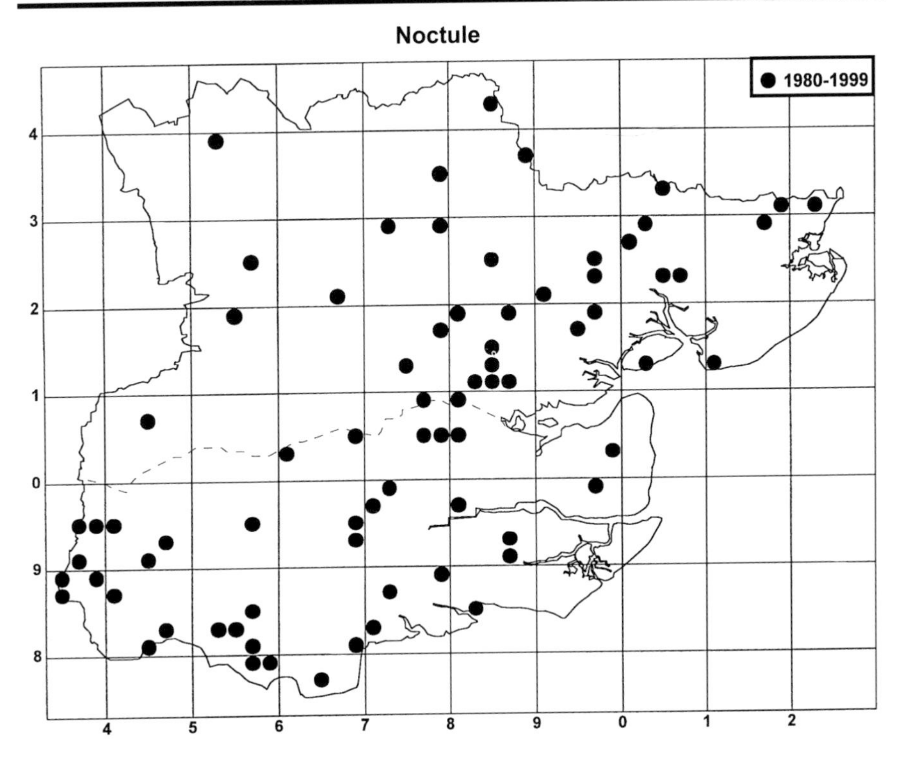

chestnut at Thundersley, 15 from an oak at Wickham Bishops, 7 from a poplar in Danbury Country Park and 7 when a cedar was felled in a garden at Kelvedon. Most other records have been made with a bat detector as bats have been observed hunting over suitable feeding areas with recent records coming from West Mersea, Tilbury, Foxearth and Stansted.

The future for the noctule, as with other large bats, is unpromising: species that feed on large insects are declining, as their prey is vulnerable to the changes occurring in the countryside. Additionally, roost sites are lost as dead trees are removed from parkland where they are perceived to constitute a danger to the general public. A new threat may be the increase in the population of the hobby, a falcon that hunts until after sunset. In recent years, hobbies have been observed chasing noctules at both Hanningfield and Abberton Reservoirs.

An unusual record was of a female noctule with a broken wing, collected at Barkingside on 1st October 1992. The bat had evidently mated prior to being taken into captivity and gave birth to a male juvenile in April, 1993. In February, 1998, both bats were still alive in captivity.

Leisler's bat *Nyctalus leisleri* (Kuhl, 1818)

Status: Scarce, declining

The Leisler's bat is closely related to the noctule but can be separated by its smaller size (forearm < 47mm) and browner colouration. The upper fur is a warm brown with a darker base to the hairs, fading to grey on the under fur. The wing membranes, face and ears are black; its narrow, pointed wings are features that are associated with fast agile flight in open spaces (Racey, 1991). Leisler's bats have been recorded only sporadically from most of Europe, but they are widespread in southern Ireland. In Britain, only 88 records were received during a 30-year period by Arnold (1993), with only four occurring during the winter months. In Essex, where there are more records than for any other county, Leisler's bats have been observed in all months from February to December and summer colonies have been found in buildings, from where the bats emerge around dusk to feed at canopy height over parkland and ponds. At Danbury Country Park, Leisler's bats can be first seen at the end of March, feeding over the car park and in storm clearings, whereas the larger noctule prefers the more open areas above the lakes. They have also been observed feeding over mercury vapour floodlights at a freight yard near the Lakeside Shopping Area at West Thurrock.

The Leisler's bat was unknown to Laver and perhaps the first record for the county is of a *"specimen of Vesperugo leisleri, which had been detected amongst skins of bats, presented by Mr Reginald Christy"* (Cole, 1906). Since it is possible that this individual may not have originated in Essex, one captured at Wenden's Ambo in 1950 (Burtsal, 1950), may have been the first county record. There were no further reports during the ensuing 30 years, until a distribution survey of bats in Essex was initiated by the Essex Bat Group. In June 1981, a male was found dead in Shelley and there were three further records in 1984. The first colony was discovered in Danbury in 1985 with subsequent roosts being found at Coggeshall, Blackmore, Bicknacre, Aveley and Little Hallingbury. Additionally, in 1988, an unweaned

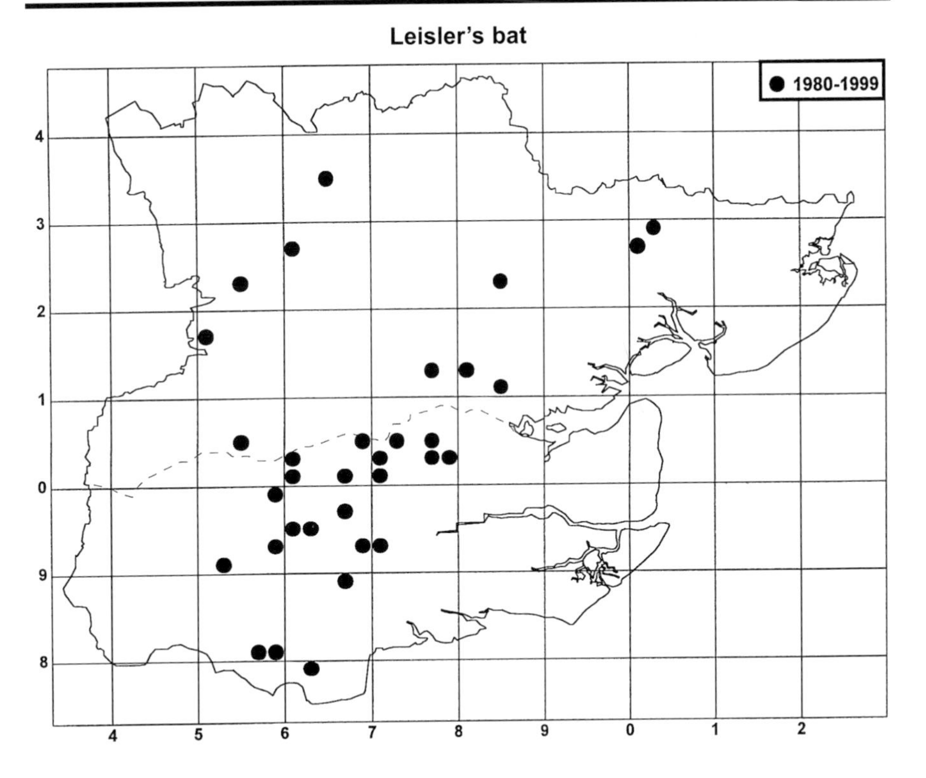

juvenile was found in Collier Row and a lactating female at Great Burstead, indicating that at least two other breeding colonies were also present at that time.

Roost sites are difficult to detect as emerging bats either fly low towards nearby cover (Bicknacre, Coggeshall and Little Hallingbury) or, where trees are not close to the roost (as at Hook End, Blackmore and Aveley), immediately gain height. In both cases the purpose is presumably to avoid advertising the location of the roost to a predator.

Another characteristic that makes this species difficult to monitor is the mobility of the summer colonies. On one estate at Coggeshall, at least three houses are used in rotation, the same pattern being followed each year. The colony collects in one house in early May staying for around seven weeks until the young have been born. In late June, the colony moves to a second house in an adjoining road, before moving to a third house in early July. On three occasions, flying juvenile bats have been found indoors at the first house during August, perhaps familiarising themselves with their prospective territory.

Along with other large bats, the Leisler's bat is declining as a result of changes in the countryside and the two largest colonies, at Aveley and Coggeshall, have decreased by nearly 70% during the last decade. Another summer colony of up to twenty bats, that used at least two houses three kilometres apart at Hook End and Blackmore, has not been located since 1995. The future seems bleak for this species and the Leisler's bat could disappear from Essex early in the new century.

Pipistrelle

Pipistrellus pipistrellus (Schreber, 1774)

Status: Common, declining

The pipistrelle is the commonest bat species in Essex and can be found feeding over farmland, open woodland, suburban gardens and along the edges of lakes and rivers. Although originally thought to have been a tree-dwelling species, pipistrelles are now found roosting in a variety of buildings from medieval churches to modern houses, invariably tucked away in crevices in brickwork or behind cladding. Recent studies have shown that instead of occurring as a single species, there are in fact two distinct phonotypes, one emitting ultrasound at 46kHz, the other at 55kHz; these are now considered to be separate species and both have been recorded in Essex. The two can be separated, not only by DNA analysis and some ill-defined morphological differences, but also by using a bat detector. In this account, both species are described together; however, separate maps, showing records collected over the last three years, have been included elsewhere.

Because of its preference for roosting in occupied buildings, the pipistrelle is the bat species most likely to be encountered by householders. During the spring, females congregate together in nursery roosts where single young are born during late June. At this time, the females emerge for two hunting flights during the night, foraging up to five kilometres from the roost before returning to suckle their young. After around four weeks, the juveniles become independent and the colony disperses. When a colony is monitored over a number of years, it is common to find several adjacent houses being occupied by the same colony – usually the 46kHz type, which appears to be more mobile than the other species.

During the last twelve years, a number of colonies have been studied by performing two emergence counts in June as part of a project to monitor pipistrelle populations in the country. The maximum figures from this survey are shown in Table 6.1. In 1990, the Maldon colony was the largest in England; since then, however, there has

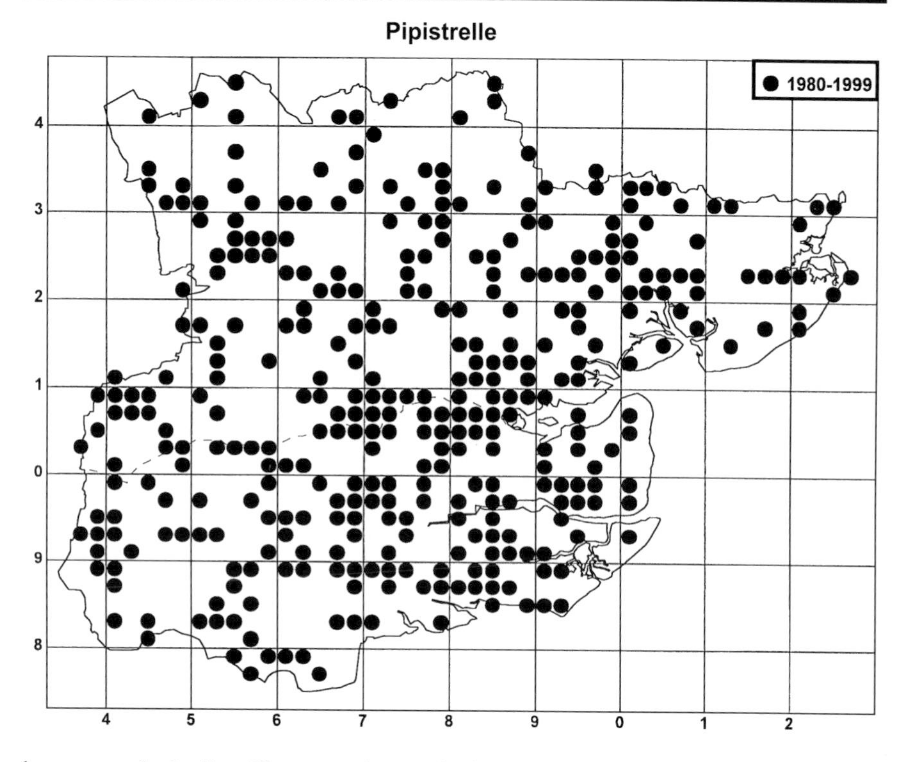

been a steady decline. However, the results from the other sites are inconclusive and demonstrate the difficulties in monitoring bats in this way.

Since the inception of the Essex Bat Group, summer roosts have been found in many different buildings including a telephone exchange, paint-spraying shop on an industrial estate, village hall, modern school and the toilet block of a public house in Roydon! The commonest site has proved to be at the gable end of houses built since 1960, the bats hiding in the soffits or between tiles and underfelt. In most cases, householders have been persuaded to tolerate their bats; however, it is sobering that despite protection, three of the four colonies holding in excess of 400 bats have been lost to home 'improvements'.

Although pipistrelles are much in evidence during the summer, there are few records of bats found hibernating. In January 1995, 30 bats were found wintering in the window frames of buildings at Goojerat Barracks, Colchester and, two years later, 53 bats were discovered when ceiling tiles were removed from a flat-roofed, upper storey apartment in Billericay. Occasionally, individuals have been found during the removal of wall cladding and others observed hibernating in the folds of heavy drapes in churches. During the winter, daytime activity has been observed on

Table 6.1 **Peak numbers of pipistrelles emerging at five colonies in mid-Essex (U = unoccupied)**

	Lt Baddow	*Lt Baddow*	*Maldon*	*Bicknacre*	*SW Ferrers*
1987	346	74	683	63	210
1988	656	82	694	78	235
1989	513	187	741	70	U
1990	147	1	1,041	86	U
1991	284	6	969	96	17
1992	277	2	921	U	214
1993	U	28	900	U	209
1994	222	67	676	97	212
1995	264	78	803	98	216
1996	54	93	688	U	244
1997	U	78	U	76	U
1998	U	129	440	65	U

several occasions, most notably on New Year's Day in 1994 and 1997 (at Thorpe-le-Soken and Bicknacre), and Christmas Eve 1997 at Danbury.

The pipistrelle is still a common feature of the Essex countryside. However, it was the decline in this species as monitored by roost counts that was the catalyst for bats being protected by statute. In 1987, it was estimated that the population of pipistrelles was 38% of that in 1978 (Stebbings, 1988); the principal causes of the decline being the changing climate and loss of suitable habitat. The pipistrelle is one species being closely monitored by the implementation of a UK government Biodiversity Action Plan: if this is successful, then other bat species will also benefit and it will ensure that the sight of feeding bats will continue to be enjoyed in the county.

Pipistrelle (46kHz)

Status: Common

The 46kHz phonotype of pipistrelle is the species found in southern Europe, the British population being at the northern limit of its range. It is widespread throughout Essex, commonly found roosting in modern houses on post-war estates where nursery colonies of usually fewer than 150 individuals gather during May and June. Colonies tend to be mobile and, over several years, often occupy a number of adjacent houses. The two species can be identified using a bat detector. Since the autumn of 1995, when separate records were first collected, the 46kHz type has proved to be more widespread than its congener.
This is the species most likely to be encountered in urban habitats, commonly found feeding over gardens and along village streets. Because of its association with built-up areas, it is also the species most likely to be found by the public and, to date, the majority of pipistrelles found injured have been of this type. There are several winter records of this species – most notably in January 1997, when 53 were discovered hibernating above ceiling tiles in an apartment in Billericay.

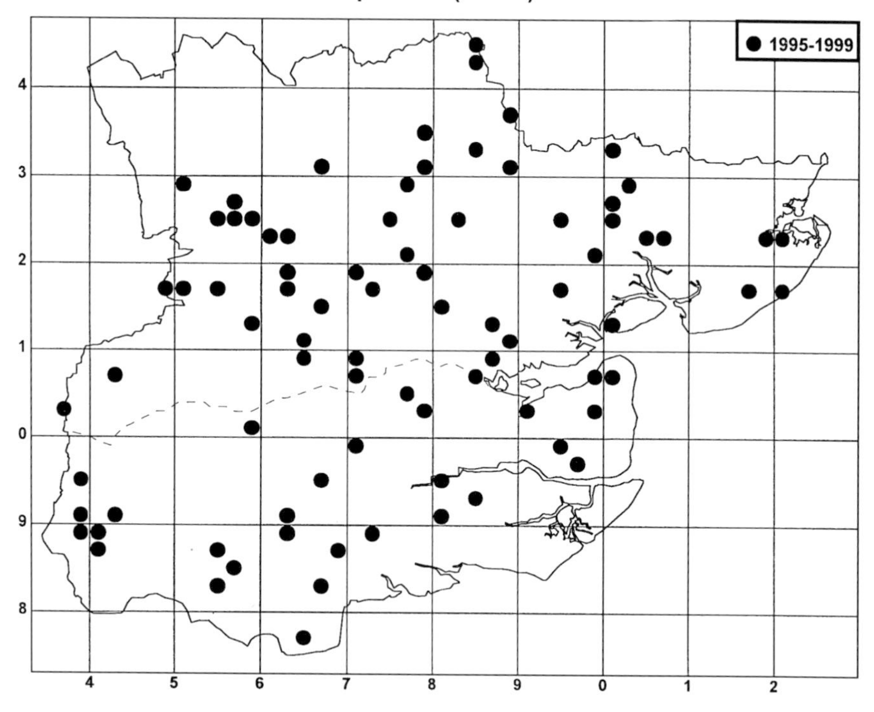

Pipistrelle (55kHz)

Status: Fairly common

This pipistrelle is typically found in northern Europe, its distribution overlapping with the 46kHz type in the United Kingdom. To date, it is less commonly found in Essex than the previous species, although nursery colonies contain greater numbers of bats. The largest colony found in the county has held over 1,000 females with several others having been recorded with more than 200 bats. As with the 46kHz species, summer roosts can be found in modern houses, as at South Woodham Ferrers, but colonies have also been discovered in older properties in more isolated settings such as those at Maldon, Debden and Baythorn End. Nursery colonies tend to be faithful to the same roost, usually staying throughout the summer.

Records of this species have been obtained since September 1995 and most have been achieved by using a bat detector. At those woodland sites, where both species have been observed foraging, the 55kHz type has been the first to emerge, feeding at canopy height for several minutes before the 46kHz type is detected. Recent evidence (Oakeley & Jones, 1998) has demonstrated a preference for riparian habitats and the early results of searching for this bat in Essex have shown that it can be detected in those areas where woodland and water are present.

Pipistrelle (55kHz)

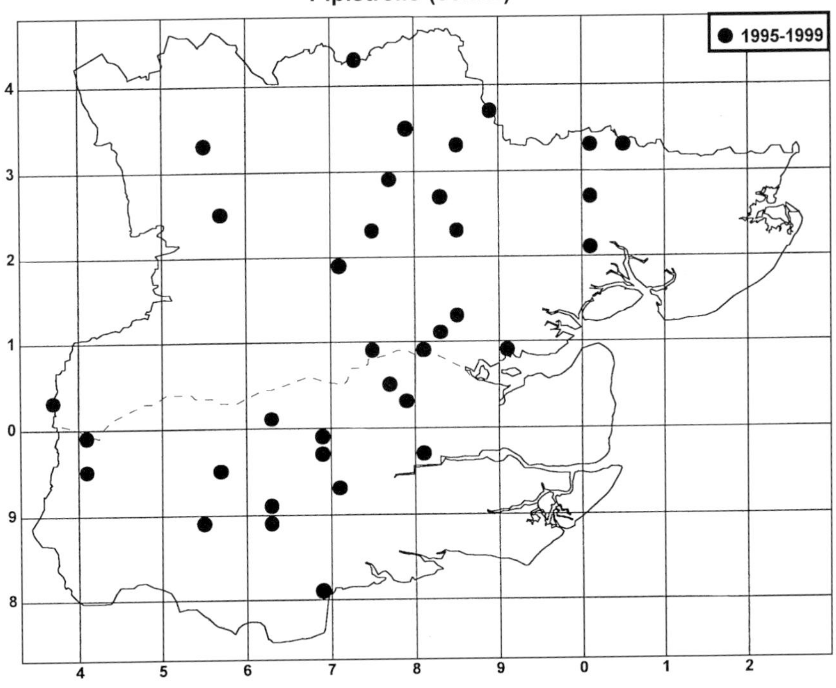

Nathusius' pipistrelle

Pipistrellus nathusii (Keyserling & Blasius, 1839)

Status: Migrant and partial resident, one record

A migratory species, widespread in northern and eastern Europe, Nathusius' pipistrelle has been identified on around 70 occasions in the British Isles (J. Russ & A. Hutson pers. comm.). It is slightly larger than the native pipistrelle with longer, shaggier dorsal fur that extends onto the upper surface of the tail membrane. The only Essex record (and the third for Britain) was of an individual photographed at White Roding in January 1985.

In 1997, Nathusius' pipistrelle was confirmed as a breeding species in the United Kingdom when colonies were found in Lincolnshire and Northern Ireland. With many of the previous individuals coming from inland locations, often during months not usually associated with migratory activity, it seems probable that this species has been resident in the British Isles for several years. It is likely that there will be more occurrences in Essex in the future.

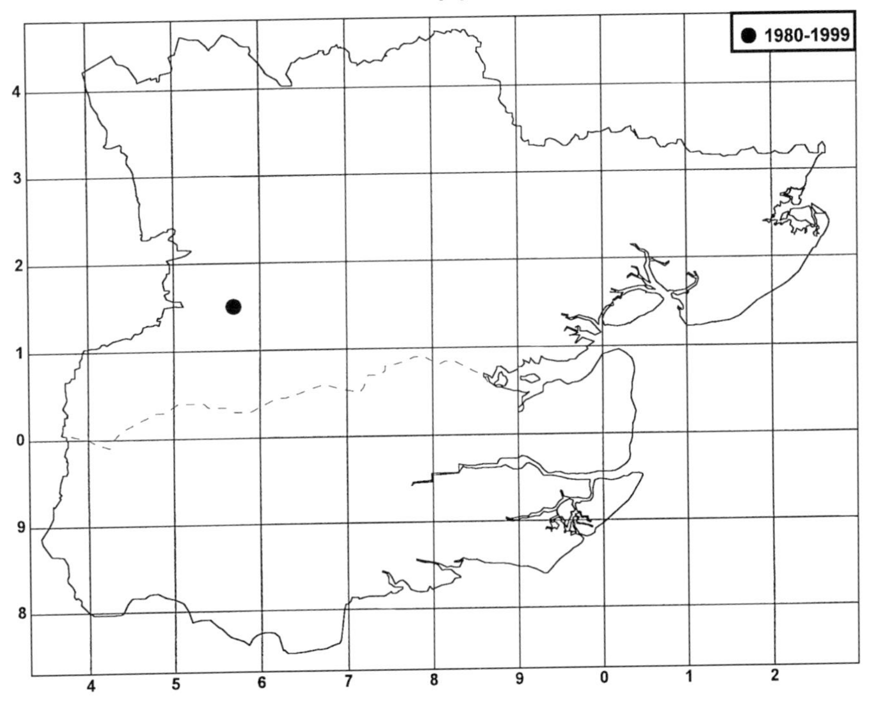
Nathusius' pipistrelle
1980-1999
4
3
2
1
0
9
8
4
5
6
7
8
9
0
1
2

Barbastelle *Barbastella barbastellus* (Schreber, 1774)

Status: Rare, one recent record

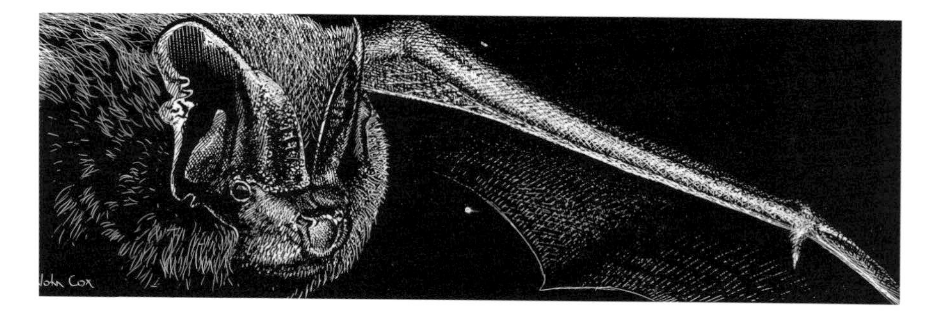

The barbastelle is a medium-sized bat, readily identified by its distinctive features. The ears are very broad and triangular, meeting in the centre of the head, the face, ears and wing membranes are almost black and the dorsal fur is dark with pale tips to the hairs, giving a frosted appearance. This species is rarely found and only two breeding colonies have been discovered in England in recent years, both since 1995. The first was in the beam of a Norfolk barn and the other, comprising 38 bats, was found in a vertical crevice in the trunk of a beech tree that had been reduced to a 5m stump by the 1987 storm. At this site, in West Sussex, radio-tracking showed that an individual was active for most of the night, feeding over tree-lined ponds and in ancient woodland before returning to the roost at dawn (F. Greenaway, pers. comm.). Several tree roosts were used during a three-week period, demonstrating how much information can be collected in a short time when using radio markers.

Laver (1898) wrote *"now that I have learned to recognise it, I do not consider the Barbastelle so rare as it is usually believed to be. Still I cannot call it a common bat."* He would identify it by its flight *"flitting slowly and in an apparently purposeless manner"* and found the species away from towns and associated with trees. Newman (1896) was also familiar with the species, but said that it was difficult to find, and claimed that it roosted during the day in the piles of wood or faggots stacked up along the side of the roads in Epping Forest.

In the 20th century there have been few records. One was captured at Wendens Ambo in 1949 and another was found behind shutters at Littlebury around the same time (K. Burtsall, pers. comm.). The favoured habitat here was parkland and the woods adjacent to the River Cam. In March 1969, during the course of a study of pipistrelles in church porches, a barbastelle was found behind a beam at St Lawrence, Bradwell (P. Racey, pers. comm.). The most recent record is of an

Barbastelle

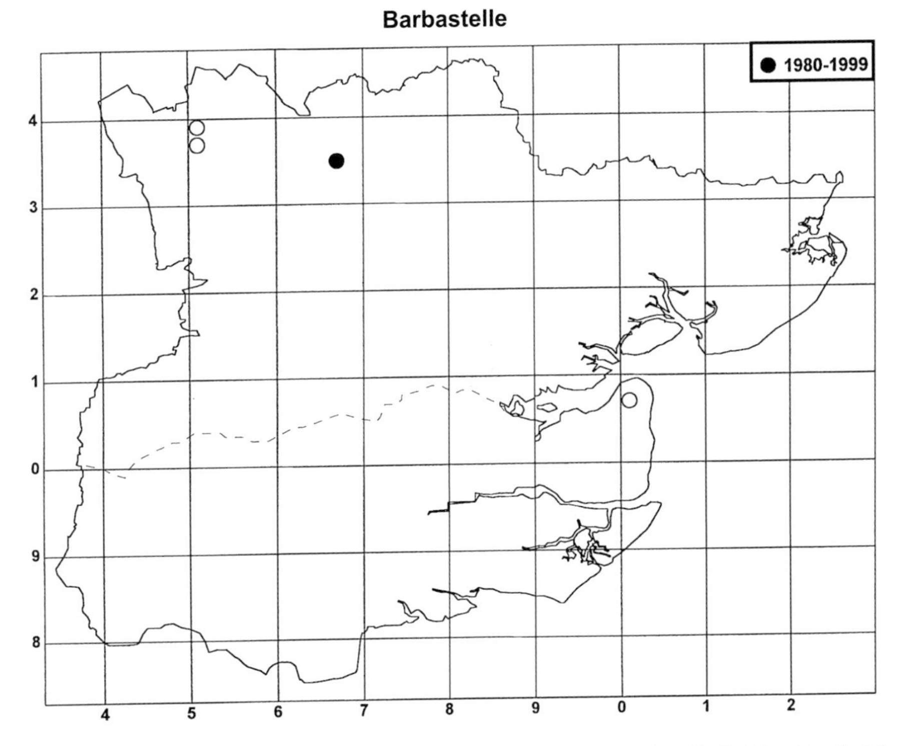

individual found roosting in the roof of a stable block at Spains Hall, Finchingfield in August 1992. Subsequent visits have failed to repeat this sighting.

It is tempting to believe that, along with some other woodland species, the barbastelle may be overlooked. Whereas the noctule is large, noisy (on a bat detector) and noticeable when it emerges around sunset, the barbastelle is much more elusive and in contrast to those species that roost in buildings, is unlikely to be found by the public. The preferred habitat of this species still occurs along the Stour (and perhaps the Colne) and the recent discovery of a colony 6km north of Manningtree offers the hope that this bat may still be present in the county.

Brown long-eared bat *Plecotus auritus* (Linn., 1758)

Status: Fairly common

This is the second most widespread bat species found in the county, having been recorded from all but the most built-up areas of metropolitan Essex and the treeless agricultural prairies. Laver (1898) found it to be very common around Colchester and considered it to be equally distributed throughout Essex. Commenting on the ears, he wrote, "*no other existing animal, so far as I know, has ears in this undue proportion... although so large, the ears do not strike one as so disproportionate as those of a lop-eared rabbit, which in comparison are really much smaller*".

Brown long-eared bats are unmistakeable with brownish fur, a pink or light brown face, large eyes and ears up to four centimetres long. During torpor, the ears are folded under the wings and when arousing are curled outwards, reminiscent of a ram's horns. Roosts are usually in older buildings, but always with ready access to woodland, parkland or mature gardens where the insect prey (detected by sight and sound as well as echolocation) is gleaned from vegetation. Although late to emerge, brown long-eared bats can be observed fluttering, butterfly-like, near foliage, at times following insects down to the ground (Greenaway & Hutson, 1990). Bats may be present in the same roost throughout the year, but the breeding groups, which are not exclusively female as with other species, usually gather in May and cluster in the ridge of roof spaces, often at the gable end or on a chimney breast. The colony can occupy several parts of the same loft, particularly when the juveniles are a few weeks old. Colonies can be difficult to count as bats may hide between the tiles and underfelt, or behind roof timbers. Several colonies, visited for a number of years have remained stable with around twenty bats, but in 1997, two larger colonies, one of 40 bats at Broad's Green and another of 50 at Wickham Bishops were counted.

Recent records have come from a number of sources. Many colonies have been discovered as a result of the surveying of roof spaces prior to remedial timber

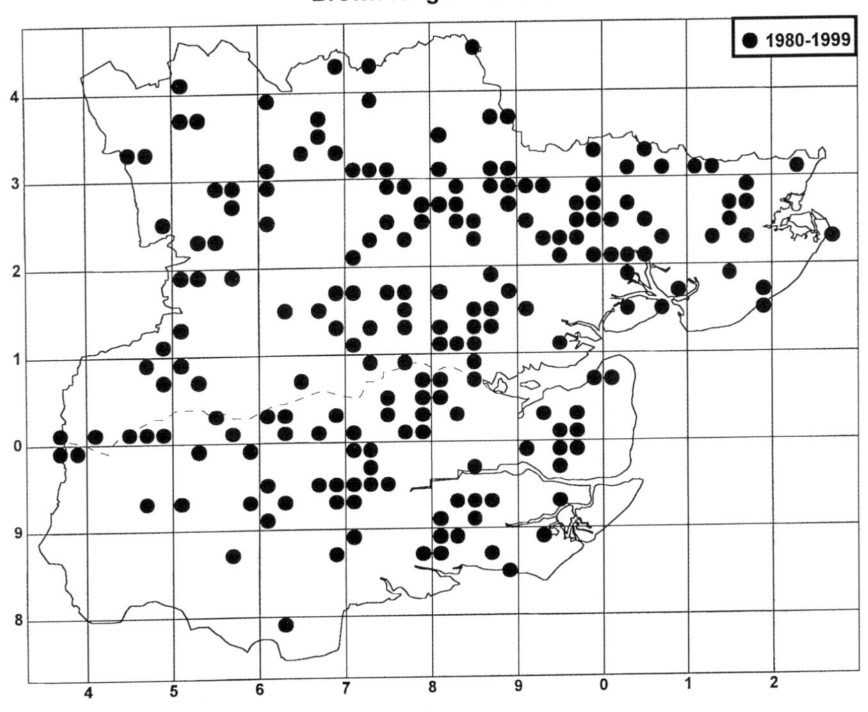

treatment taking place. Probably the commonest victim of the toxic chemicals used 30 years ago, brown long-eared bats have successfully re-occupied lofts where safer, newer alternatives have been used; in some cases breeding within nine months of chemicals being applied. The presence of this species can also be detected from its habit of perching while consuming large prey items. The wings of nymphalid butterflies and noctuid moths, together with droppings can be found beneath such perches, usually in porches, barns, outbuildings and churches. Brown long-eared bats often roost in churches but their presence is not always apparent – at Lamarsh and St Nicholas, Ingrave, bats are present in the roof space, but droppings are not found in the aisles. At St Peter and St Paul, Stondon Massey, bats gain access to the tower by landing on the bell ropes and crawling up into the belfry.

Because of the habit of following insects to ground level, brown long-eared bats are vulnerable to cats and each year, a number of bats with broken wings or torn membranes are brought to the attention of the Essex Bat Group. Rarely, bats are taken by avian predators and the remains of one unfortunate individual was found in a barn owl pellet from Tillingham.

Although frequently encountered in summer, there are few records of brown long-eared bats in hibernation sites. A sedentary species, the habitat surrounding the Grays deneholes is unsuitable for this bat and only occasional individuals are recorded. In contrast, the wartime bunkers at Coggeshall, which have been adapted by fixing bat-bricks inside them and partially blocking the entrances, are in prime habitat. Up to twenty bats breed in a nearby summer roost and use the bunkers for hibernation. As many as four in one bat-brick have been counted.

In suitable areas the brown long-eared bat is common – four colonies are known bordering Danbury Common – but the removal of hedgerows and woodland in the past, together with the use of toxic chemicals in roof spaces, has contributed to the decline of this species. Brown long-eared bats are dependent on older properties and will require a more enlightened building industry, together with the sympathetic support of roost owners, to be able to maintain the population at its current level.

Three species of lagomorphs are present in the British Isles – the rabbit, the brown hare and the mountain hare (which is confined to Ireland, parts of Scotland, the Peak District and the Isle of Man). Once included in the order Rodentia, the lagomorphs, which comprise the rabbits, hares and pikas, have several distinctive characteristics. Unique among these is the habit of refection whereby soft faecal pellets produced during the day are eaten and then excreted as hard pellets, having passed through the alimentary canal for a second time. Lagomorphs are also separated from rodents by their short tail, large caecum and naked area around the nostrils that is covered by retractable flaps of skin. All lagomorphs are herbivorous, with both cheek-teeth and incisors that grow continuously.

The rabbit and brown hare are common in Essex with the rabbit penetrating well into some heavily urbanised areas of the county (having been observed grazing in railway sidings at Stratford and in the heart of Docklands). Records of rabbits have come from sightings of live animals, the presence of burrows and road casualties. The brown hare is separated from the rabbit by its larger size, long ears (with a black tip), long hind legs and black marking on the upper surface of the tail. It is most often recorded from arable land, particularly during the winter months before growing crops conceal its presence.

The brown hare has been the subject of several recent national surveys, initiated by the concern about an 80% decline in the population during the 20th century. Several 1km squares in Essex have been surveyed as part of this research and the species has also been included in the Essex Biodiversity Action Plan. Although the extent of any decline in the county population is uncertain due to lack of historical data, the future achievement of the Action Plan's objectives will guarantee that the current status and distribution of the brown hare will, at least, be maintained.

Rabbit

Oryctolagus cuniculus (Linn., 1758)

Status: Abundant, increasing

The rabbit is common throughout Essex, occurring wherever there are areas of short grass or closely grazed agricultural pasture. New areas of scrub and surface cover are readily invaded by expanding colonies although the population can be temporarily checked by outbreaks of myxomatosis (which is endemic in the county). Rabbits are also to be found in deciduous woodland, particularly where predator control is undertaken by gamekeepers; however conifer plantations are less hospitable and here, the rabbits are restricted to the clearings and rides. Breeding occurs between January and August when litters of between three and seven young are born at monthly intervals. The young appear at burrow entrances after eighteen days and are weaned a week later (Cowan, 1991). Although there is high pre-natal mortality, a female rabbit in an expanding colony can produce twenty live offspring during a breeding season - enabling a rapid expansion of the population (Lloyd, 1970).

The rabbit was introduced to Britain by the Normans – the first archaeological evidence (dated between the 11th and 13th centuries) of their presence comes from Rayleigh Castle (Sheail, 1971), with further material from *c.*1100 found at Hadleigh (Veale, 1957). By the 13th century, warrens were established: the locations of some survive to the present day as place names, such as at the headquarters of the Epping Forest Conservators (The Warren) at Loughton and the Warren Golf Course at Woodham Walter. Further evidence of medieval rabbit farming comes in the form of artificial warrens or 'pillow mounds' that are present in Epping and Hatfield Forests. These consist of flat-topped hummocks of varying sizes into which holes were bored, the rabbits being pushed in using long poles. Soon afterwards, they inevitably escaped and began to colonise the surrounding area. As rabbits became more common, so their value declined: by the 19th century they became the diet of the poor rather than the delicacy of the rich (Rackham, 1986). By this time, the

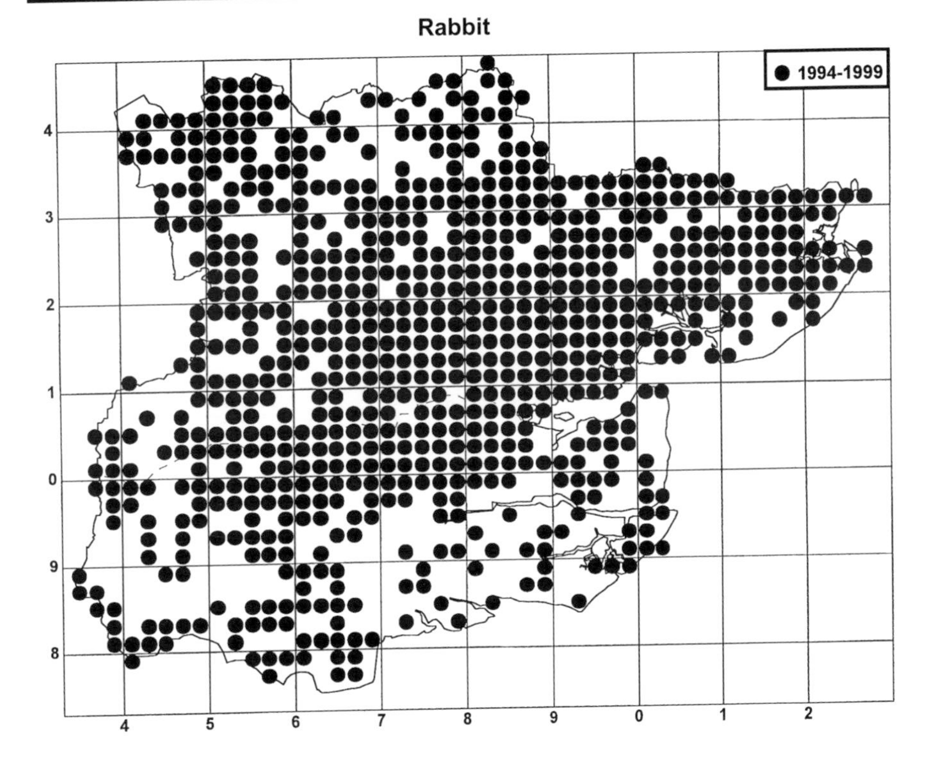

increasing interest in game and its associated predator control (together with the creation of suitable habitat as a result of changes in agricultural methods) allowed the population to increase to the extent that in 1898 Laver wrote, *"this destructive creature is very common in all parts of Essex, and little need be said about it."* Evidence of the explosion in the population comes from the game book of the Great Parndon estate where the number of rabbits shot or trapped, almost quadrupled during the last quarter of the 19th century.

By 1953, it was estimated that 100 million rabbits were present in Britain. The introduction of myxomatosis killed over 99% (Thompson, 1956) although there is little documentary evidence of its impact in Essex. However, the legacy of this disease in the county can be seen on our heaths and commons, where the establishment of 'myxomatosis birch woods' dating back to the 1950s (a good example is present at Layer Breton Heath) occurred as a result of reduced grazing by rabbits. Seear (1964) reported that the rabbit population fell markedly after 1953 and that local increases were often later wiped out by new outbreaks of the disease. The 1986 atlas (Hughes), perhaps through under-recording, failed to record the species in many areas of north-west Essex and suggested that *"there appears to be*

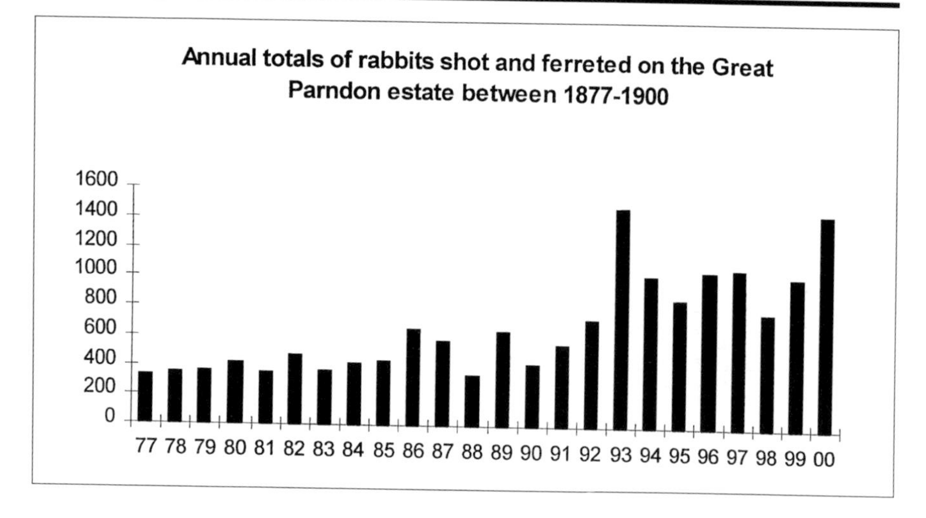

only a gradual upward trend in the rabbit population, with greater increases in isolated areas."

The rabbit can now be seen in all suitable areas of Essex, perhaps only being excluded from parts of the highly urbanised south. Despite the continuing presence of myxomatosis, mortality caused by the disease has been reduced to 40–60% by an increase in genetic resistance (Ross & Sanders, 1984); the new threat of viral haemorrhagic disease, first discovered in Britain in 1992, appears to have receded and it has not been found in Essex. Nationally, the population is thought to be 40% of pre-myxomatosis levels and increasing (Harris *et al.*, 1995): this increase is also being seen in the Essex countryside as new areas such as the verges of new roads are rapidly colonised. The rabbit seems certain to thrive in the new century.

Brown hare

Lepus europaeus Pallas, 1778

Status: Common

The brown hare was introduced to Britain during Roman times and has become a familiar feature of the Essex countryside. However, a recent national survey (Hutchings & Harris, 1996) has suggested that the population today may be only 20% of what it was 150 years ago. Laver (1898) records *"I shall say little about this animal as it must be well-known to everyone"*, yet in 1903 he wrote that it was *"formerly very frequent, but in some districts approaching extinction as a consequence of persecution, the results of the Ground Game Act. In need of protection."* Although the increase in the human population and the spread of industrialisation would also have contributed to this decline, the Ground Game Act 1880, which permitted tenant farmers, rather than just landowners, to shoot hares was considered to be the main reason. The protection afforded to hares on the 85% of Britain farmed by tenants was thereby removed and the population of hares declined as a result of overshooting.

Hutchings and Harris (1996) described the impact of this legislation on the hare population on a large shooting estate in Norfolk, an impact that was mirrored on the Great Parndon estate near Harlow at the end of the 19th century. With protection removed after the introduction of the Act, hares were perceived to be pests and overshooting led to an inevitable reduction in numbers. As numbers declined, the pressure of hunting reduced and the population recovered, only for the cycle to be repeated during the 1890s, leading to Laver's call for protection for the species in 1903. Following this second decline, the population in the south-east, as measured by game bag numbers, recovered up to 1930 (Tapper & Parsons, 1984). Further increases were seen during World War II, when more land was converted to arable and the introduction of myxomatosis in 1953 saw hares benefit from a decline in the rabbit population (Barnes & Tapper, 1986).

At this time, hares were considered to be very common in north and mid-Essex, with large numbers killed on farmers' shoots. For example, in the 1961/62 winter,

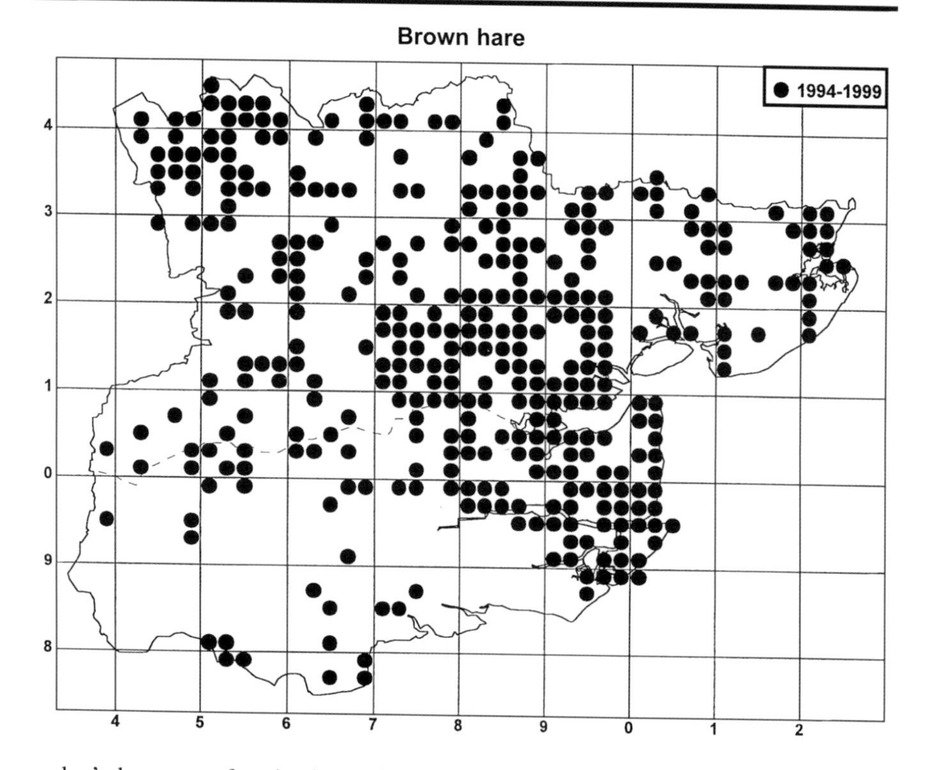

a day's bag was often in the region of four to five hundred hares in north Essex (Seear, 1964). Since then, the national population has declined with the main factor thought to have been agricultural intensification. Brown hares do best in diverse arable landscapes where a range of food is available throughout the year; the trend towards large areas of monoculture, such as winter cereals, means that food is short during the summer when the crops are tall, woody and inedible.

During the present survey, hares have been found to be widespread throughout Essex with good numbers recorded in the north-west and from coastal areas such as the Dengie and Foulness. Most records have been obtained between November and March when hares are most visible, either lying up in forms in winter crops or 'boxing', where unreceptive, near-oestrus females are trying to ward off the attention of males (Holley & Greenwood, 1984). Double figure counts from single fields have been made during the winter from Saffron Walden, Foulness and Tollesbury. Hares were also recorded in coppiced woodlands especially those that are surrounded by arable land. The area where a decline has been noticeable however is on land within the M25. Hares are now rarely reported from Epping Forest and Rainham Marshes where they were frequently recorded during the

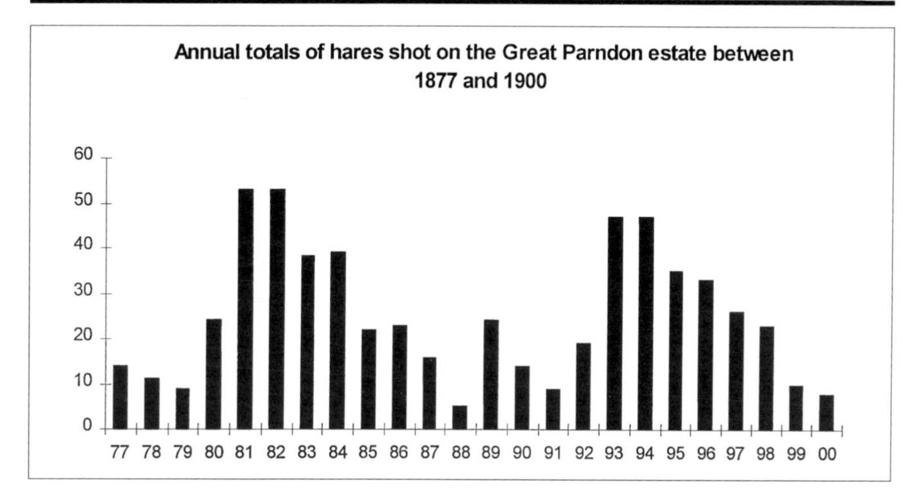

1960s, and it would appear that the growth of the road network has created a barrier to the recolonisation of these areas from outer Essex. The national survey conducted during the winters of 1991/92 and 1992/93 concluded that in arable areas, hare numbers were most likely to increase where there was an improvement in habitat richness (e.g. set aside, headlands, hedgerows), particularly in those areas where the numbers were not significantly reduced by culling (Hutchings & Harris, 1996). Organised shoots still occur in many areas and illegal coursing has been reported from the north-west of the county. In 1997, the police forces of Essex, Bedfordshire, Cambridgeshire and Hertfordshire combined in 'Operation Tortoise' to combat illegal coursing around the borders of these counties. Local landowners were also involved, resulting in a big decline in coursing in north-west Essex although there have been recent reports of the problem reappearing in the Maldon area.

Brown hares are indicators of a habitat-rich rural environment. Their future is the subject of a Biodiversity Action Plan drawn up by conservation bodies in Essex, which will promote the uptake of agri-environmental schemes that consider the needs of hares when implementing changes in land management. With an increase in the availability of food and cover after ploughing and harvesting, the brown hare should continue to be a common sight in our arable landscape.

Rodents form the largest order of mammals, with around 1,500 species occurring throughout the world. They are characterised by a single pair of incisors in both jaws that grow continuously during their lifespan. There is a large gap, or diastema, between the incisors and cheek-teeth, the jaw musculature being adapted for gnawing. Thirteen members of this order have been recorded in Essex during the last 200 years, although two are now extinct. The red squirrel survived in the county until 1972 and the coypu was introduced and eradicated during the second half of the 20th century. The musk rat (*Ondatra zibethicus*), which never reached Essex, and the coypu remain the only two introduced mammals that have been successfully removed from Britain by deliberate pest control campaigns.

Of the remaining rodents, the grey squirrel, recorded from 81% of the tetrads in the county, proved to be the most widespread species found in the last five years. By contrast, the ship rat, present at only a few buildings at Tilbury, was the most restricted in its distribution. The second arboreal member of this group is the common dormouse, which at present is mainly found at ancient woodland nature reserves.

Most of the rodents are small mammals, like shrews, studied by the combination of live-trapping, 'bottle-hunting' and owl-pellet analysis. The results of these studies are summarised in the insectivore introduction (Table 5.1, page 25). The important thing to note is that each method of study identifies a different species as the most abundant. This is partly because the study methods sample different habitats but is mainly a result of the differing biases of each method.

Small mammals also have large annual changes in abundance as rapid breeding in the summer adds juveniles to the population. Mortality rates are high throughout the year but probably highest in winter. The difficulties of making accurate estimates of these changes in abundance is illustrated in the graph below: it shows the annual cycle of abundance of wood mice as measured by live-trapping in a wood and by owl-pellet analysis. Both cycles share an October peak but in other respects the patterns are precise opposites. This may be genuine: perhaps the barn owls hunting in open habitats sample a population which peaks in summer and autumn and the woodland population peaks in winter when mice return to woodland habitats from the fields. Alternatively, it may be that owls are best at catching juvenile mice and traps at catching territory-holding adults. The message is to treat any one source of data with caution.

The rodents also include the only Essex examples in recent centuries of an introduced species replacing its closest relative completely (the grey squirrel replacing the native red squirrel during this century and the common rat ousting the black rat, itself an introduced species but of longer standing).

While the pest-control campaigns against coypu and grey squirrels provided many records for the maps the same cannot be said of the mouse and rat control industry.

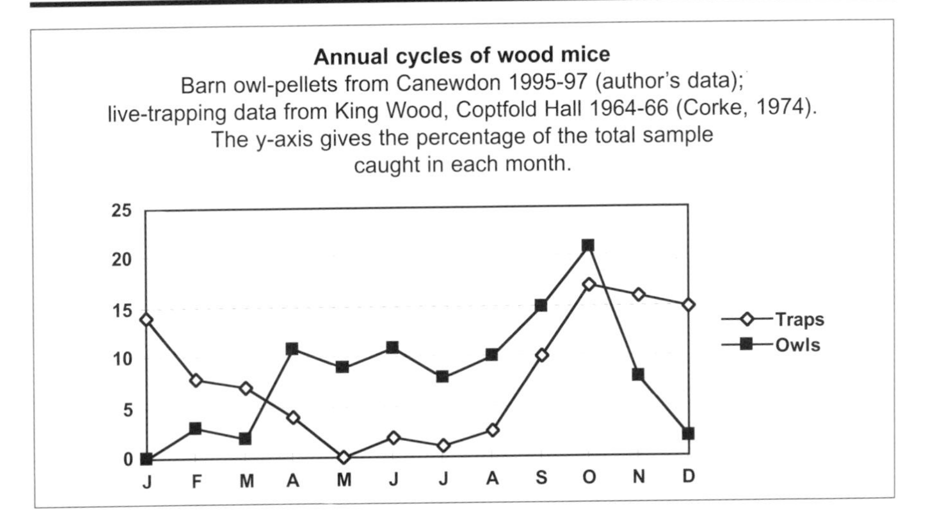

A certain understandable secrecy surrounds the location of infested premises and mice are not usually identified to species level before poison is laid. The map for house mice is probably the worst example of under-recording in this book.

Due to their high reproductive rate, rodents have the potential to be the most successful group in Essex. Several species are declining however; the field vole, water vole, harvest mouse and dormouse due to habitat loss and the house mouse, common rat and ship rat as a result of changes in the countryside and improved control methods. Fortunately, there is a high public regard for the water vole and the dormouse, and conservation measures are in place to ensure their survival in the new millennium.

Red squirrel

Sciurus vulgaris Linn., 1758

Status: Extinct

"*This elegant and active little mammal is so well known that very little need be said about it. It occurs in all parts of the county where suitable spots (that is woods) are to be found.*" Seventy-five years after Laver's comments, the red squirrel was extinct in Essex. The decline and eventual disappearance of this species was well described by Harris (1973/74) and the following account has been adapted from his review.

Although common in the late 19th century, red squirrel numbers declined rapidly in the period between 1903 and 1914 in south-east England, due to an outbreak of coccidiosis. During this time, in 1910, C.E. Green introduced continental red squirrels (*S. v. fuscoater*) onto his estate in Epping and jet black and dark-tailed squirrels were recorded in the area in the following years. They caused problems, especially in nearby gardens, and numbers declined until, by 1919, Stubbs (1923) reported an increase in the population of native squirrels (*S. v. leucorus*) at Theydon. The British race recovered further in the 1920s and these animals lived alongside descendants of the introduced stock for twenty years, with the last melanistic squirrel being recorded near Parndon in 1943. A similar pattern of decline and recovery had also taken place in eastern Essex and the 1945 England and Wales Squirrel Survey (Shorten, 1946) found that in a survey of 303 of the county's 332 parishes, red squirrels were present in 126 (42%). However, the final decline was about to start and by 1950, only 88 parishes had red squirrels. The last record from Belfairs Nature Reserve was of an individual seen in 1948 (Spooner & Bowdrey, 1988). At this time the only place in west Essex with red squirrels was Epping Forest: these had gone from the main forest area by 1957 (Wheeler, 1958) and outlying woods two years later. In 1958, the red squirrel was last seen in Hatfield Forest (Rackham, 1989) and by 1960, they were present only in east and north-east Essex.

The red squirrel's preferred habitat is large stands of mixed woodland, from where, as the population increases, it can overflow into less suitable habitats such as small woods and gardens. For centuries, the red squirrel had occupied a niche where it had been able to prosper, without competition. Gamekeepers had ensured that one

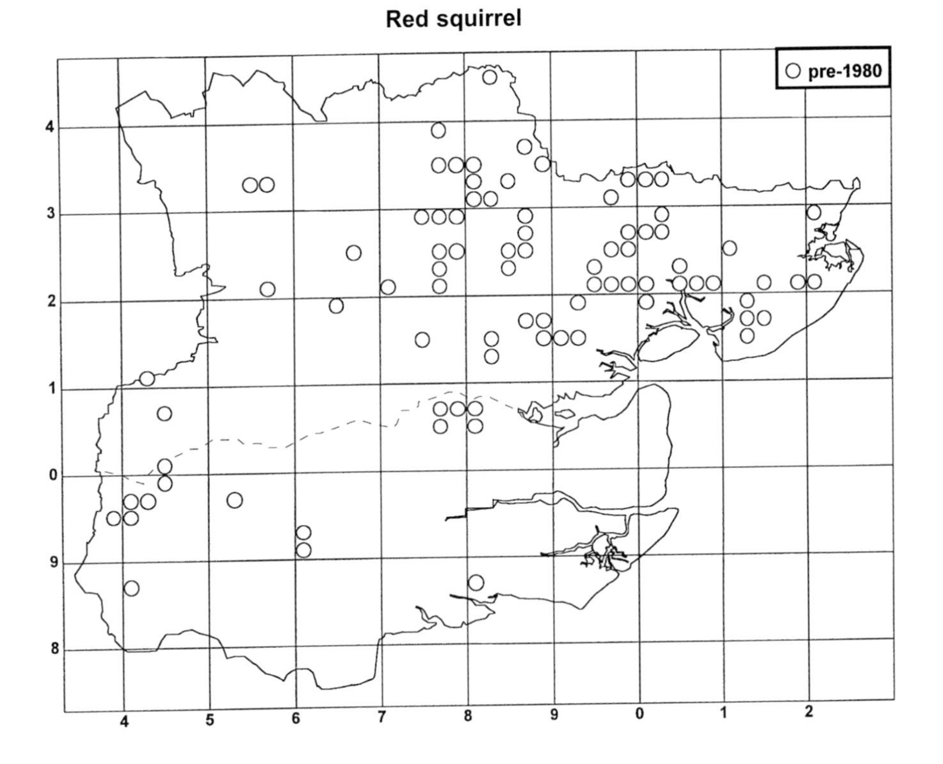

predator, the pine marten, was eradicated and the major causes of mortality were prolonged spells of very cold weather and starvation in the event of a poor autumn seed crop. When competition arrived in the form of grey squirrels, the red squirrel retreated into areas of mixed woodland such as those around Colchester where they were able to coexist for a time; however, it was the absence of pure conifer that ensured its extinction in Essex. Some animals survived for a time in built-up areas of Colchester where, presumably, food was supplied by local residents, thereby reducing the intensity of the competition from the American intruder.

After 1970, red squirrels occupied just three areas of the county. The only reliable records for that year came from Weeley Hall Wood (where some were shot) and Lexden Park. However, the MAFF Squirrel Survey of 1971 found them to be present at St Osyth, Little Oakley and, surprisingly, the Warren Golf Course in Woodham Walter. Also in 1971, individuals were seen at Kirby-le-Soken and Little Baddow. The presence of red squirrels in the Danbury area, where they had not been seen for fifteen years, caused Harris to conclude that they had probably been introduced.

Red squirrel decline (redrawn from Harris, 1973/74)

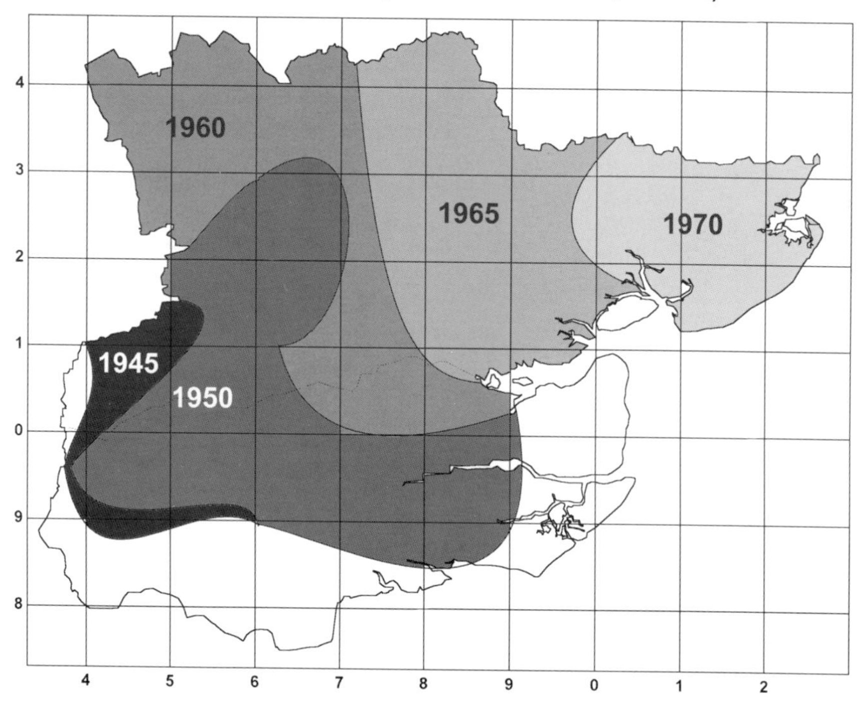

A last attempt to delay the inevitable saw the introduction of three males and three females from Rendlesham Forest, Suffolk into the coniferous area of Thorndon Park in 1968 or 1969. They may have been responsible for a number of unconfirmed reports from Brentwood and Shenfield around that time, with the last sighting occurring in the summer of 1972.

Against this background of virtual extinction by 1970, the report of a red squirrel from Harlow in 1985 seems likely to be a case of mistaken identity.

Grey squirrel

Sciurus carolinensis Gmelin, 1788

Status: Abundant, increasing

"... the quadrupeds of Britain are so few, that every new species is a great acquisition"
White (1789)

The comment by Gilbert White has been used before as an introduction to this species (Harris, 1973/74) and much of our information on the spread of the grey squirrel in Essex comes from that account. Although the first evidence of the grey squirrel in the United Kingdom dates from 1828, it was not until later in the 19th century that the widespread importation and release of American squirrels took place. Between 1876 and 1929, 33 introductions were made of which only one (at Bushey) was unsuccessful. Probably the early ancestors of our Essex squirrels were the ten released at Woburn Park in 1890; this colony prospered to such an extent that eight further introductions were made using their descendants, including 91 sent to London Zoo during 1905–7 (Middleton, 1931). From Regent's Park, the animals spread in most directions; however, the absence of open spaces to the east and the industrial area and reservoirs of the Lea Valley acted as a barrier and it was some time before the invasion of Essex began. The first record is of an unconfirmed sighting of a grey squirrel in Wanstead Park in 1917 (Middleton, 1930), followed by an authentic report from Gaynes Park, Epping in 1921 (Watt, 1923). Prior to 1930, there were two further records from the south-west of the county and one from Stanway in 1927.

It seems likely that the colonisation of Essex was delayed by a poor beech mast crop in 1930; the weakened squirrels then succumbed to an outbreak of coccidiosis, the same disease that had earlier decimated red squirrel numbers (Middleton, 1932). However, this proved a temporary respite and, although prevented from reaching Essex via the Lea Valley, the early pioneers arrived at Roydon in 1933 and from there moved south towards Epping Forest. The Grey Squirrel Survey of 1934–35 produced only three reports from Essex and at that time there had been only an occasional sighting of a grey squirrel in Epping Forest. However, by the autumn of

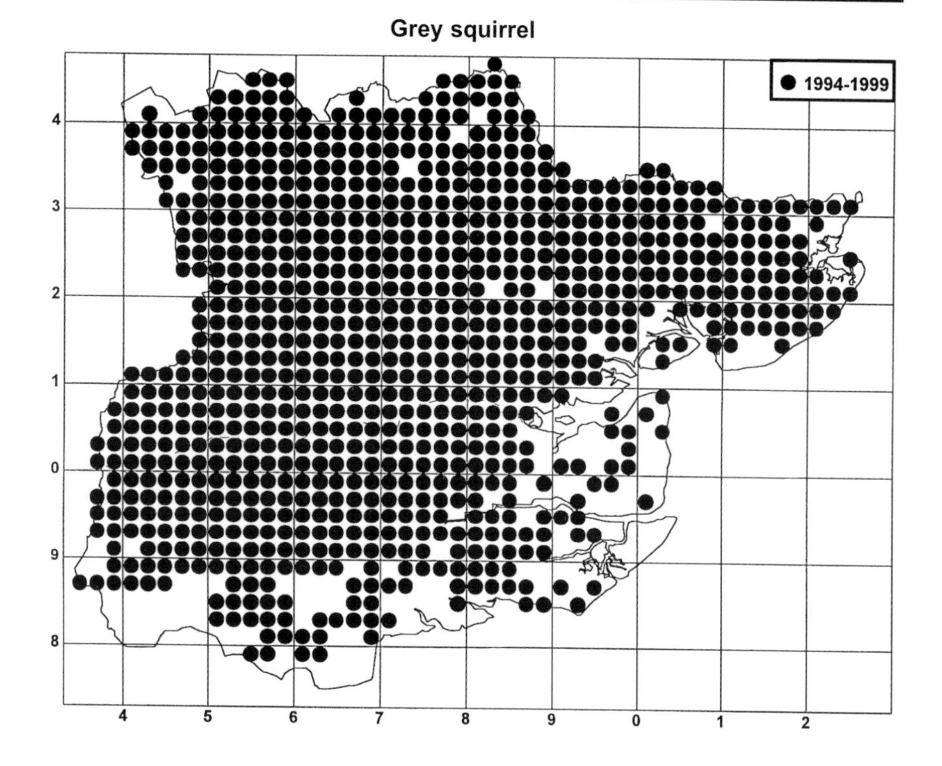

1937, they had arrived in force and the ensuing control measures had killed 150 squirrels. Johnston (1938) conceded that grey squirrels were still present, but suggested that the threat to the native species had passed its most critical stage!

The eastward spread was slow to occur, in contrast to other counties, and only six further records had been confirmed by 1937 (Parsons & Middleton) with the grey squirrel making limited progress in Essex until 1945. This was, however, the lull before the storm and, with the eastern boundary moving twenty miles in the next ten years, two-thirds of the county had been colonised.

The Squirrel Survey of 1959 (Lloyd, 1962) showed that the eastward migration, after 1955, had slowed down. This was particularly so in south-east Essex, with its large tracts of urbanised and treeless habitat along the Thames. However, in the north-east, with more suitable countryside, Colchester had already been reached. There were three possible reasons for the delay in further colonisation. Another low mast crop in 1954, followed by a poor breeding season were probably the main factors, but additionally, the squirrel bounty was doubled in 1955. Although this may have had a negligible effect in most areas, the forest keepers at Epping were

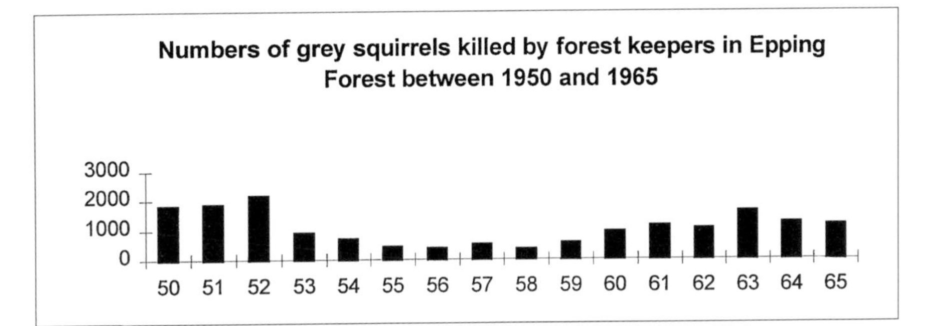

carrying out rigorous control measures during the winter months. Between 1950 and 1965, the forest was systemically covered two or three times a year – the squirrels being shot after being dislodged from their dreys. Assuming the same effort was made each year, it is clear that there was a decline in the population during the mid-1950s which was reversed by the end of the decade. Despite such efforts, by 1960, the distribution of the grey squirrel in Essex looked very similar to that of today with only the intensively farmed areas inside the sea walls left uncolonised.

In the 1971 Squirrel Survey, conducted by MAFF, grey squirrels were absent from only 23 parishes, mostly in coastal areas:

Barling Magna	Foulness	Harwich
Little Bromley	Mistley	Tolleshunt Major
Beaumont-cum-Moze	Goldhanger	Helions Bumpstead
Little Oakley	Peldon	West Mersea
Canvey Island	Great Clacton	Langenhoe
Little Totham	Thorpe-le-Soken	Wix
East Mersea	Great Wakering	Layer Breton
Manningtree	Tollesbury	

Today, the presence of grey squirrels has still to be confirmed from only Canvey Island and Foulness.

In Essex, the grey squirrel occurs in a wide range of habitats, preferring mixed or broadleaved woodland but also thriving in parks, hedgerows, gardens and urban areas with mature trees. They feed predominantly on seeds and plant material, which are often obtained by foraging on the ground. The breeding season is between February and July when one or two litters of two to four young are produced in a drey or tree hole. It is in September that young squirrels are most vulnerable with many becoming road casualties at this time when dispersing in search of new territories. Three-quarters of juveniles fail to survive their first winter

Spread of the Grey squirrel (redrawn and updated from Harris 1973/74)

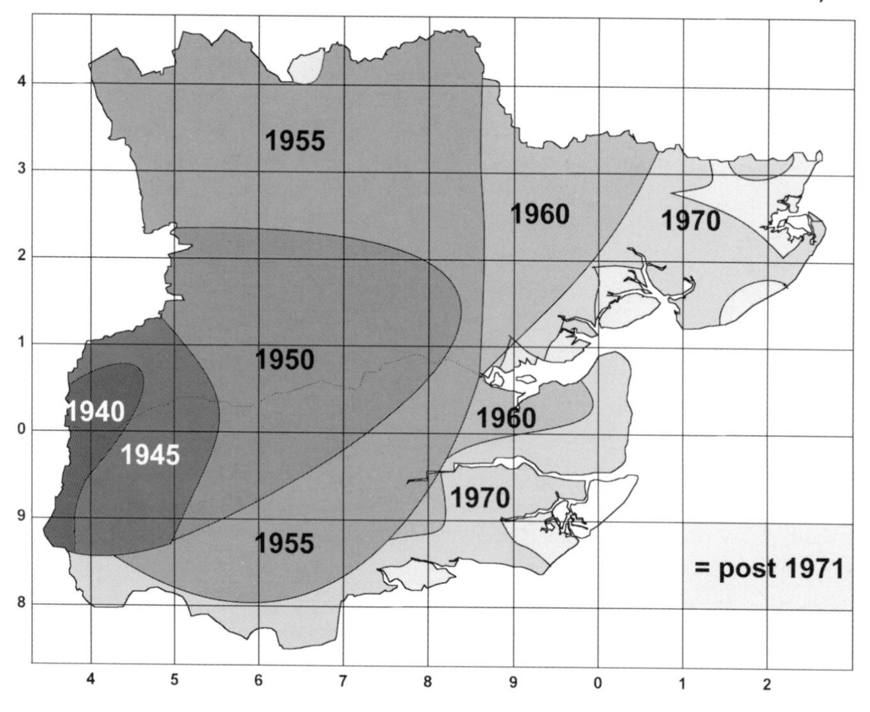

but those that do may live for up to seven years (Gurnell, 1991). Occasionally, albino specimens are reported and a juvenile, now in the collection at Southend Museum, was found dead at Howe Green on 29th October 1985.

Of the many records collected during the last five years, most have been of dreys, visible during the winter in deciduous trees, live sightings and road casualties – which show a peak in September. It is at this time that dispersing squirrels can appear in sub-optimal habitats with autumn individuals seen at Wat Tyler Country Park, Old Hall Marshes and parts of the Dengie peninsula. Although on a much reduced scale, the spread of the grey squirrel has continued in recent years. Mersea Island has been colonised and other coastal areas have reported their first squirrels (including one individual seen taking the eggs of little terns in Hamford Water). Regular sightings at South Woodham Ferrers were first confirmed in 1996, and there are occasional records from St Lawrence Bay, Steeple.

The grey squirrel is perhaps the most widely recorded mammal species in Essex – its remarkable invasion having colonised most of Essex in 30 years. Today, squirrels attract mixed emotions – regarded as vermin in woodland, as well as being fed and encouraged as a common visitor to some urban gardens.

Bank vole

Clethrionomys glareolus (Schreber, 1780)

Status: Abundant

This reddish brown vole is widespread throughout Essex, particularly along hedgerows and in mature deciduous woodland with a thick shrub layer. Both bank voles and field voles occur in grassland habitat; the bank vole being found where bramble and scrub offer cover from predators; the similar field vole preferring the more open areas. The diet is primarily herbivorous, consisting mainly of fruits and seeds; however, fungi, moss, dead leaves (in winter), roots, flowers, grass, insects and worms have all been recorded. The breeding season is from April to October, with litters of usually four young being produced every three to four weeks. Life expectancy is a few months, and by winter the population consists entirely of animals born during the year (Alibhai & Gipps, 1991). The population can fluctuate markedly and is strongly influenced by the success of the tree seed crop with numbers of bank voles being greater during the summer following a successful seed crop than after a poor season (Mallorie & Flowerdew, 1994).

Laver (1898) considered that the bank vole was uncommon and had only seen two specimens, suggesting that under-recording was also a problem for Victorian recorders! At this time, it also seems likely that caution may have been exercised before identifying a bank vole, as the species was still relatively new, having been first described from an Essex specimen in 1832. Today the bank vole is commonly found in suitable habitat but has not adapted to the urban areas of the county. Many records have come from live-trapping, with this species being caught more frequently than any other apart from the wood mouse. There were also several sightings of live animals – their diurnal activity makes bank voles easier to observe than other small mammals.

The bank vole is widely preyed upon by owls, mustelids, cats and foxes, although its preference for hedgerows and areas with cover afford it some protection from avian

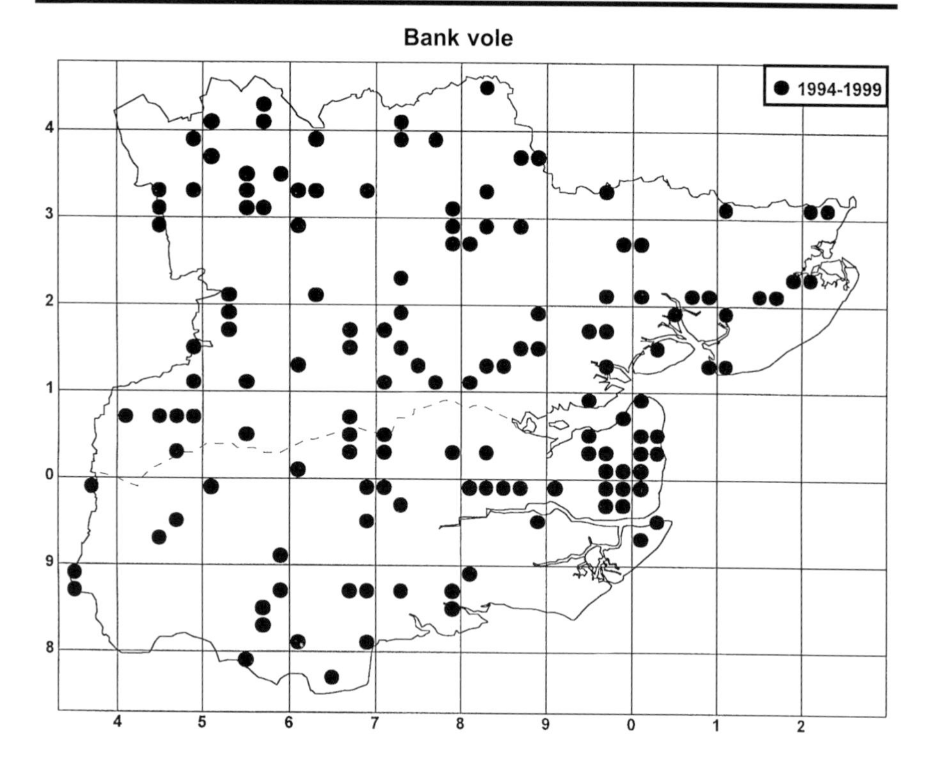

predators. As a prey item in the diet of a pair of barn owls at Canewdon, the bank vole occurred less commonly than the field vole, constituting 3.2% of the mammalian prey compared with 4.8% of the total prey of barn owls present at nineteen sites on the Dengie peninsular (Love, 1998).

Exceptionally, colour variations are recorded and Laver described the finding of an albino near Chelmsford in August 1885 that was forwarded to London Zoo. In September 1981, an albino was trapped near Brentwood, and several generations of albino bank voles were bred until the strain died out some months later (see Plate 8)

The bank vole is not threatened in Essex and should remain abundant in the future. With new hedgerows being planted, a growth in farm woodland schemes and the continuation of long-term set aside, the bank vole could well increase in numbers over the next few years.

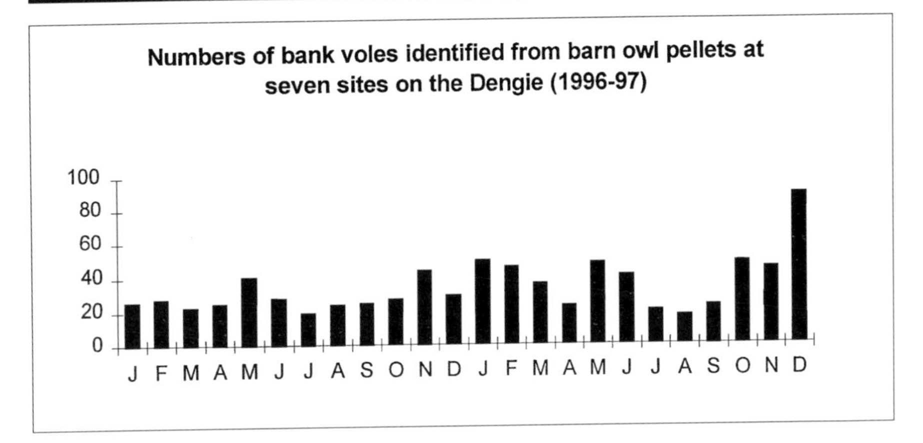
Numbers of bank voles identified from barn owl pellets at seven sites on the Dengie (1996-97)
100
80
60
40
20
0
J F M A M J J A S O N D J F M A M J J A S O N D

Field vole

Microtus agrestis (Linn., 1761)

Status: Abundant, declining

This small, greyish-brown vole is common throughout Essex wherever rough, ungrazed grassland remains, also occurring at lower densities in woodland edges and rides and hedgerows. The field vole can be separated from the bank vole by the lack of chestnut coloration in the dorsal fur, and the smaller, less prominent ears. Evidence of their presence in grassland comes from well-defined runways amongst tussocks, together with small accumulations of green droppings and nibbled grass stems. The breeding season lasts from March to October, when successive litters of four to six young are raised – the highest densities being achieved in summer and early autumn (Gipps & Alibhai, 1991). In a two-year survey of barn owl pellets at Canewdon, although less plentiful than wood mice, field vole numbers increased in spring and early summer before declining (perhaps due to predation), with a second peak later in the year.

Although less marked in Britain, field vole populations are cyclical, with periods of abundance followed by periods of scarcity. Historically, there were occasions when the numbers reached plague proportions: "*About Hallowtide last past [1580] in the marishes of Danesie Hundred, in a place called Southminster, in the Countie of Essex, a strange thing happened: there suddenlie appeared an infinite multitude of mice, which, overwhelming the whole earth in the said marishes, did sheare and gnaw the grasse by the roots, spoiling and tainting the same with their venomous teeth in such sort that the cattell which grased thereon were smitten with a murreine, and died thereof...*" (Holinshed, 1586). History repeated itself over sixty years later on Foulness *when "an Army of Mice, nesting in Ant-hills, as Conies in Burroughs, shaved off the grass at the bare roots, which, withering to dung, was infectious to Cattle*" (Fuller, 1662).

Both authors went on to describe how the plague was followed by an increase in the number of owls feeding on the voles. The field vole is a favoured item in the diet of the grey heron, kestrel, four species of owl, fox, stoat weasel, badger and domestic cat and many of the recent records have been the result of the analysis of barn owl pellets, with others coming from Longworth trapping, the reporting of cat victims and sightings of live animals, often when lifting sheets of corrugated iron set in suitable habitat.

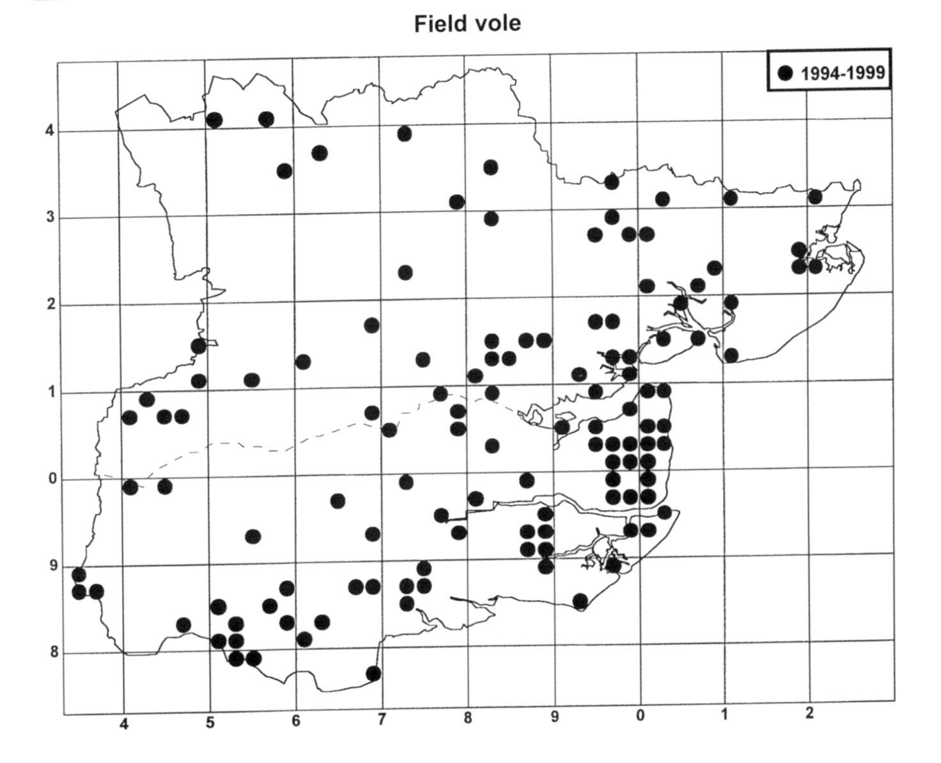

In recent years in Essex, the field vole has declined due to an increase in grazing associated with the rise in the rabbit population and the loss of marginal land to development with the ploughing of field edges and the 'tidying up' of roadside verges also contributing. With rabbit numbers likely to increase further, it is improbable that the field vole will recover the ground it has recently lost.

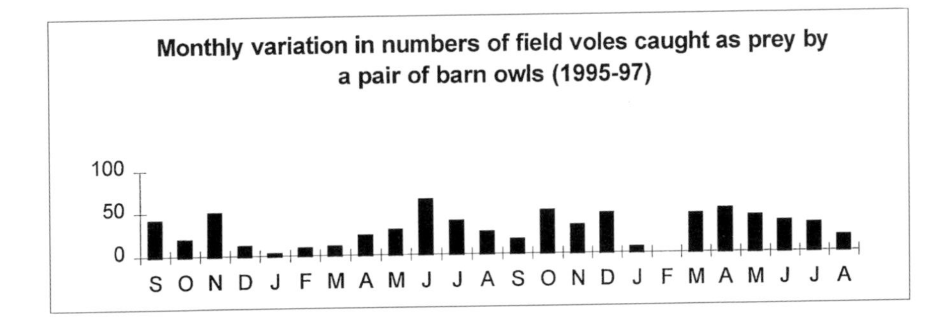

Water vole

Arvicola terrestris (Linn., 1758)

Status: Fairly common, declining

The water vole is a creature of slow-flowing rivers, streams, ditches and ponds bordered with steep banks that offer sites for burrows and a dense fringe of emergent vegetation to provide cover and a plentiful food supply. Because this type of habitat has been degraded through pollution, human interference (such as new roads and development) and canalisation, water vole populations have declined. The recent spread of the introduced mink is believed to have posed an additional threat. In 1989–90, a national survey was carried out to assess the current status of the water vole: part of the project involved revisiting sites from historical records dating back to 1900. Of these, 68% had lost their water voles and the authors predicted that the figure could rise to 94% by the turn of the century – a rate of loss greater than that of any other British mammal. East Anglia fared better than most areas: 60–80% of sites with historical records were still occupied by water voles (Strachan & Jefferies, 1993). This finding may be due to the relative scarcity of mink in East Anglia, because the decline in the water vole has been more marked where mink are widespread.

In Essex, where there are few mink records, it seems more likely that habitat fragmentation, canalisation of river banks (with subsequent removal of emergent vegetation) and, at some sites, drought, have played a greater part in any reduction in the population. It is difficult to state the extent to which Essex water voles have declined, because their historical distribution is poorly documented. Laver (1898) wrote that the water vole was "*common in all parts of Essex wherever there are sluggish streams or where stagnant water exists in sufficient quantity to hide it*". Hughes (1986) described the species as "*a familiar sight in Essex along well-vegetated river banks*", although the limited number of records made it difficult to assess its true status. At that time, water voles were present along the Roding and the Lea in East London (TQ38, TQ48) but were not recorded in central Essex. During the 1989–90 national survey, 70 Essex sites were surveyed. Of these, 57 (81.4%) produced positive evidence of water voles and the species was still present at 86.7% of the historical sites.

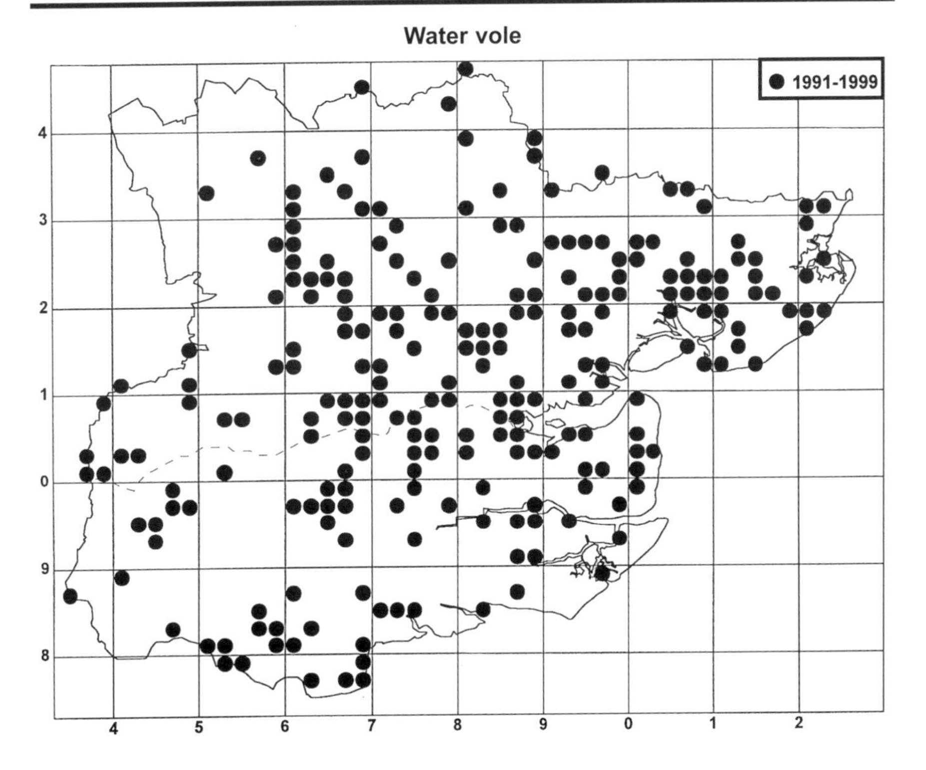

The current map includes records collected by Geoff Gibbs along the Chelmer during a NRA Breeding Bird Survey in 1991–92, as well as all records from 1994 onwards. Fortunately, the water vole is still present along all the river systems in the county, with apparently thriving populations being reported from Old Hall Marshes (C. Tyas, pers. comm.). At Rainham Marshes; an estimated population of 150 voles at this site in late 1997, was considered to be the largest in the Greater London area (B. O'Dowd, pers. comm.). In 1997, the national office of the Wildlife Trusts organised a survey, by volunteers, called 'Water Volewatch'. The identification of latrines and feeding 'lawns' at the entrance to burrows was described on a recording form and positive sightings were received from more than twenty sites in Essex, covering the main river systems. Although water voles usually favour slow-moving water, they were also found in the brackish borrow-dykes behind the sea walls of tidal rivers; reports came from the Dengie, Tollesbury, Foulness and Two Tree Island, where part of their territory is affected by the incoming tide. Water voles are recorded as prey items less frequently than other small rodents and only one report, from Aveley, was received of a water vole being caught by a cat. Barn owls occasionally prey upon water voles and twelve were identified from owl pellets collected at Canewdon and fifteen from Old Hall Marshes (representing 0.4% and 0.5% of total prey items respectively).

The most recent survey for this species (co-ordinated by the Environment Agency and the Essex Wildlife Trust) took place during the summer of 1998 following the inclusion of the water vole in the Essex Biodiversity Action Plan. The objectives of the survey were to identify key sites in Essex for water voles and mink so that baseline distribution maps for both species could be drawn, and future population trends could be monitored. In addition, the results would also be used to formulate a conservation strategy for the water vole in the county.

The survey was conducted on twelve river catchments throughout the county: 500m sections of river were surveyed at 3km intervals using a database previously tested by the Environment Agency. So that non-riverine aquatic habitats might be included, water features such as moats, gravel pits and dykes were also surveyed in a number of randomly-selected 1km squares. In total, 428 river sections and 108 non-riverine sites were investigated, and information was also collected on the suitability of the habitat for water voles. The presence of latrines at a site was considered to be evidence of breeding and these 'core' sites were recorded separately from those where burrows, footprints, feeding 'lawns' or food remains were found.

Table 8.1 **The number of positive and 'core' sites for water voles in Essex recorded along twelve river catchments during the Essex Water Vole Survey, 1998 (Thompson, 1999)**

Catchment	*Number of sites surveyed*	*Number of positive sites*	*Percentage of positive sites*	*Number of "core" sites*	*Percentage of "core" sites*
Blackwater	54	25	46.3%	19	35.2%
Chelmer	83	35	42.2%	29	34.9%
Colne	17	12	70.5%	10	58.8%
Crouch	26	5	19.2%	3	11.5%
Dengie	44	12	27.3%	11	25.0%
Mardyke	14	2	14.3%	1	7.1%
North Thames	21	2	9.5%	1	4.8%
Roach	16	2	12.5%	1	6.3%
Stour	67	37	55.2%	20	29.9%
Tendring	36	27	75.0%	25	69.4%
Cam	7	0	0	0	0
Roding	43	10	23.3%	9	20.9%
Total	**428**	**169**	**39.4%**	**129**	**30.1%**

Of the 108 non-riverine, aquatic habitats, eighteen (16.7%) proved positive for the presence of water voles.

It is evident from the results that the water vole is widespread in the north of the county; the survey demonstrated that suitable habitats were present in the Tendring peninsular and along the Stour and Colne catchments, rather than in the south. However, the mink is also more abundant in north Essex (50% of the positive sites were from the Stour catchment); there is some evidence that the water vole may now be largely confined to the tributaries of the Stour as a result of predation by mink. The results from the latest survey show that the percentage of occupied sites in 1999 was lower than it had been in the 1989–90 national survey, suggesting a decline of more than 50% in sites with water voles in some parts of the county. Further surveys along the Cam and the upper reaches of the Colne are planned in 1999, so that a comprehensive understanding of the water vole's distribution is known prior to instituting appropriate conservation measures. It is envisaged that these will include habitat improvements to avoid the isolation of colonies, the minimising of water level fluctuations (particularly on the Stour) and a review of the practicalities of mink control measures in some river catchments (Thompson, 1999).

Although the water vole was already a Red Data Species (Morris, 1993), it was not until early 1998 that the species was added to Schedule 5 of The Wildlife and Countryside Act – ensuring that consideration of its needs are taken into account when waterway management plans are being devised. Now that our knowledge of this species is better than ever (it is planned to repeat the latest survey at the same sites in 2003), there is hope that the 'core' sites identified in 1999 will be conserved. If this can be achieved, together with the restoration of other sites through sympathetic bankside management, a species that can produce five litters of six young in a year has the potential to increase its population in Essex.

Wood mouse *Apodemus sylvaticus* (Linn., 1758)

Status: Abundant

The wood mouse is found throughout Essex and may be the most widely distributed mammal in Britain. It can be found in all but the dampest habitats, including both coniferous and deciduous woodland, arable land, coastal grassland, gardens and the greener areas of our large towns. Wood mice are opportunist feeders taking seeds, fruits and green plants in proportion to their relative abundance, with buds, invertebrates and fungi also taken when available (Watts, 1968). The population fluctuates seasonally with a peak in autumn and early winter. High mortality then occurs during the colder weather until breeding commences in March, with successive litters of four to seven young produced until October. A long-term survey to study the population dynamics of small mammals (Mallorie & Flowerdew, 1994) showed that, for wood mice, numbers were also influenced by the quality of the autumn seed crop. Perhaps as expected, higher densities of mice were present in the winter and summer after a good seed crop – with between 130 and 200 per hectare having been recorded (Gurnell, 1981) – than after a poor season.

The seasonal variation in the population can be demonstrated by analysing the contents of owl pellets. In a two-year study of a pair of barn owls (*Tyto alba*) at Canewdon, numbers of wood mice peaked in October of both years, with troughs between January and March (author's data). Both winters had protracted cold spells with occasional snow cover reducing the availability of wood mice as prey; however the subsequent increase in numbers coincided with the start of the breeding season.

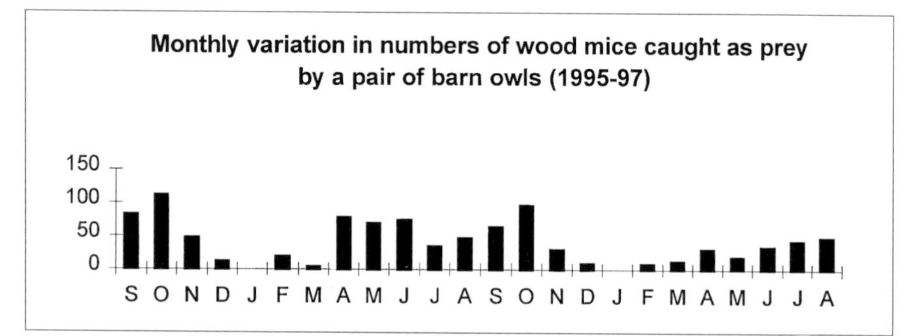

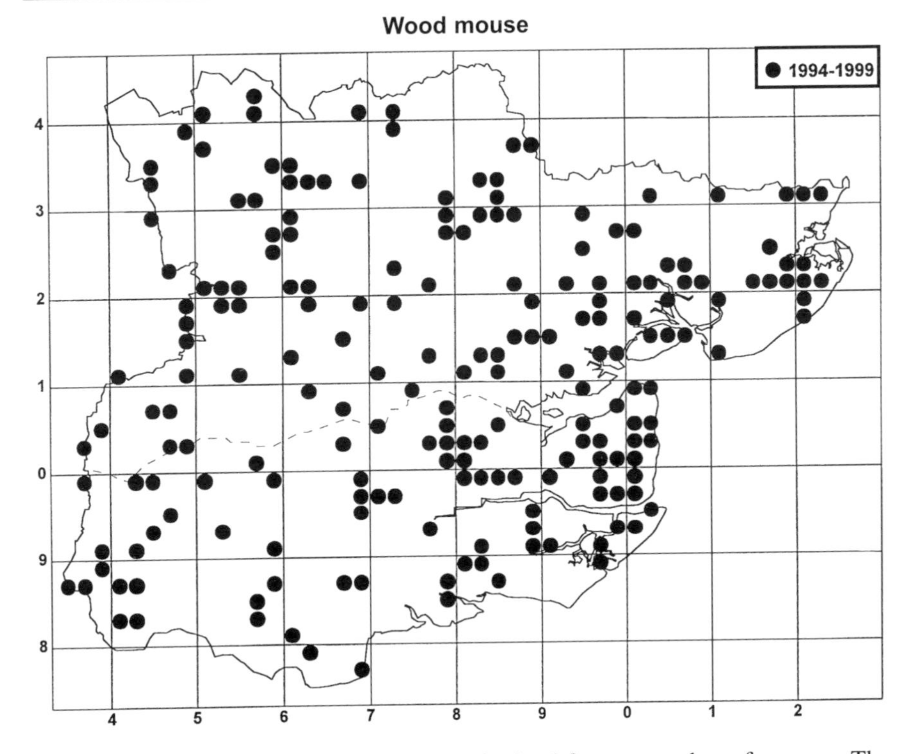

Records for the current survey have been obtained from a number of sources. The wood mouse is the species most frequently caught in Longworth traps, and the majority of inland records are of trapped animals. Barn owls have a mainly coastal distribution in Essex and the analysis of pellets has produced evidence of the importance of wood mice in their diet. Even in these less wooded areas, wood mice comprised 39.2% of the prey at Canewdon, 8.8% at Tollesbury, 14.8% and 21.6% from two sites at Old Hall Marshes and 23.8% from three sites on Foulness – a total of 1,950 wood mice! Other predators include mustelids and foxes and a number of records are of dead animals brought in by domestic cats. Evidence that wood mice are good climbers comes from regular reports of animals being discovered in bird boxes up to four metres above the ground.

The gaps in the distribution reflect the difficulty of recording nocturnal small mammals, rather than an absence of wood mice. With its ability to adapt and thrive in all habitats, the wood mouse will remain our most abundant mammal.

Yellow-necked mouse *Apodemus flavicollis* (Melchior, 1834)

Status: Fairly common

The yellow-necked mouse has a limited range in Britain, being found in eastern and southern England, south Wales and the English-Welsh border counties. The reasons for this restricted distribution are uncertain but it seems that areas with a fairly high density of ancient woodland and high summer temperatures are favoured. In Britain it is rare for the density of yellow-necked mice to exceed that of the wood mice with which they always occur but in some parts of Europe this species is the dominant *Apodemus*.

The yellow-necked mouse seems intolerant of urban areas and is restricted to countryside with ancient woodlands although it can use other types of woodland within these areas. Yellow-necked mice have more brightly coloured dorsal fur and whiter undersides than the wood mouse, with a distinct yellow collar extending between the fore-legs; in juveniles, the collar is greyer, but still visible. When fully grown, Essex yellow-necked mice average 40%-50% heavier than a wood mouse of the same sex and age (Corke, 1974).

The yellow-necked mouse was first recorded in Essex in 1905 (Cole) from a specimen trapped in a storeroom at Wakes Colne, some ten years after it was first identified as a British species distinct from the wood mouse (de Winton, 1894). By 1915, Laver, in comparing the distribution of the yellow-necked mouse with the polecat in Essex, wrote that "*This is in a very different condition and instead of approaching extinction is more frequent apparently. It is only during the last few years that it has been so generally recognised. It is found in most parts of Essex. If a long-tailed Field Mouse (i.e.* Apodemus*) is caught in a storeroom in a house in this country it is generally of this species. It cannot be said that the ordinary* sylvaticus *never enters houses, for it does so at times, but much more rarely than the Yellow-necked variety or species; this being the one usually found in the storeroom in the house, or in the gardener's seed-room.*" This species is well-known for entering rural houses and of the records where full information was available (recently contributed to a national atlas) 50% were from houses compared with 2% for wood mice (Arnold, 1993).

Yellow-necked mouse

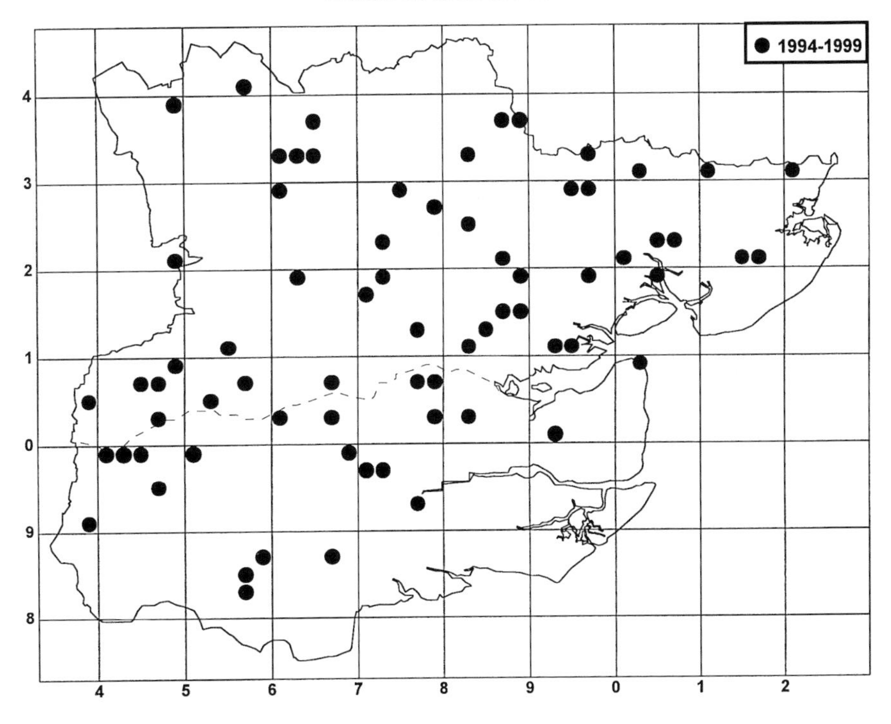

A glance at the distribution map shows that the yellow-necked mouse is present throughout most of Essex with the exception of the suburbs of London and the south-east area. It is most commonly associated with mature deciduous woodland, and most records are of animals caught in Longworth traps set in this habitat. In a long-term trapping study in Essex, it was found that where both *Apodemus* species occurred together, the yellow-necked mouse accounted for a fifth of the captures (Corke & Harris, 1972) – recent trapping supports this finding. Favoured situations appear to be amongst roots of trees toppled by the 1987 hurricane, along banks acting as woodland boundaries and also in species-rich hedgerows. The habit of entering rural buildings in autumn has produced several records, notably from the Essex Wildlife Trust Visitor Centre at Abberton, Bradwell Bird Observatory, the author's garage at Bicknacre and the warden's house at Fingringhoe Wick (remote from ancient woodland)! In addition, yellow-necked mice have also been found in roof spaces at Maldon and Pattiswick during surveys to locate bats. At Little Leighs these mice carry huge numbers of acorns a minimum of a hundred metres to store them in the roof space of a bungalow (D. Scott, pers. comm.)

A recent source of records has been the erection of nest boxes for dormice in several Essex woodlands. Yellow-necked mice are good climbers and have been regularly found up to four metres above ground in boxes, suggesting that they may also favour tree holes and cavities in pollards. A radio-tagged male mouse in central Essex moved 300m, from its woodland nest-site to a farmyard, and back in the course of one night (D. Corke, pers. comm.). Although it was caught at ground level its main nest site seemed to be high in a tree where it remained most days. In 1998, a national survey was initiated to establish the distribution and habitat requirements for this species (Marsh, 1999). If yellow-necked mice are such arboreal mammals as they appear to be, the curious finding of this survey that active woodland management and the absence of ivy-covered trees are good predictors of where yellow-necked mice will be caught, might be explicable. All the survey work was done with ground-level Longworth traps. Perhaps, when they have the chance of living in the canopy, the mice do not descend so often to be caught in the traps.

A new study of this species by a Cambridge-based PhD student has just begun in Essex. When completed this may solve some of the many mysteries which surround the ecology of the yellow-necked mouse. Meanwhile it seems there is little evidence that justifies the inclusion of this species in the UK Red Data Book (Morris, 1993).

Plate 1 (above). Leucistic (semi-albino) hedgehog, Dovercourt
Photo: *Chris Gibson*

Plate 2 (below). Mole drinking at dog's bowl in Essex garden
Photo: *Bob Glover*

Plate 3 (above). Leisler's bat, Galleywood Photo: *Alastair Shay*

Plate 4 (below, left). Natterer's bat, Grays deneholes
Photo: *Frank Greenaway*

Plate 5 (below, right). Parti-coloured bat, Chadwell Heath
Photo: *Alastair Shay*

Plate 6 (above, left). Hare resting in wheatfield Photo: *Bob Glover*

Plate 7 (above, right). Rabbit Photo: *Bob Glover*

Plate 8 (below). Albino bank vole, Brentwood Photo: *John Dobson*

Plate 9 (above). Yellow-necked mouse, Bicknacre Photo: *John Dobson*

Plate 10 (below). Harvest mouse, Bicknacre Photo: *Alastair Shay*

Plate 11 (above). Town fox, Thundersley Photo: *Alastair Shay*

Plate 12 (below). Country fox, Hockley Photo: *Bob Glover*

Plate 13 (above). Weasel, scavenging a rabbit road casualty
Photo: *Bob Glover*

Plate 14 (below). Stoat with the corpse of a hare Photo: *Bob Glover*

Plate 15 (above). Fin whale, Foulness
Photo: *Bob Glover*

Plate 16 (left). Sowerby's beaked whale, Shoeburyness Photo: *John Skinner*

Plate 17 (below). Common seals basking on Foulness Point Photo: *Bob Glover*

Plate 18 (left). Red deer hind in milk, Bendysh Wood Photo: *David Cor*

Plate 19 (above). Muntjac, High Wooc Photo: *Brian Eastc*

Plate 20 (below). 'Wild boar', Tollesbu (see page 193) Photo: *Bob Glo*

Harvest mouse *Micromys minutus* (Pallas, 1771)

Status: Fairly common, declining

Weighing a mere six grams, this is our smallest rodent. The harvest mouse can be distinguished from other mice by its small size, orange brown dorsal fur (contrasting with the white under-fur) and long, prehensile tail. During the summer and autumn, they live above ground, building distinctive, well-camouflaged nests by weaving living grass leaves together. The breeding nests are spherical, up to ten centimetres in diameter, whereas smaller, more superficial structures are used by individual mice. In early winter, as the surrounding vegetation dies, the nests are more obvious and provide an opportunity for recording the presence of this species. Harvest mice overwinter at ground level, the breeding season beginning in May when the vegetation has grown sufficiently to support the breeding nests. Successive litters, of one to seven young, are born with females able to become pregnant at five weeks old (Harris & Trout, 1991).

Laver (1898) reported this species as widespread and recent evidence confirms that this is still the case. However, a national survey in 1996 targeted sites where harvest mice had been present twenty years earlier. Of 24 sites in Essex, nests could only be found in 50%; the required habitat having disappeared at the other sites. Where harvest mice were absent, the commonest causes were increasingly intensive farming methods, housing development and the tidying up of roadside verges. Although harvest mice were once associated with corn ricks and cereal fields, today they are most commonly found in reed beds, ditches, along field edges and hedgerows where monocotyledons are supported by fences and bramble and also in plantations. Evidence of harvest mice has been found in the protective tubes used to support young trees, and also in willow plantations along river valleys at Nayland, Coggeshall, Lamarsh, Felsted and Rivenhall, where the surrounding vegetation is allowed to grow. Nests are constructed in a variety of plants but searching in common reed (*Phragmites*), reed grass (*Phalaris*) and cocksfoot (*Dactylis*) has proved most profitable with nests being built up to a metre above ground. Summer litters are vulnerable to cold weather and heavy rain but a large population can rapidly build up in good conditions – for example, in September 1988 at Bicknacre, 43 harvest mice were counted during the cutting of part of a field that had previously remained uncut for five years. However, mortality can be very high, with

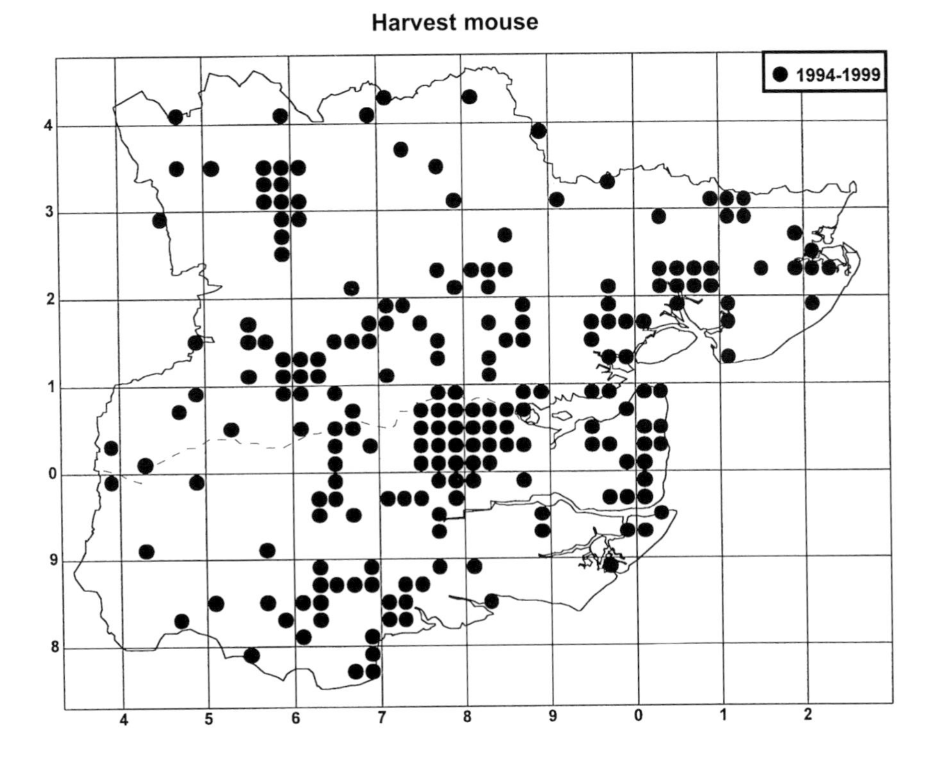

harvest mice vulnerable to predation by many species, including pheasants. In a two-year period on the Dengie, the barn owl population captured 549 harvest mice – 3.2% of all prey items. Numbers caught increased during July, reaching a peak in October that coincided with the end of the breeding season and the destruction of suitable habitat through harvesting (Love, 1998).

Today, the harvest mouse occurs mainly in damp habitats and field margins, and the quality of these habitats will influence the number of mice that survive the winter and breed in the following spring. Of available winter sanctuaries, it is unmanaged hedgerows that support the largest populations of small mammals; however many of these have been lost as fields have increased in size (Perrow *et al.*, 1992). Although the distribution map shows that the harvest mouse is widely scattered throughout Essex, much suitable habitat in inland areas has been lost to development and agriculture, causing fragmentation of the population and leading to local extinctions. Assuming that the present management of the countryside continues, perhaps the future for this species will be in the damp inland river valleys, safe from drainage schemes, and the drainage ditches, reedbeds and rough grassland still present in the coastal regions of the county.

House mouse

Mus domesticus Schwartz & Schwartz, 1943

Status: Common, declining

Although proven to have been present in this country since the Iron Age (Yalden, 1977), the house mouse is thought to have declined during the last 50 years as a result of changes in farming practice and improvements in methods of rodent control.

Formerly the third commonest small mammal of arable land (after the wood mouse and bank vole), the use of modern harvesting machines rather than the threshing of cereals for storage in ricks has eliminated a habitat where house mice could pass the winter. Today they are commonly associated with farm buildings, particularly those housing pigs and poultry, or in grain stores where food is readily available (Berry, 1991).

There is evidence that the house mouse was much more common in Victorian Essex. Fitch (1890) described a Finchingfield farmer, who hired four boys to kill the mice found to be infesting a wheat rick and, with additional help from men on top of the stack, accounted for over 3,000. Additionally, there were five further ricks within a 50 yards radius that were also considered to be infested! Laver (1898) wrote "*Who does not know this foul-smelling but nevertheless pretty little beast? Houses, buildings and corn-ricks are its favourite haunts, and it does not occur in this country except in their vicinity.*" During the present survey, the house mouse was rarely found in open countryside. This species thrives where there is an absence

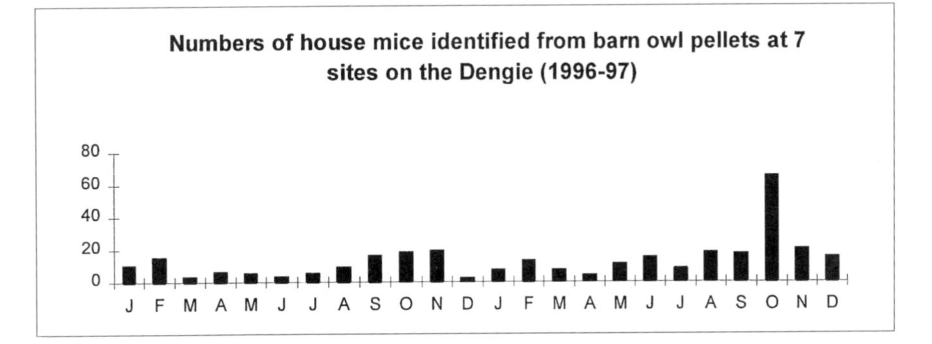

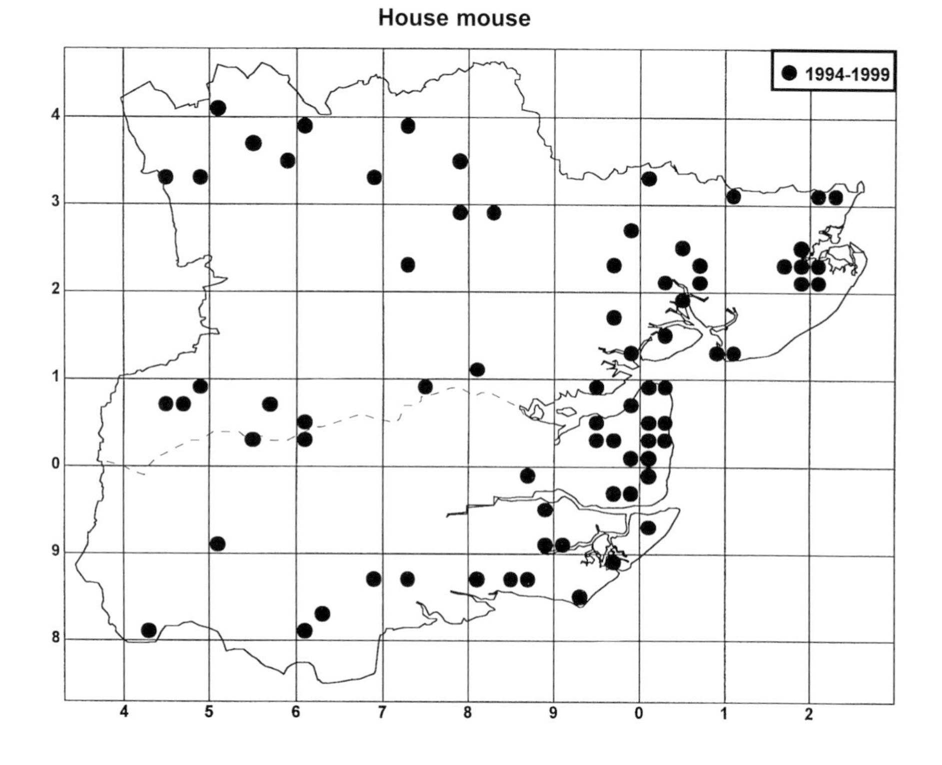

of competition from other small mammals, particularly the wood mouse (and in buildings, the common rat), and most records were from houses, often where pet food was stored, or from farm premises. In favourable conditions indoors, litters of five to eight young are born at monthly intervals, the population multiplying eight-fold during the year (Berry, 1968). As a commensal pest, the house mouse is more likely to be taken by the common rat than owls or carnivores and the 245 house mice identified from barn owl pellets on the Dengie, represented just 1.4% of the prey items during a two-year period. As with most other small mammals, numbers peaked in the autumn, at the end of the breeding season (Love, 1998); however, predation has a limited impact on the population, house mice being more vulnerable to a fall in temperature and the advent of frosts, particularly if accompanied by a shortage of food (Berry, 1991).

It is unlikely that the house mouse will ever again achieve the abundance of a century ago. However, it will continue to be a largely unobserved pest, living in close association with the human population.

Common rat

Rattus norvegicus (Berkenhout, 1769)

Status: Common

Although the common rat is now common throughout the British Isles, it is a fairly recent arrival. It is probable that this species originated in eastern former Russia or China, spreading into Europe early in the 18th century, before reaching Britain around 1728 in shipping from Russia. Colonisation was rapid and the highly adaptable common rat displaced the black rat, which was widespread in earlier times. It soon became established, particularly in habitats where the available food is supplemented by the presence of the human population. Today the common rat is commonly found in farm buildings, refuse tips, sewers and in the hedgerows bordering arable land. In summer and autumn, they are associated with cereal crops; in winter with maize and kale (planted as cover for pheasants and partridges); and are found in root crops throughout the year. Additionally, common rats readily take to water and thrive in the vegetation beside inland rivers as well as along the sea walls of the Essex coast. In favourable circumstances, the breeding season is continuous with females producing up to five litters of six to eleven young. Clearly there is the potential for large numbers to rapidly build up; however juvenile mortality may be as high as 99% in saturated populations (Taylor *et al.*, 1991).

Laver (1903) described the common rat as "*much too abundant*" and a plague of rats in Essex in the spring of 1890 was reported in several newspapers (Fitch, 1890):

"*One day last week no less than 318 rats were killed from two stacks which were being threshed on Freebourne's Farm, in the occupation of Mr J. Wakelin.*" (Essex Standard 8th March, 1890)

"*During the last few days, at a small farm in Laindon parish, upon some stacks of wheat being threshed by a steam threshing machine, no fewer than 594 rats and about 1,000 mice were killed*" (Essex Weekly News 25th April, 1890)

Today, the common rat is present throughout the county, although under-recorded. Many records are of road casualties, and sightings of live animals are usually associated with the availability of supplementary food. Although feeding activity is

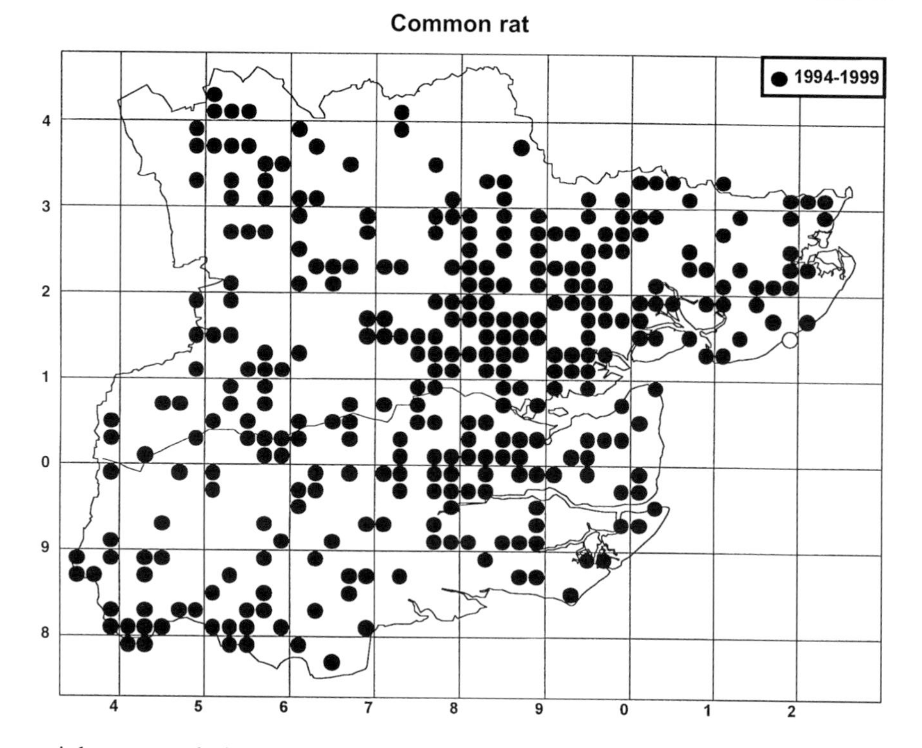

mainly nocturnal, the presence of discarded food at picnic sites or the provision of grain for game-rearing can tempt young rats to feed in the open.

Young rats are taken by owls, mustelids, foxes and cats but adults are too aggressive for small predators such as weasels and owls. A study of barn owl pellets on the Dengie showed that common rats peaked as a prey item in September and October – coinciding with the period of abundance following the breeding season and indicating the greater vulnerability of young as they dispersed (Love, 1998).

In recent years the common rat has declined. Although the increases in landfill sites, fly-tipping and crop yields have provided new opportunities, the loss of hedgerows and ditches, the elimination of cereal stacks and improvements in hygiene and control methods have ensured that the rapid population explosion described by Fitch has not recurred. Above all, the common rat has demonstrated a remarkable ability to survive, despite the best efforts of game-keepers, Environmental Health Officers, Pest Control organisations and those in chemical companies responsible for developing new rodenticides. This is a species destined to remain a common pest in both urban and rural landscapes with the potential to increase rapidly if control is relaxed.

Ship rat *Rattus rattus* (Linn., 1758)

Status: Rare, present at one site

The ship rat, or black rat, is our rarest rodent, occurring only at Tilbury Docks (where it is subject to ongoing control measures), the population having been maintained by occasional reinforcements from visiting ships. The ship rat was first introduced to Britain in Roman times, as evidenced by the finding of a skull and other bones in a Roman well, constructed around the 3rd century, in York (Rackham, 1979) with further influxes probably occurring on ships returning to this country from voyages overseas. Prior to the Roman finds, it was thought that the ship rat arrived with the returning Crusaders (Barrett-Hamilton & Hinton, 1910–21). The fleas carried by this species transmitted bubonic plague (Black Death) in Europe during medieval times. Ship rats were widespread until the arrival of the common rat (*Rattus norvegicus*) in the 18th century (Twigg, 1984). By the end of the 19th century, the species had declined and Laver reported that "*it is now almost extinct, although still occurring about the docks and other places in the East-end of London*". Unlike the common rat, ship rats are not found in sewers and underground tunnels, preferring to occupy dry, warm sites such as dockside buildings, grain silos and flour mills where they survive in cavity walls, wall panelling and false ceilings (Taylor, 1991). In 1950, Fisher, commenting on its status in London, wrote that "*certain fashionable flats, clubs theatres and cinemas are infested... it is the dominant rat in the Oxford Street area*". At that time there were reports from East and West Ham, Dagenham, Purfleet and Tilbury, although East Ham was "*apparently free in 1956*" (Bentley, 1959) with an intriguing record of one being caught in an aviary at Brentwood in September, 1951. Unfortunately, the exact location is unknown (Fitter, 1960). The ship rat was reported from Poplar and Silvertown during 1961, but there were no new records for nearly twenty years.

The recent status was reviewed by Twigg (1992) and in 1979, control measures were required at a chemical factory in Dagenham. In August 1983, ship rats were found in a cargo of wool on board a ship at Tilbury, and four years later, they were reported from grain silos at Tilbury, where they are still present. Port of London Authority records from 1985–89 show that 23 foreign ships at Tilbury had active

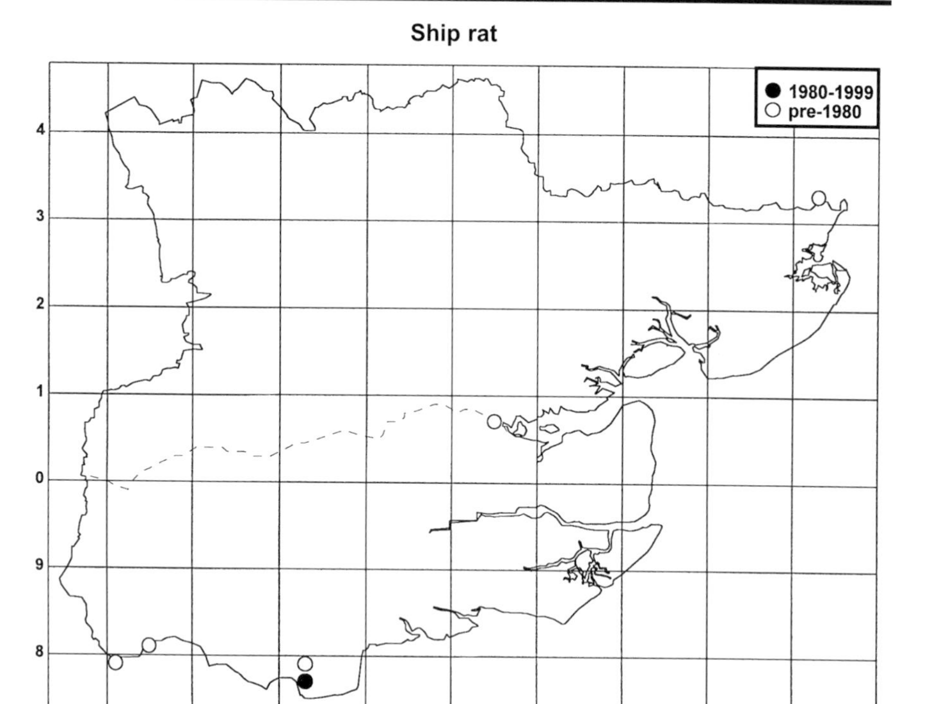

infestations of ship rats and the species was also found on two Dutch barges, in for conversion. However, the Port Health Authority at Tilbury and the River division of the Port of London Authority have not recorded evidence of infestations of ship rats since that time (J. Evans, pers. comm.).

With more efficient inspection and control measures and the widespread use of containerisation, the prospects for the future of the ship rat at Tilbury seem bleak. Twigg (1992) speculated that the opening of the Channel Tunnel could lead to an increase in inland records as continental lorries travelled, uninspected, to different regions of the country but there is no evidence of this happening. There have been isolated records from food warehouses during this period but nowhere has a colony become established. With a population of around 1,000 animals in Britain, a conservation case could be made for captive breeding and reintroduction, but the ship rat is unlikely to attract much public sympathy if it disappears. Perhaps the best chance of observing an Essex specimen is in a museum and a young male, captured at Fullbridge, Maldon in 1910 during the unloading of a barge from London, can be seen in the collection at Colchester.

Common dormouse *Muscardinus avellanarius* (Linn., 1758)

Status: Scarce, declining

Familiar to many people only from photographs, the dormouse is rarely seen and has been the subject of considerable recent conservation interest. The dormouse was formerly present throughout most of England and Wales yet has declined in the 20th century through loss of habitat and inappropriate woodland management. It is now locally distributed in southern England and Wales with the Essex population amongst the most northerly in the country.

Dormice prefer ancient woodland with a varied understorey, coppice woodland and species-rich hedgerows. They rarely range more than 70m from the nest and the optimum habitat will include a variety of shrubs and trees to provide cover for nesting and a supply of food throughout the year. In spring, dormice seek out hazel catkins and the flowers of hawthorn before moving on to those of oak, sycamore and honeysuckle. Insects make up most of the diet during summer until the fruits of bramble, yew and holly become abundant – hazel nuts being eaten to gain weight prior to hibernation in the autumn. The single litter of usually four young is born during July, although this may be delayed by poor weather (Bright & Morris, 1996).

Laver (1898) considered the dormouse to occur "*where the oak and hazel abound, and where there is sufficient woodland or overgrown hedgerow to protect it*". He also reported capturing dormice – "*I have occasionally taken them licking up the 'sugar' I had placed on the tree trunks for the purpose of attracting moths at night.*" During the 20th century, the distribution of the dormouse in Essex retracted, as the dense growth of unmanaged coppice woodland shaded out the shrub layer, and other ancient woodland was cleared to make way for development, agriculture and forestry. Dormice were recorded for the last time in Epping Forest in 1943 (Corke & Harris, 1972) and, with only a few records to consider, Seear (1964) described the species as rare in Essex.

As with other nocturnal small mammals, the dormouse can be easily overlooked. Visual records are rare and their presence is often proved by the finding of summer nests or hazel nuts, gnawed in a distinctive manner. The resurgence in interest in the dormouse in Essex started with the 'Great Nut Hunt' of 1993, part of English Nature's Species Recovery Programme (Whitten, 1990). This was a much-

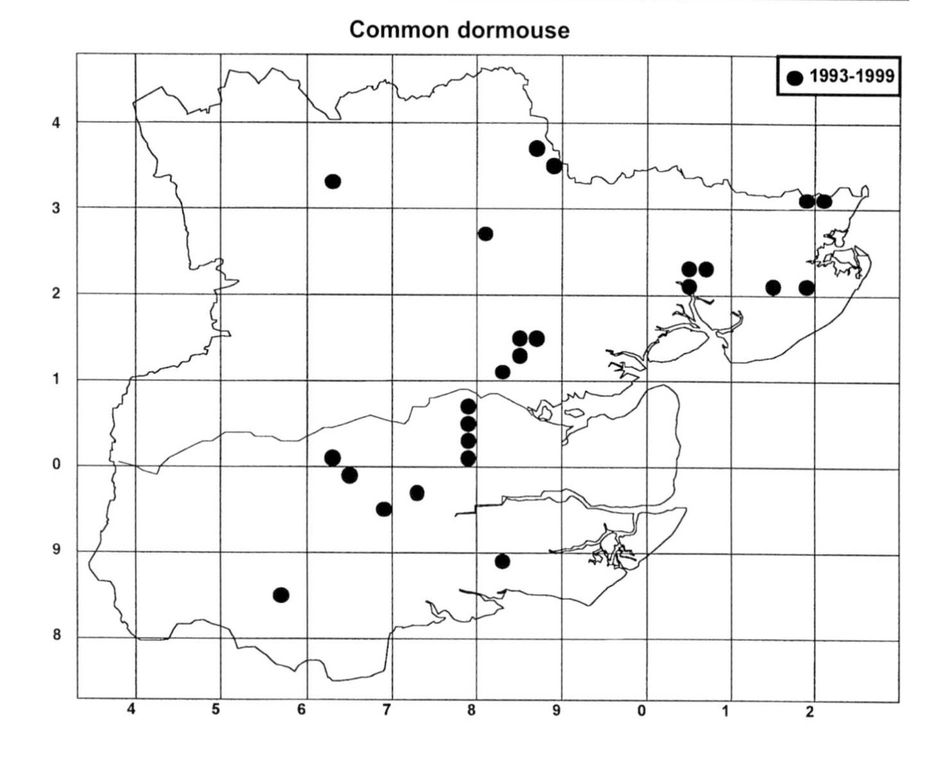

publicised project that encouraged the public to search for gnawed hazel nuts. Information packs offered guidance on identification and those nuts that had potentially been opened by dormice were sent to English Nature for confirmation. In Essex, 57 sites were visited, 4,890 nuts found of which 18, involving 7 sites, proved positive for dormice (Bright *et al.*, 1996).

These successes were the catalyst for the next phase in the Essex Wildlife Trust's project to conserve dormice in the county. Studies from elsewhere had shown that dormice will use tree holes, squirrels' dreys or birds' nests as sites for their breeding nests. However, coppice woodland, although rich in food, tends to offer few tree holes and it is in these woodlands that nestbox schemes have proved so succesful, in some cases increasing the population density within months (Morris *et al.*, 1990). During the years following the Great Nut Hunt, nearly 700 nestboxes were sited on Trust reserves and other managed woodlands such that an occupancy rate of over 15% was achieved within four years. Evidence of breeding is regularly observed with family groups of up to six dormice being found in some boxes. This programme is continuing to expand with new reserves and suitable private woodland being selected for future projects.

A feature of Essex woodlands containing dormice is that they are often smaller than twenty hectares – the area described as the minimum for the long-term survival of a viable population of dormice (Bright *et al.*, 1994). Where smaller blocks of habitat occur, it is important that they are interconnected by hedgerows or overgrown scrub so that juveniles are able to colonise new areas. Such woodland is often present along stream valleys, the damp surroundings having spared it from agricultural intensivisation. A project in Tendring involving landowners and conservationists is seeking to improve woodland management and to create links between those woods where dormice are still to be found (R. Cottrill, pers. comm.). Most records from the current survey have come from these nestbox schemes with two reports, from Crowsheath Wood and the Backwarden Nature Reserve, of hibernating dormice being disturbed by winter woodland management programmes. With the dormouse fully protected under the Wildlife and Countryside Act 1981, the monitoring of nestboxes is undertaken by licenced members of the Essex Wildlife Trust and it is anticipated that more volunteers will be required in the future as new schemes are initiated. Fortunately, the taking of dormice by cats is a rare occurrence; however, one at Mill Green was reported by its owner to have caught up to 25. When asked to produce an example so that the identification could be confirmed, two were delivered within a few days! (G. Smith, pers. comm.). An additional record was of one disturbed by a gardener at Thorpe Hall during February, 1998.

At present, the dormouse is mainly known from nature reserves. However, it is now the subject of a Biodiversity Action Plan (see page 206) and there is an ongoing commitment to the sympathetic woodland management required to conserve the species in Essex. There is a clear need for a distribution survey (in the same way that the water vole has been targeted) to identify those areas where the dormouse is still present. This could be achieved by searching for the breeding nests in autumn – a method that has proved successful in Tendring where nests have been found in bramble and holly; through an extension of the nestbox schemes that are proving so productive and by the organising of more 'nut hunts'. If more sites could be identified and protected, then after a century of uncertainty, the future could be assured for the dormouse in Essex.

Table 8.2 Nestbox occupancy by dormice 1994-1998 (data supplied by Essex Wildlife Trust)

Reserve	*Number of boxes used by dormice (total number of boxes)*				
	1994	1995	1996	1997	1998
Danbury Complex					
Backwarden	0(55)	10(55)	9(55)	6(55)	0(54)
Birch/Martins Wood	0(10)	4(10)	1(15)	3(15)	4(10)
Blakes Wood	0(12)	0(22)	1(23)	1(23)	2(23)
Little Baddow Heath			1(10)	2(8)	5(17)
Pheasanthouse Wood	1(10)	0(10)	0(10)	3(10)	2(10)
Poors Piece	0(10)	7(11)	0(13)	3(12)	5(15)
Scrubs Wood	1(14)	1(14)	7(22)	4(25)	15(30)
Spring Wood					1(10)
Thrift Wood		1(15)	1(15)	1(15)	2(15)
Woodham Walter Common			1(20)	3(25)	4(40)
Other Reserves					
Brookes Reserve					1(30)
Captains Wood			7(35)	9(31)	24(53)
Copperas Wood		1(10)	2(10)	4(10)	1(27)
Cranham Marsh		0(16)	0(16)	0(16)	1(30)
Crowsheath Wood		2(10)	2(15)	3(15)	2(26)
Loshes Meadow					0(20)
Pound Wood	2(40)	8(38)	4(31)	11(28)	3(30)
Roman River Valley			?(10)	1(8)	0(18)
Shadwell Wood		0(15)	0(12)	0(12)	0(18)
Shut Heath Wood			0(15)	0(15)	0(32)
Villa Wood			7(16)	10(46)	5(39)
Weeleyhall Wood		1(31)	4(31)	0(34)	4(37)
West Wood			0(20)	0(20)	0(30)
Total	**4(151)**	**35(257)**	**47(394)**	**64(423)**	**81(614)**
% occupied	***2%***	***13%***	***12%***	***15%***	***13%***

Coypu

Myocastor coypus (Molina, 1782)

Status: Extinct

The coypu is a South American rodent that was introduced into Britain in 1929 as a captive farm animal to produce nutria (the fur of the coypu) for the fur trade. Fifty fur farms were soon established but the combination of lower profitability as the price of nutria fell and the outbreak of the Second World War meant that all farms had closed by 1939 (Lever, 1994). The first escapes had already been recorded in Sussex in 1932 and by 1940, feral populations were present in Norfolk, Suffolk and Buckinghamshire. The early optimism that the feeding habits of coypus might be beneficial because of their clearing of dykes and broads was soon dispelled as the burrowing by the increasing population caused damage to dyke walls and river banks. However, it was their fondness for root crops, particularly sugar beet, and the damage to reedbeds and marsh plants that led to their addition to the Destructive Imported Animals Act of 1932.

The first Essex record refers to an individual seen at Rowhedge in 1938 but this was almost certainly an escape from a nearby fur farm at Alresford. A second fur farm was present at Dedham and a note in the archive at Colchester Museum records that coypu were released from here in 1940. Not surprisingly, it was in this area of Essex that coypu became established and were present on the north side of the Stour near Dedham in 1955 with the first county record from this time (Owen, 1960). In 1958 juveniles were seen at Lamarsh and in 1959 another juvenile was killed at Rayne – a subsequent three mile search of Pods Brook by MAFF officers failed to find any further animals. In 1960, two were caught on the Chelmer at Stebbing and kept in captivity at Colchester Natural History Museum. Between 1960 and 1965, a concerted effort was made to eradicate the coypu and it was estimated that trapping and the cold winter of 1962/63 accounted for 90% of the population. During this time, 140 were killed at Manningtree, twenty at Woodham Walter, one was found dead on the railway line at Audley End and others were reported from Stebbing, the Dunmow area and Thaxted. In December 1961, an adult was caught in a snare near the Stort at Roydon and another trapped at Mountnessing (Seear, 1964). In 1963, additional records of animals killed came from Tillingham, Thorpe-le-Soken, Glemsford and Dedham (Corke, 1965). After this programme of trapping, coypu

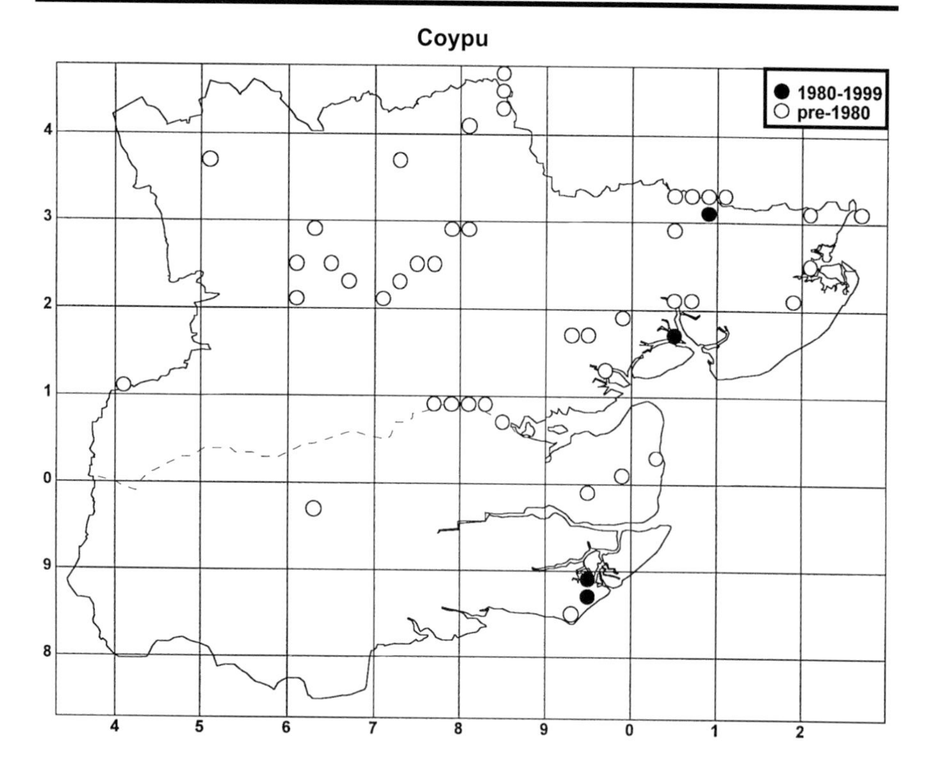

were confined to a small area of East Anglia and there were no Essex records during 1967/68 (Scott, 1969). However, a succession of mild winters and an easing of the control measures saw a further spread in the 1970s, with coypu being present at Abberton Reservoir at the end of the decade.

In 1981, MAFF instituted a ten year campaign to finally eradicate the coypu. In January of that year, one adult and four juveniles were killed at Lawford by a Tendring Pest Control Officer, who presented the animals to Colchester Museum and in April 1982, one was seen on the Fingringhoe Ranges (Winter, 1983). The last Essex specimens, at Great Wakering, were killed during this period and in 1989 the coypu was declared extinct in Britain.

Although a popular subject of national newspaper headlines and television documentaries, many people would be surprised to find that this group of mammals comprises 20% of the mammal species recorded in Essex. That this is the case perhaps owes more to our ancestors as observers, and in many cases, hunters, than to the current status of cetaceans in Essex coastal waters. One of the first accounts of an Essex mammal is of a porpoise caught off Mersea in 1299. The event was recorded and is translated from the Latin of The Wardrobe Accounts of King Edward I (Society of Antiquaries, 1787): *"Charges in respect of a whale per the Sheriff of Essex – To John de la Lee, Sheriff of Essex and Herts, for moneys paid by him to divers persons in charge of a certain whale caught off the island of Merseye [Mersea]; for one empty cask bought to put the whale in; for salt bought to salt the same; for the carriage of the same from the island aforesaid to Staunford to the court; together with the expenses of one man with a team conducting the said whale there in the month of May £0 14s 8d"*

In the above account (Christy, 1906), Staunford is Stanford-le-Hope, about 30 miles from Mersea. Harting (1906) plausibly argued that the whale was probably a porpoise on the grounds that the whale was either very small or the cask very large. However, even 700 years ago, a stranded cetacean was considered a 'Royal fish' and was taken to the sovereign who was present with his court at Stanford. Today, much of our knowledge of these mammals comes from details of strandings along the coast. An act dating from the 14th century, De Praerogativa Regis, conferred ownership to the Crown of any stranded cetacean and today, these are reported by coastguards to HM Receivers of Wreck who pass on the details to the Natural History Museum in London. Periodically, the data are published and Essex records have been obtained from this source. In many cases the presence of a corpse on an Essex tideline is not an indication of the variety of mammals offshore, but merely a feature of the wind and tidal currents prevailing in the southern North Sea.

Whales and dolphins are divided into two groups: the large whales with baleen plates (Mysticetes) that are plankton feeders and the toothed whales (Odontocetes) that feed on fish and other marine prey. Of the 23 species occurring in British and Irish waters, thirteen (five mysticetes and eight odontocetes) have been recorded in Essex. Additionally, the sperm whale (*Physeter macrocephalus*) is the subject of two historical reports; one was captured in the Thames and brought ashore at Blackwall around 1732 and two were washed up at unknown locations on the Essex coast following an east coast storm in1763 (Laver, 1898).

The 20th century has seen a massive reduction in the number of cetaceans in the North Sea. Up until 1950, the large whales were hunted, for some species almost to extinction and for others to less than a quarter of their previous population. As their numbers declined, the pressure of whaling was transferred to smaller species such as minke whales, northern bottlenose whales and pilot whales. In 1986, a ban on the hunting of all species was introduced by the International Whaling Commission: however, Norway continues to take minke whales and pilot whales are exploited by the Faroe Islanders.

During the last 30 years, the decline of coastal species in Essex such as the porpoise has been due to less direct action by man. The discharge of pollutants into the North Sea by industrialised countries, run-off of agricultural chemicals, the decline of fish stocks as a result of over-fishing and the increase in heavy shipping and pleasure craft, causing sound disturbance, have all made our offshore waters less hospitable.

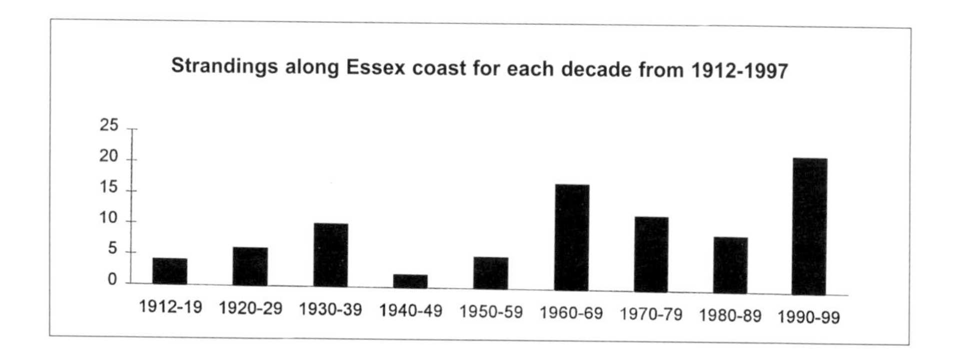

The increase in strandings during the last decade is difficult to interpret. Could it be due to an increase in observer activity or cetacean numbers, or sadly, the increased vulnerability of those animals remaining in the southern North Sea? The porpoise is the subject of an Essex Biodiversity Action Plan that seeks to identify the conservation measures required to retain this species as a feature of our coasts. Let us hope it succeeds.

Occasionally, stranded animals cannot be identified, usually owing to their state of decomposition. Those involving Essex are:

7th August 1939	East Mersea	one, 5.49m
9th August 1956	East Mersea	two, 3.66m
9th August 1956	East Mersea	one, 4.57m
4th August 1967	Canvey	one, 3.05m
25th September 1981	Clacton Sailing Club	one, 1.83m
30th June 1992	Shoeburyness	odontocete
26th May 1994	Havengore Creek	odontocete
22nd November 1994	Martello Bay, Clacton	odontocete

Humpback whale

Megaptera novaeangliae Borowski, 1781

Status: One record

This large whale can be separated from the other large rorquals by its habit of lifting its tail flukes clear of the water when commencing a steep dive. The flukes are distinctively butterfly-shaped and notched with the undersides showing an area of white coloration; the extent and shape of which is variable and allows individuals to be identified and monitored in the same way that ringing has enhanced the study of birds. Humpback whales can grow to 15m and weigh up to 65 tonnes with a life expectancy of at least 30 years (Evans, 1991).

The humpback whale is a migratory species with a worldwide distribution. The routes to the polar regions are well known and in some parts of their range, humpback whales can experience disturbance from over-enthusiastic whale watchers. Commercial whaling earlier in the century plundered this species during its migrations to such an extent that the population in the southern hemisphere is now only 3% of that present before exploitation. The population in the northern hemisphere has declined by nearly 50% with numbers currently around 7,000 (Evans, 1987) of which several hundred are in the north-east Atlantic.

Summer is spent in the Greenland Sea and off Iceland and Norway, where between 50% and 70% of body weight is put on as blubber on a diet of mainly krill and some fish species. In late autumn, the humpback whale travels over 7,000km to the warmer waters off North Africa and the Cape Verde Islands to give birth and mate. Little feeding is done during this period; however the warmer water is more hospitable to calves with thin layers of blubber (Macdonald, 1995).

Humpback whale

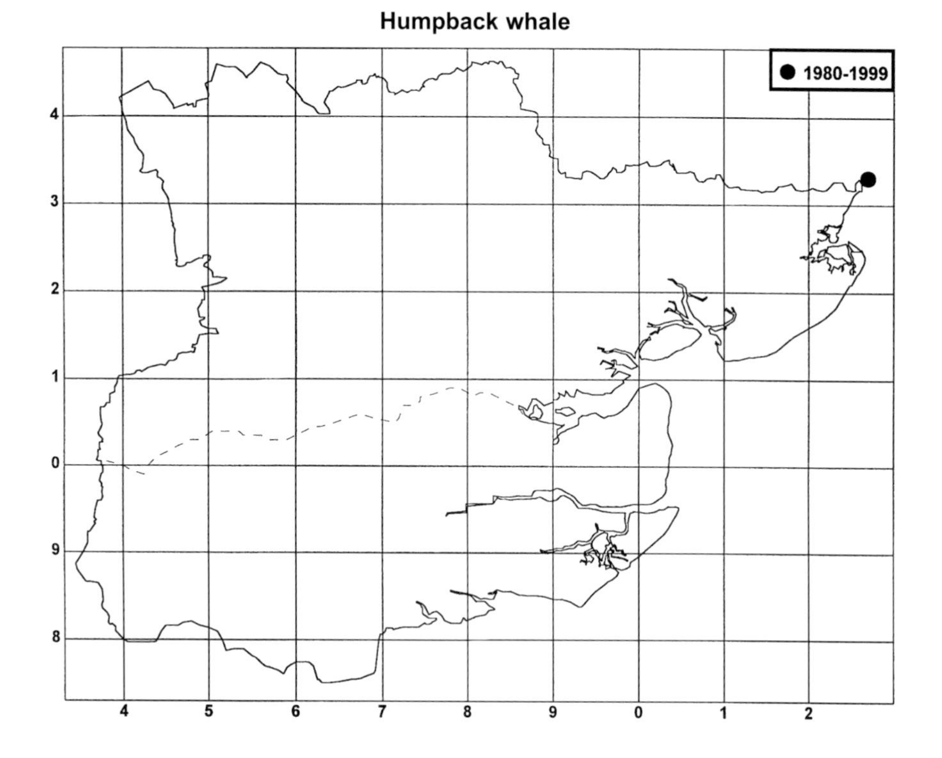

As a coastal species, the humpback whale is occasionally seen from northern headlands but the appearance of a 10m, 30 tonne juvenile in Harwich harbour on 3rd June 1995 was a remarkable occurrence. First spotted at high tide in early morning by the Harwich inshore life-boat, an operation was launched to return the whale to the sea. A harbour launch and the coastguard followed the animal into the River Orwell, before it turned and headed up the Stour. Here there was a danger of the humpback stranding in the shallow waters off Mistley and a flotilla of boats was organised to persuade it to head towards open water. The mouth of the Orwell was blocked with volunteers' boats, all generating noise from engines and horns to ensure that the whale continued its journey eastwards, and eventually, after six hours of gentle persuasion, the humpback whale returned to the North Sea (Ellis, 1995).

This unexpected event constitutes the only Essex record.

Fin whale

Balaenoptera physalus (Linn., 1758)

Status: Rare, six records

The fin whale is the largest mammal recorded in the county. Females are on average larger than males and can grow to 24m and weigh up to 80 tonnes. This species is identified by its small dorsal fin sited about two-thirds along a body with grey coloration on the upper side and white below, including the underside of the tail flukes and inner surface of the flippers. It can live for up to 90 years.

Fin whales are rarely seen from land. The north-east Atlantic population numbers between 9,000 and 14,000 and a proportion of these are thought to migrate northwards along the continental shelf in spring, returning in the autumn. During the summer they are occasionally seen from western Britain and Ireland where they feed on fish such as herrings, sand-eels, cod and pollack, some cephalopods and small crustaceans.

There are several Essex records. A *"finner whale"* was captured at Grays in 1849 which measured 17.7m in length with a girth of 9.2m (*Zoologist* 1849, p. 2620), and another was taken in the Thames in May 1859 (Bell, 1874).

An individual that generated much public interest was found stranded in the Crouch on February 12th 1891 (Crouch, 1891). It was first found lying in shallow water near Holliwell Point, the alarm was raised and in half an hour about 30 men with ropes were attempting to secure the animal. The whale was shot *"many times"* until it died and was then towed to Burnham where a crowd had already formed. It was claimed for the Crown by HM Customs and later auctioned for £17 10s to a Mr J. Prior of Southminster and Messrs. J. Hawkins and H. Cook of Burnham. Later the same day it was claimed by solicitors acting on behalf of the Lord of the Manor, Sir Henry Mildmay, owner of the royalty of the river. The news caused considerable interest in the area and the specimen was exhibited in the Malting Yard. A total of 1,300 people paid for admission, lured by both the prospect of seeing a whale and

Fin whale

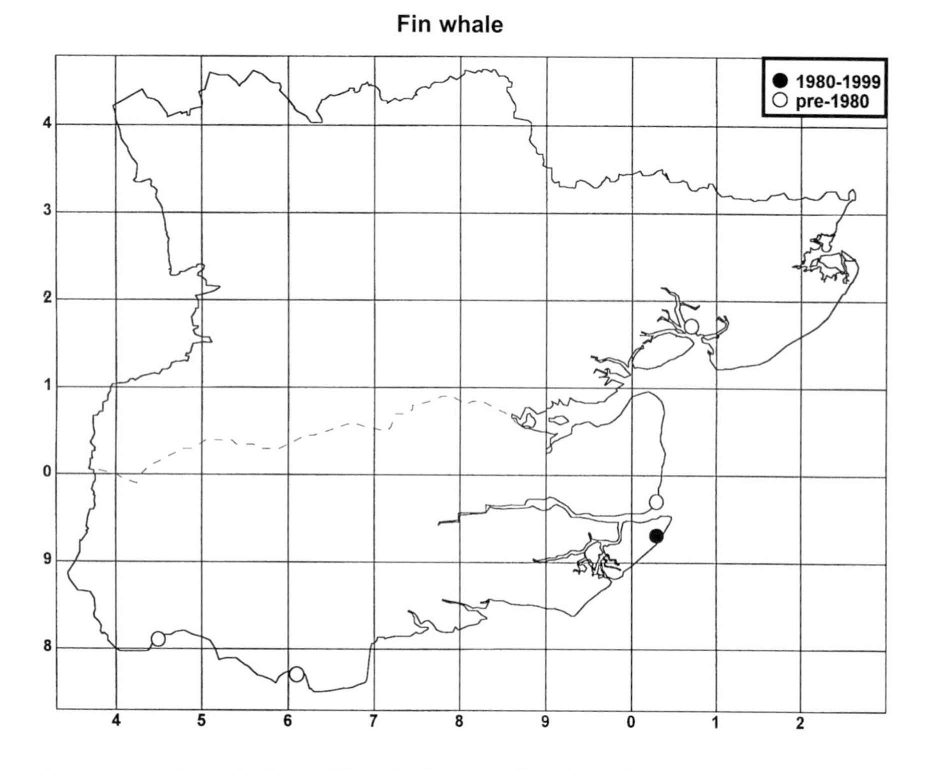

cheap trains at single fares! The whale was a female and measured 14.2m. On the 7th April 1891, another rorqual was seen in the Crouch, on sandbanks near the mouth of the river, by the crew of one of the boats that had previously towed the earlier whale. It was reported as about 15m long and apparently made a successful escape on the following tide (Fitch, 1891).

On 27th November 1899, another female, measuring 20.3m, was stranded at Gallions Reach, near Barking Creek, having been *"chased by tugs for four hours before being run ashore"*. Two days later, the decomposing body burst, revealing two calves, both of which died shortly afterwards. One was later stolen, the other measuring 5.4 metres, was exhibited with its mother (Anon, 1900).

There are two records for the 20th century. On 30th September 1962, a fin whale measuring 12.5m was stranded at Brightlingsea and on 28th October 1995, another, 20.5m in length, was found on the shoreline on Foulness. Baleen plates from this individual were extracted and are in Southend Museum.

It is estimated that the world population is now at 22% of that which prevailed before hunting decimated numbers. The fin whale was fully protected in 1986.

Sei whale

Balaenoptera borealis Lesson, 1828

Status: Rare, five records

The sei whale has not been recorded in Essex since 1948. A large whale, with females measuring up to 21m in length, the sei whale can be identified from the dark, steely grey coloration on the back, flanks and rear of belly, with a paler greyish white colour on the throat grooves and anterior part of the belly. The dorsal fin is sickle-shaped, up to 60cm high and situated just less than two-thirds distance along the back. This species is rarely observed at sea, preferring the deeper waters of the continental shelf, migrating north to Iceland and the Greenland Sea during the summer and returning to temperate waters off north-west Africa in winter. In northern seas, the diet consists of several fish species, squid and copepods (Evans, 1991).

Laver (1898) recorded the presence of four sei whales in Essex waters. The first occurrence was of an individual in the Thames that eventually stranded at Hope Reach, near Gravesend in 1859. The second, a male 8.83m long, was found by fishermen having become beached near the mouth of the Crouch on 1st November 1883. After experiencing *"considerable difficulty they succeeded in capturing and killing it"* and transported it to Southend where it was later exhibited. The litigious Sir Henry Mildmay (see also the account for fin whale), as Lord of the Manor of Burnham, claimed ownership of the whale as a 'royal fish' and the case reached the High Court of Justice (before Mr Justice Chitty) and was reported in *The Times* of 8th November 1883. The whale was eventually purchased by the Australian Museum at Sydney (Flower, 1886).

Four years later, on 19th October 1887, another male was discovered on the foreshore outside the entrance to Tilbury Docks. Measuring 10.77m it was found lying nearly level with the top of the sea wall and was thought to have been stranded

Sei whale

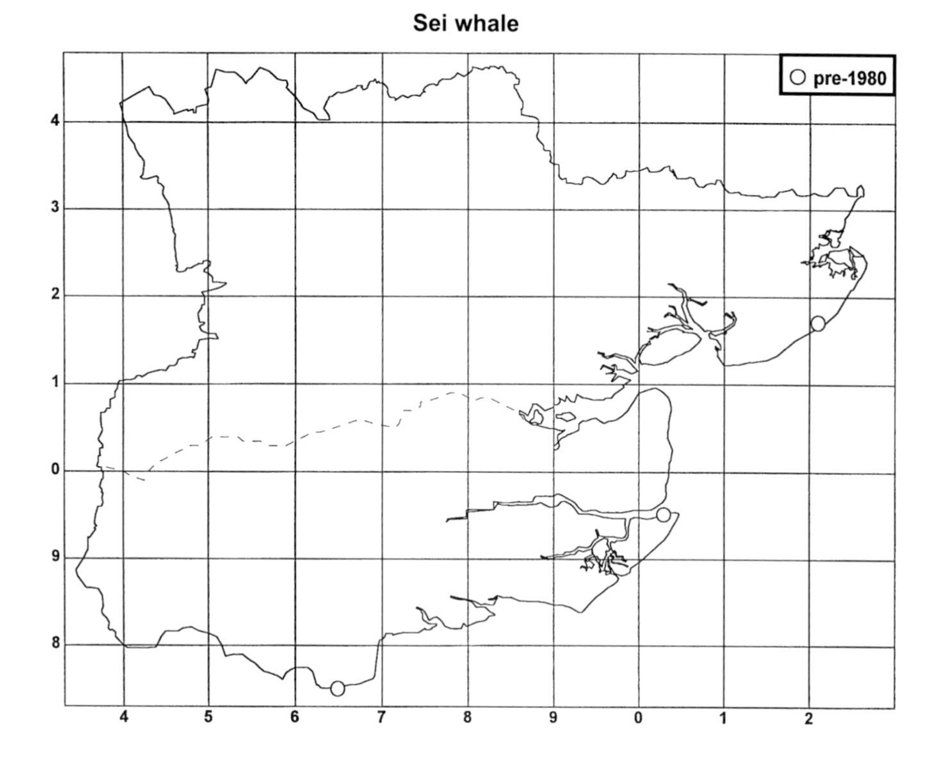

whilst pursuing the shoal of sprats and abundance of shrimps and eels present in the Tilbury area at the time (Crouch, 1887). The body was towed away by a tug, hoisted onto three trucks by a derrick belonging to the Dock Company and exhibited in the Engineer's yard at Tilbury before being bought by a Mr E. Gerrard. The following year, another sei whale occurred in the Thames estuary before entering the Medway and stranding along Gillingham Reach.

The only record for the 20th century is of a small specimen of 4.88m that stranded at Little Holland on 12th September 1948 (Fraser, 1974).

It has been estimated that nearly 80% of the population of sei whales in the northern oceans (around 50,000 whales) were hunted prior to the ban on commercial whaling in 1986. Crouch (1888) described a whaling station in West Finmark that received 771 whales of this species during 1885 and in Scotland, catches of sei whales off the Outer Hebrides fell from 375 between 1903 and 1928 to just three in 1950–51 (Evans, 1991). With the species exploited almost to extinction, it seems unlikely that the sei whale will occur again in Essex.

Minke whale *Balaenoptera acutorostrata* Lacepede, 1804

Status: Rare, four records

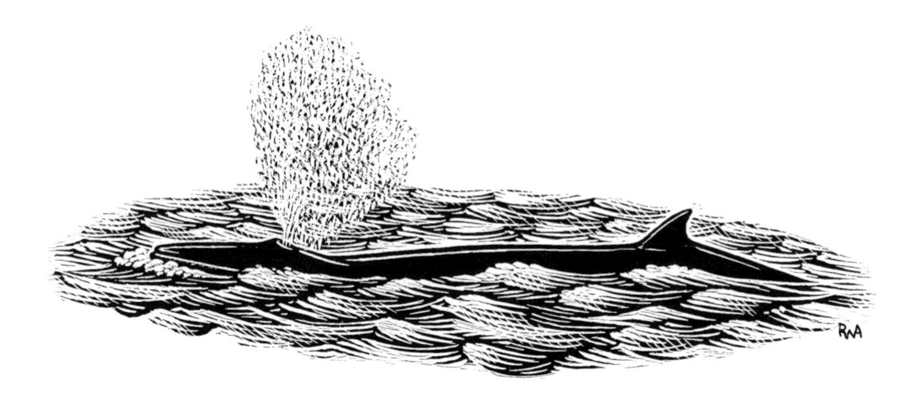

The minke whale, the smallest and commonest of the baleen whales to occur in northern seas, has suffered least from the pressure of commercial whaling because it generates less profit than the larger rorquals. During the summer, the minke whale is frequently reported from Atlantic coasts – often within sight of headlands – and is regularly observed in the northern North Sea.

The first Essex record is of a young female, 5.08m long, that had been driven ashore and killed at the head of Mayland Creek on 23rd September 1900 (Fitch, 1900). There have been two recent occurrences of individuals stranded alive; both involved young animals of around 4.5m in length. The first of these, at Purfleet in October 1996, died before it could be returned to the river – despite the efforts of several volunteers and the Tilbury Fire Service. The second (and most recent) stranding occurred on 9th March 1999 at Holland Haven.

The only live sighting of a minke whale was in Harwich harbour in the summer of 1986.

Minke whale

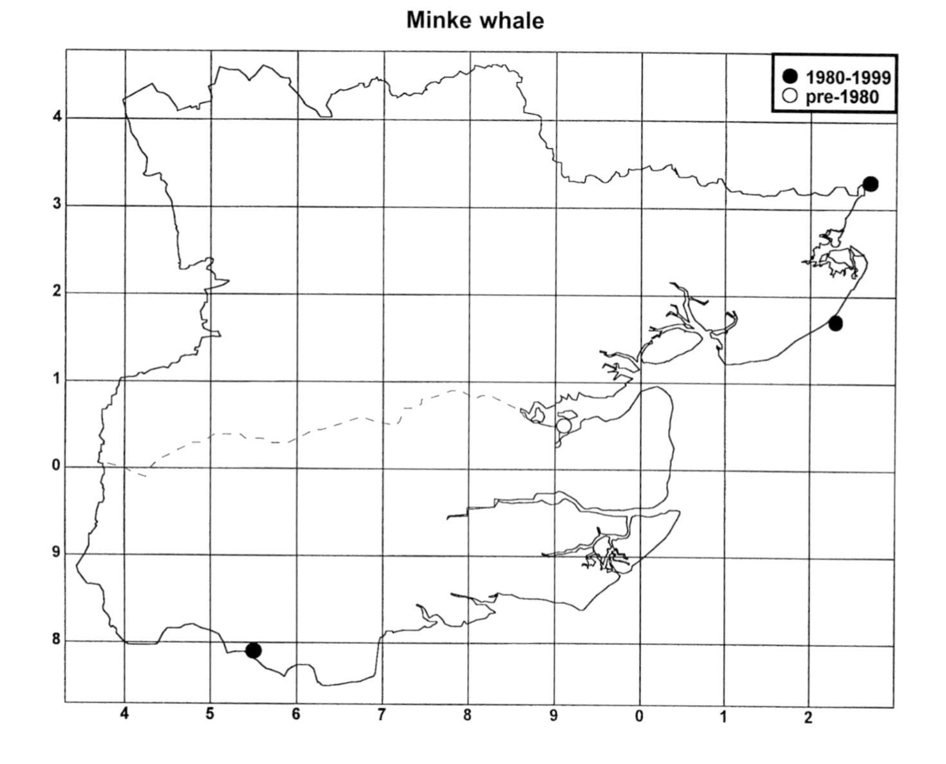

Narwhal

Monodon monoceros Linn., 1758

Status: One record

The narwhal inhabits the Arctic Ocean feeding on cuttlefish, squid, crustaceans and fish. The species is found close to loose pack ice and annual migrations are determined by ice formation and drift. The narwhal lacks a dorsal fin and males have a distinctive tusk that can reach 3m in length.

Occasionally individuals appear in temperate waters and there are six records for Britain. One was a sighting involving two individuals off Orkney in 1949 and the other reports are of strandings. These have occurred in 1648, 1800, 1808 and two in 1949 from the Thames estuary (Evans, 1991). Of these, one 3.94m long, was found at Rainham on 17th February of that year. With global warming producing an increase in sea temperature, this exceptional record is unlikely to be repeated.

Narwhal

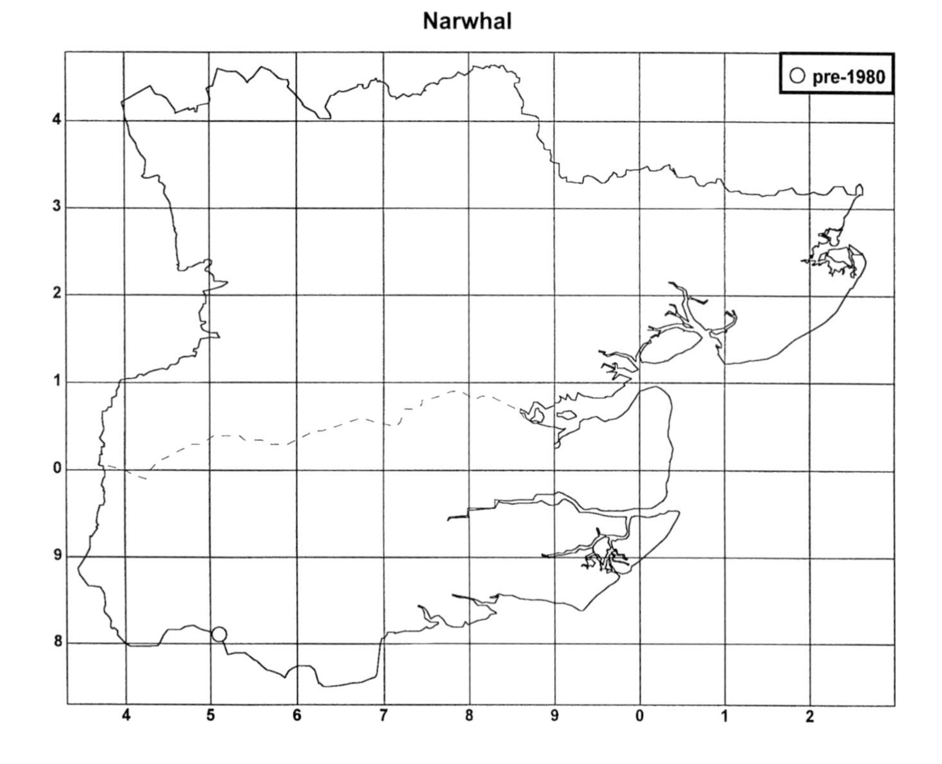

Northern bottlenose whale *Hyperoodon ampullatus* (Forster, 1770)

Status: Rare, no recent records

The northern bottlenose whale is characterised by a prominent dolphin-like beak, bulbous forehead, two V-shaped throat grooves and, in males, the presence of two pear-shaped teeth of 3–4cm projecting at the tip of the lower jaw. The female has no visible teeth although vestigial teeth can be found, unerupted, in both jaws. This is the largest of the beaked whales recorded in British and Irish waters growing to a length of 9.5m. The northern bottlenose whale is variable in colour – from chocolate brown to greenish brown above, and lighter on the flanks and belly. The single young is born in April or May, after a gestation period of twelve months, and is independent after a further year. (Evans, 1991).

Northern bottlenose whales are found in polar seas, usually in deeper waters. In spring, a migration takes place from the temperate seas around Madeira and Cape Verde, northwards following the edge of the continental shelf to the Greenland Sea, Spitzbergen and the seas off Iceland and Norway. The summer is spent gaining weight on a diet of mainly squid and some pelagic fish species before a return migration in the autumn.

Essex has played a major part in the classification of this species with specimens from Maldon (1770), the River Thames (1789), *"near London"* (1804) and *"Essex"* (1828) all being described by different authors. Since then there have been seven records. In July 1891, two male bottlenose whales were recorded in the Thames – one was found near the Nore lightship and towed into Leigh and the other seen at the entrance to Barking Creek (Laver, 1898). The records for the 20th century all refer to strandings.

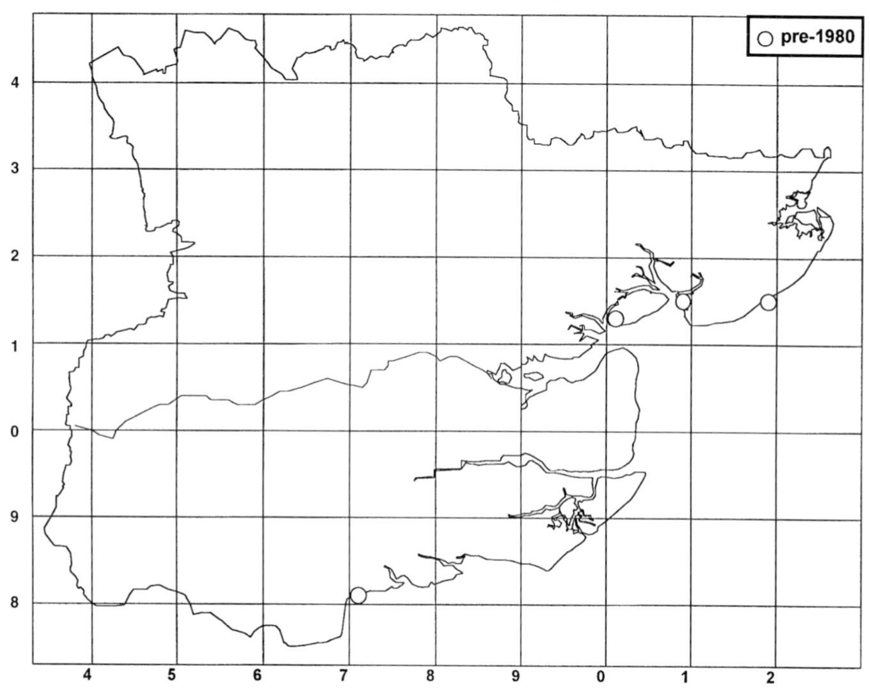

9th October 1916	Mucking	5.49m
30th July 1939	West Mersea	9.14m
30th July 1939	West Mersea	5.49m
31st July 1939	Clacton	6.40m
27th July 1975	Point Clear Bay	6.50m male

As with other whales, northern bottlenose whales tend to occur in groups and these usually comprise up to ten individuals. A school was present in Essex offshore waters in the summer of 1939 and a record of an unidentified odontocete, 5.49 metres long stranded at East Mersea on the 7th August of that year, may also have been of this species.

As the populations of the baleen whales were depleted by commercial whaling, so smaller species such as the northern bottlenose whale were hunted for oil and animal food. The Norwegians exploited this species until 1977 and the recent decline in strandings along the British coast, and in the number of sightings in the deep waters off western Scotland and Ireland, may well be due to this activity.

Sowerby's beaked whale *Mesoplodon bidens* (Sowerby, 1804)

Status: Rare, four records

The beaked whales are rarely observed at sea and knowledge of their distribution is known mainly from the pattern of strandings that have been monitored during the 20th century. They are characterised by a distinctive beak extending from the skull and an absence of teeth in the upper jaw. The Sowerby's beaked whale has a moderately long slender beak and the males are distinguished by a single pair of exposed teeth half-way along the lower jaw. As these teeth only erupt in males, it is thought that they may play a role in fights in which males compete for females – the presence of scars on the surface of older males adding further support for this view. The dorsal coloration is dark grey, fading to paler grey on the flanks and belly, with light spots and scarring on the upper surface and flanks (Evans, 1987). Reproduction is thought to take place in the spring. The juvenile, measuring around 2.4m, is born after a gestation period of about a year and is weaned after a lactation period of a further twelve months (Pourreau, 1988).

Sowerby's beaked whale is known mainly from European waters, particularly the northern North Sea. There has been an increase in strandings in recent years – of 43 reports between 1913 and 1985, 53% occurred after 1963 with recent records from the Northern Isles, eastern Britain and the Channel coasts of southern England (Sheldrick, 1989)

There are four Essex records with two, presumably from the same social group, being stranded on the same day. The identification of the individual at East Tilbury was confirmed from examination of a tooth and vertebra and the skull from the female found at Shoebury is in the collection at Southend Central Museum.

16th July 1939	Westcliff	4.52m
29th November 1959	East Tilbury	
22nd September 1989	Coryton	
22nd September 1989	Shoebury	4.1m

Sowerby's beaked whale

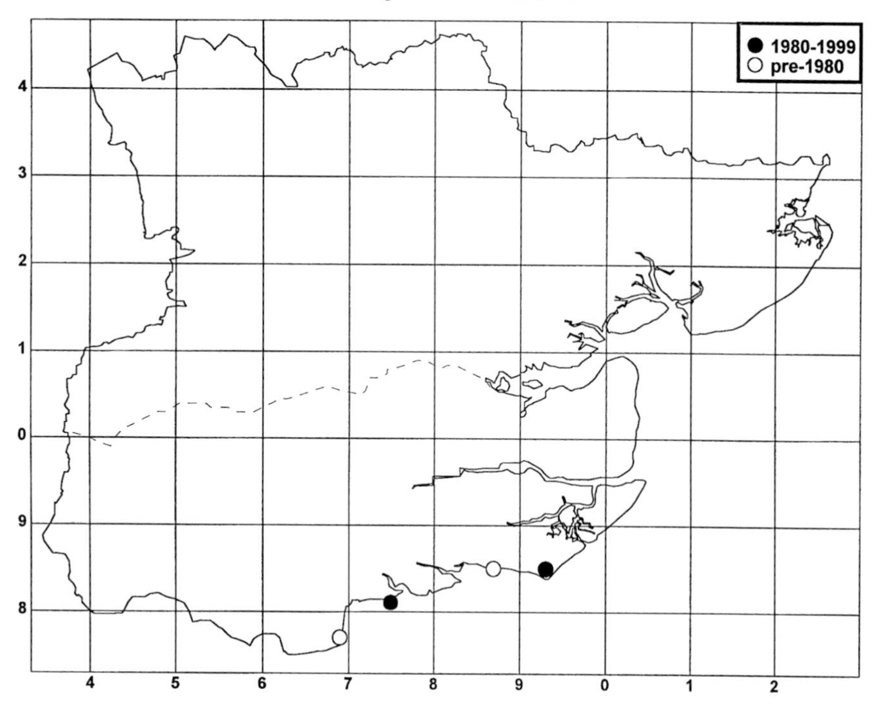

Harbour porpoise

Phocoena phocoena (Linn., 1758)

Status: Rare

The porpoise, rarely reaching two metres in length, is the smallest cetacean occurring in British and Irish coastal waters with the population mainly distributed along the Atlantic coasts of Scotland and Ireland and in the northern North Sea. Although formerly common off the Essex coast, this species has declined in the English Channel and southern North Sea during the last 30 years and is now only rarely recorded in the county. When seen at sea, the porpoise can be identified from its dark grey upper surface and the small triangular dorsal fin situated halfway along the back. The diet consists of several fish species together with crustaceans and cephalopods (Evans, 1991).

For Laver (1898), the porpoise was *"so common that I have not thought it necessary to give any records of capture"* and in July 1904, *"a shoal was driven ashore at West Mersea, about six were killed but the rest got away"*. In the Rochford Hundred in the mid-1950s, it was described as a *"common visitor to the shores of the Hundred, from the Thames to the Crouch at Creeksea"*, yet now it is most commonly found stranded along the shoreline. Although porpoises can be seen in all months of the year, they are most likely to be sighted between July and September when the young are born in coastal waters. The only four sightings during the last decade have all been made by birdwatchers, with fourteen strandings during the same period.

21st September 1990	one seen off Sales Point, Bradwell
10th April 1993	our seen off Colne Point
20th September 1997	one seen from Southend Pier swimming out of the river
2nd December 1997	one seen off Canvey Point

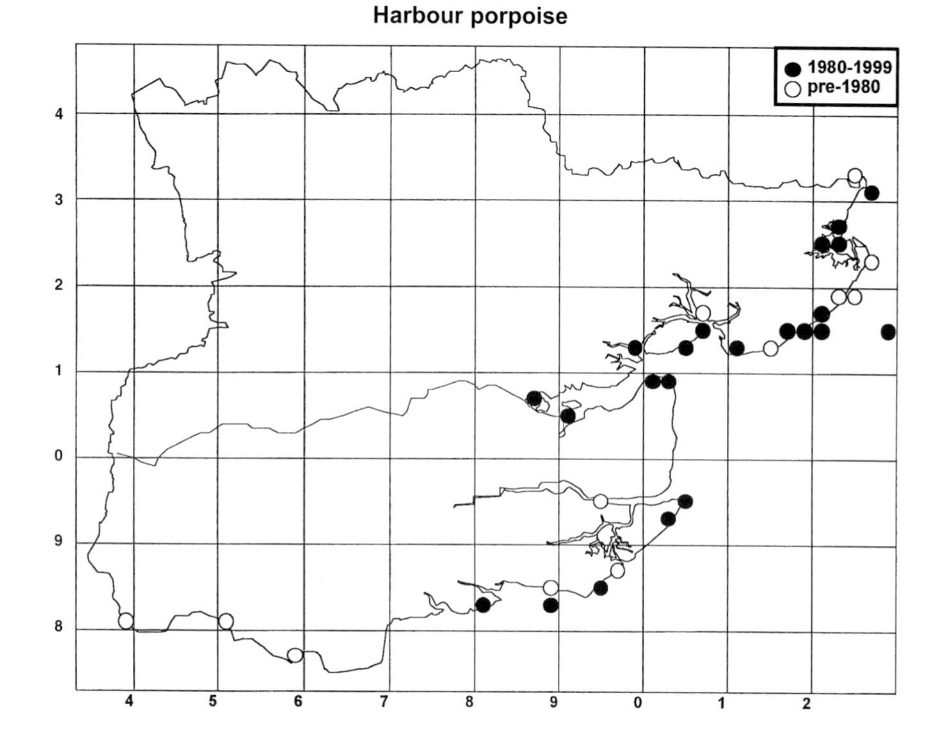

The table of strandings shows a clear peak in April, although this differs from the national picture where a late-summer peak can be demonstrated. On four occasions more than one animal was involved. Three, presumably from the same social group, were stranded over six days at Frinton in December, 1924, a female and her calf were stranded at West Thurrock on 29th April 1964, two were found at Bradwell on 21st April 1966 and two at Clacton/Holland on 16th September 1991. In recent years, the increase in recreational activities such as speedboats and jetskis in several Essex estuaries has enhanced the risk of direct collision and the high frequency sounds generated by these craft disturb small cetaceans (Evans, 1995). As more people become involved in these leisure pursuits, it seems certain that the porpoise will never be more than an infrequent visitor to our coast.

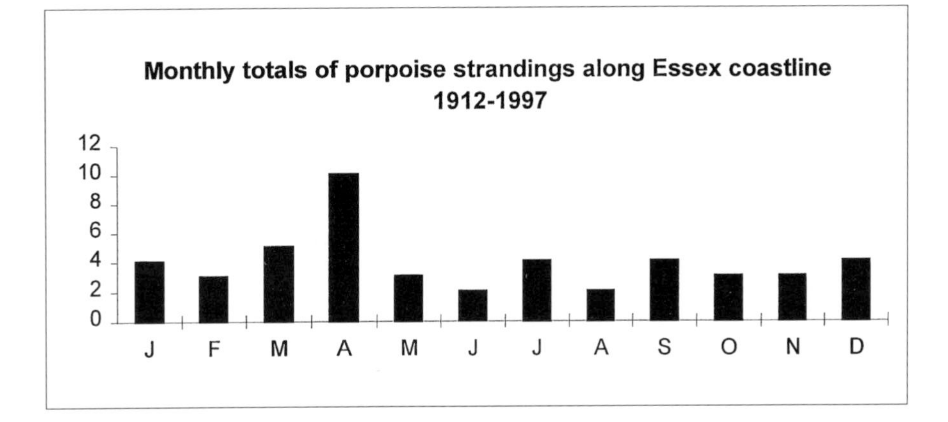
Monthly totals of porpoise strandings along Essex coastline
1912-1997
12
10
8
6
4
2
0
J
F
M
A
M
J
J
A
S
O
N
D

Common dolphin

Delphinus delphis Linn., 1758

Status: Two records

The common dolphin has a worldwide distribution but in the United Kingdom is most commonly found off south-western coasts, with small numbers occasionally entering the North Sea. This species may be identified by its small size (less than 2.5m) and distinctive hourglass pattern of creamish yellow on the flanks.

There are two Essex records. On 12th March 1938, an individual measuring 2.28m was stranded at Clacton and on 8th March 1993 another was found on the shoreline at Foulness Point. Evidence that this species sometimes enters the Thames estuary comes from stranding records at Putney in August 1935 and Millwall in April 1937. Additionally, two were seen alive at Chiswick during two days in November 1947 (Fitter, 1949).

Common dolphin

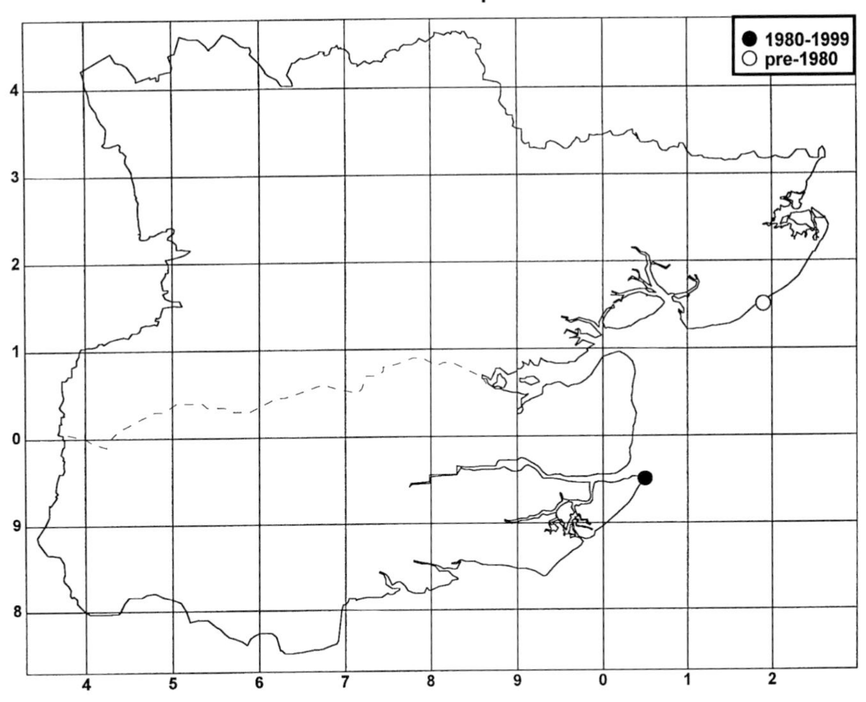

Common dolphin / Striped dolphin

Delphinus delphis / Stenella coeruleoalba

Status: one record

Although the striped dolphin occurs mainly in tropical and temperate waters, there have been a number of recent British records from Atlantic and Irish Sea coasts. Some of these have occurred as a result of the re-examination of specimens previously identified as common dolphins – a species with a similar appearance, particularly when stranded in poor condition (Berrow & Rogan, 1997).

The only record for the county was of an individual, unable to be specifically identified, found dead at Cudmore Grove on 1st August 1990.

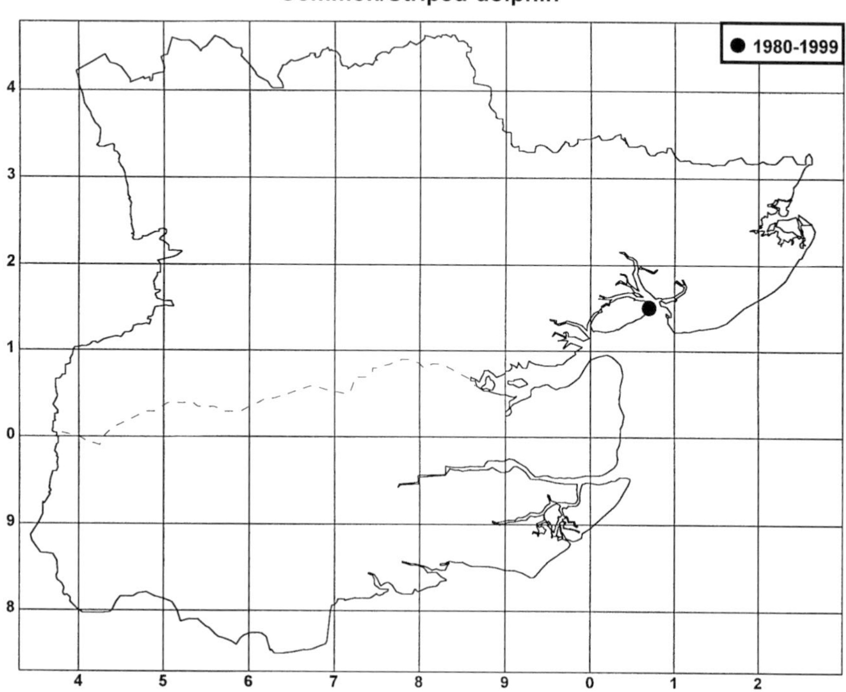

Bottle-nosed dolphin

Tursiops truncatus (Montagu, 1821)

Status: Rare, no recent records

The bottle-nosed dolphin was once a common sight in the estuaries and bays of Essex but is now rare in the southern North Sea – with pollution, disturbance from an increased level of sea-going leisure activities and the reduction in fish stocks all contributing to a recent decline in the population. When seen, the bottle-nosed dolphin can be recognised by its grey coloration; dark on the back fading to lighter grey on the flanks and white on the belly. The sickle-shaped dorsal fin is centrally placed along the back and records are usually of either individuals or small groups of up to 25 animals. In southern England, there are recent reports of this species from Dungeness and the Sussex coast, but the last Essex record was of a stranded individual at Walton in 1972.

The bottle-nosed dolphin has a world-wide distribution, with most sightings occurring within ten kilometres of land. The diet is varied, including many fish species, squid and cuttlefish and life expectancy is around 25 years. The single young is born between March and September and weaned after nineteen months, females breeding every two to three years (Evans,1991).

Laver (1898) commented that he had often been close enough to this species to identify it from a boat and described the fate of several individuals. In 1829, one was captured in the Thames near the Nore lightship and its skeleton kept in the museum of the Royal College of Surgeons. Around 1880, a female measuring 3.05m was captured off Harwich (caught by a cod hook in the lip), followed by another female being shot in the Colne on 5th September 1881 and two more suffering the same fate in the River Colne the following year. Describing an incident in the River Colne in 1892, Laver wrote *"On the morning of May 29th last, a man named John Crosby was waiting by the side of Mill Creek, Fingringhoe, when he discovered some large Porpoises in a shallow part of the creek, unable to pass*

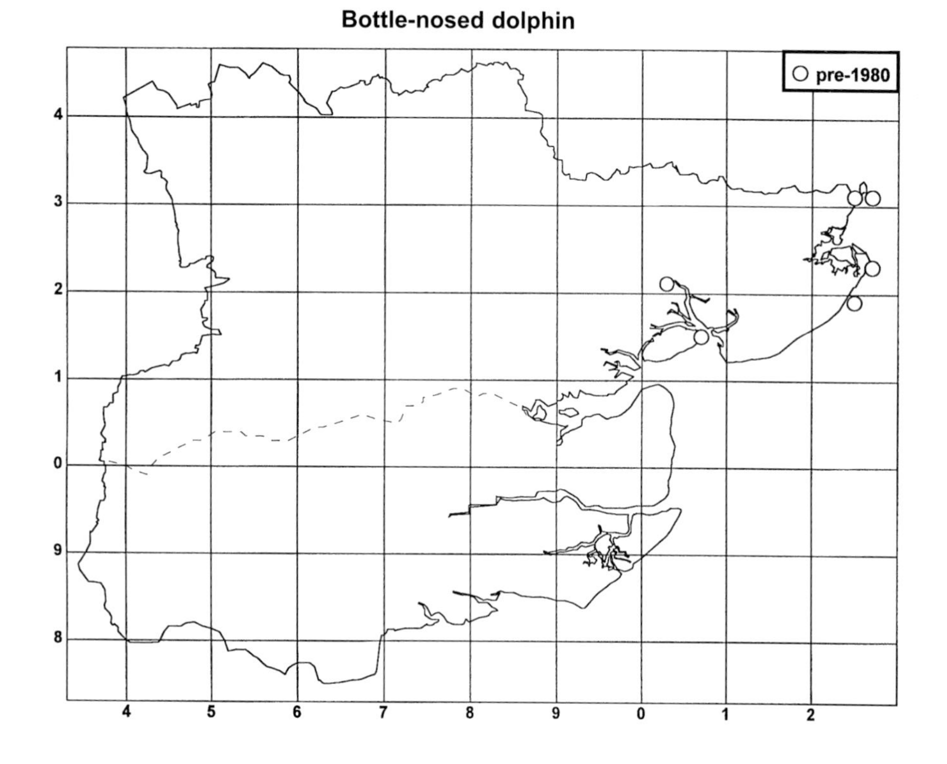

downwards, in consequence of the receding tide leaving too little water on a bank below. With the help of some of his friends whom he had called to his assistance, a slip noose of rope was passed over each, and they were drawn onto the marsh and dispatched by cutting their throats, pig-fashion. I saw them in the afternoon, and found them to be two male and one female 'Bottle-noses', Delphinus tursio, *a Dolphin not rare in our estuaries. The female measured 10ft 3 inches, the largest male 10ft 1 inch and the lesser 5ft 10 inches, from the tip of the nose to the notch in the fluke, respectively."*

During the 20th century, the only records have been of stranded animals.

26th July 1914	Dovercourt	3.12m
2nd December 1924	Frinton	3.05m
12th October 1928	Walton	1.52m
1st September 1932	Frinton	2.49m
3rd June 1957	Dovercourt	3.66m
28th May 1972	Walton	3.66m

Occasionally, bottle-nosed dolphins have occurred in the Thames with four records from the London area before the Second World War (Fitter, 1949) and two strandings at Waterloo Bridge and Chiswick during the mid-1950s.

It is perhaps this species, through its presence in dolphinaria, that has done most to heighten public awareness of the threats to cetacean populations around the world. Sadly, many of those problems are all too present in our inshore waters and the bottle-nosed dolphin seems likely to remain a very rare visitor to the Essex coast.

White-beaked dolphin *Lagenorhyncus albirostris* Gray, 1846

Status: Rare, no recent records

This large dolphin prefers the temperate and subpolar waters of the North Atlantic and is the commonest species found in summer off the north coast of Scotland, the Faroes, Iceland and West Norway. It occurs in the northern North Sea but, in common with other species, is rare in the southern North Sea and English Channel. The diet consists mainly of fish such as cod, herring, whiting, mackerel, capelin and haddock, but octopus, squid and some benthic crustaceans may also be taken. The white-beaked dolphin can reach 2.7m in length, and is identified by its black back, fading to grey behind the dorsal fin, a short pale beak (which may not be visible in the field) and a sickle-shaped dorsal fin situated halfway along the back (Evans, 1987).

The first Essex record concerned a school of around nine white-beaked dolphins in the River Colne on 11th September, 1889. Laver (1889), wrote that *"they were first seen by the pilot of the iron railway bridge at Alresford, and by Mr Barton, of Alresford Lodge, near the bridge, but whether the 'school' consisted of seven or nine is not quite clear. Mr Barton armed himself with his rifle, and from a punt, shot at several, and managed to capture two. One specimen was 9 feet 6 inches long (probably an adult), and the other 6 feet 6 inches, both being females. One that he shot at got into deeper water, and was picked up next day by Henry Barr, a fisherman at Wyvenhoe, being 9 feet 6 inches long, adult, sex not noted. Another of his wounded ones, also 9 feet 6 inches long, was captured by the crew of the yacht 'Valfreyia.' Thus, five specimens were taken at one time of this rare dolphin in our river."* The fifth animal was one that was driven aground and killed with a pocket knife. The editor of *The Essex Naturalist* went on to propose the establishment of a Natural History Museum for such specimens and commented, *"the opportunity of securing another Essex Delphinus* [sic] *may possibly not occur again, if there be a*

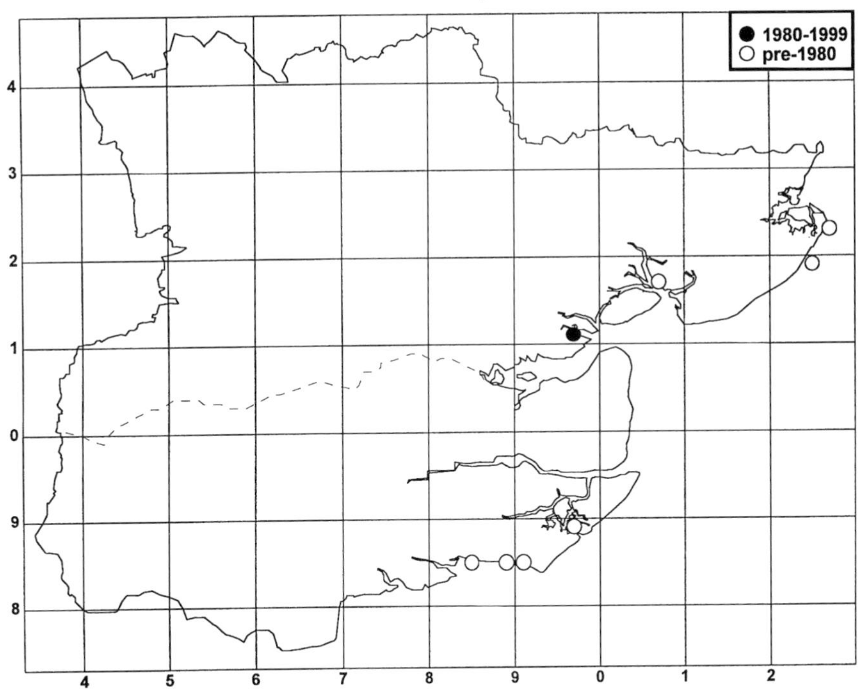

'schoolmaster' abroad among the dolphins to warn his pupils of the end of five of the confiding animals who were so foolish as to visit the inhospitable waters of the Colne."

The other nine Essex records all refer to strandings, with seven occurring in 1977.

3rd November 1964	Walton	2.51m female
21st March 1977	Frinton	2.13m female
21st March 1977	Frinton	2.22m female
April 1977	Havengore Creek	
21st September 1977	Southend	2.50m female
21st September 1977	Southend	2.59m female
21st September 1977	Westcliff	2.48m female
22nd September 1977	Thorpe Bay	2.64m female
10th April 1982	Old Hall Marshes	2.56m female

Additionally, two dolphin skulls found on Havengore Island in 1944 were thought to be of this species (D. Hunford, pers. comm.). The skull of the 1977 dolphin from Havengore was removed and put in a compost heap, then recovered and cleaned in the autumn of 1978, with its identification confirmed by the Natural History Museum, London (Wilson, 1979). The number of records for 1977 suggests that there was a school of white-beaked dolphins in the southern North Sea at that time, a number of which died and were brought by the tide to our coastline. The lack of records since 1982 coincides with the increase in shipping and leisure activity that have contributed to the scarcity of cetaceans in Essex coastal waters.

Killer whale

Orcinus orca (Linn., 1758)

Status: One record

This, the most charismatic cetacean, is also the most recognisable. The powerful black and white body and tall, conspicuous dorsal fin is rarely seen from south-eastern coasts; however, the killer whale has a world-wide distribution, occurring in both tropical and polar seas (Evans, 1991).

There are several historical accounts of the presence of the killer whale in Essex. Laver (1898) writes that three specimens were captured in the Thames at the end of the 18th century and a skull, obtained from a stranding on the Essex coast, is in the Natural History Museum. Another individual is mentioned by Dale (1732) and Laver himself *"saw two whales which had been killed in one of the creeks of the Blackwater. These, I have no doubt, were of this species, but no record was kept of them, and I do not recollect what became of their bones. Probably they went, as usual, for manure."*

There is one recent record, of an individual, 5.64m long, stranded at Walton on 20th September 1963 (Fraser, 1974).

Killer whale

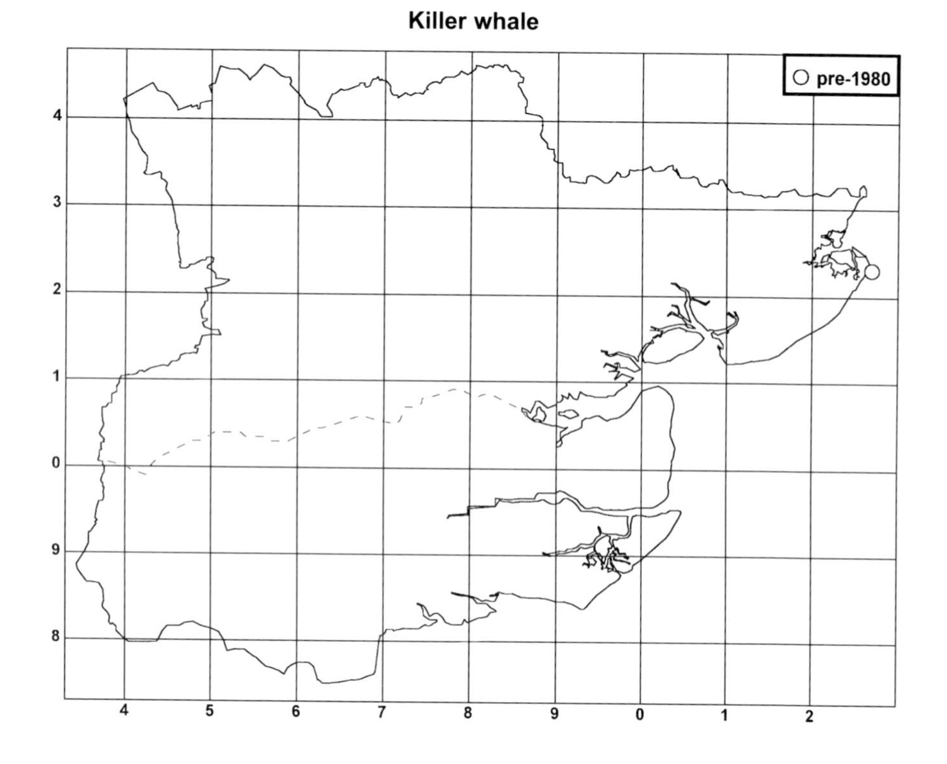

Risso's dolphin

Grampus griseus (Cuvier, 1812)

Status: One record

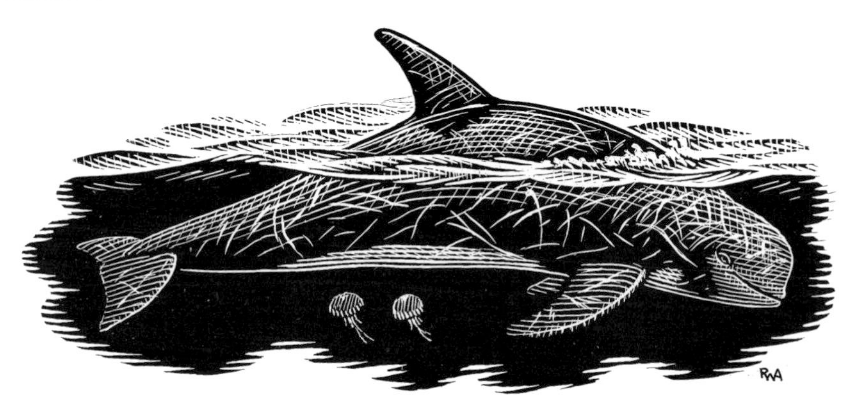

This is a large greyish dolphin with a blunt, rounded head and tall dorsal fin, centrally placed along the back. During mating, there is aggressive interaction between adults: this may account for the scars often seen on the head and body. Risso's dolphin occurs on Atlantic coasts and also in the northern North Sea, being rarely found further south and in the English Channel (Evans, 1991).

The sole Essex record (the fifth for Britain) was made on 5th September 1885 (Laver, writing in 1898 recorded the date as 1887) on the saltings on the north side of the Crouch near Creeksea. After being taken to the other side of the river, it was eventually boiled down for its oil. The remains of the skull and lower jaw were obtained and submitted to the Natural History Museum where the identification was confirmed. At the time, this was the furthest east and north that the species had been recorded (Laver, 1898).

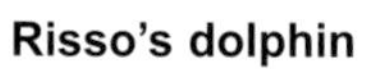

Risso's dolphin

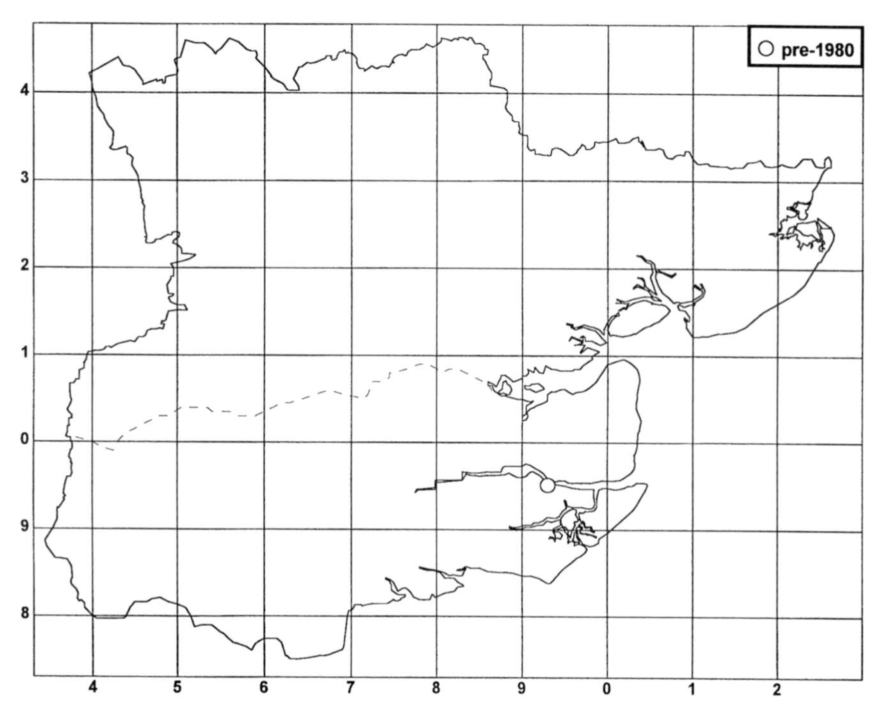

The carnivores first appeared around 58 million years ago and comprise 236 modern species worldwide. They are distinguished by the presence of large, conical canine teeth and specialised carnassial teeth for shearing and cutting their prey. Nine species have been recorded in Essex during the last 200 years, two of which – the pine marten and polecat – are now extinct. Two others, the ferret and mink, are present in the county after escaping from captivity. All nine species are members of the order Carnivora although the badger is omnivorous.

Another feature shared by all species (except the ferret) is that they have been subject to various methods of 'predator control'. The pine marten and polecat were eradicated by Victorian gamekeepers, whose modern-day counterparts actively control foxes and mustelids in woodland used for pheasant rearing. The badger has suffered from 'badger digging' (an activity that has fortunately declined in recent years following improved legislation) and the mink has been trapped at a few sites in Essex to protect ground-nesting birds. At present, four hunts still pursue the fox in Essex; and, despite their efforts, its numbers are increasing. Hunting of otters, which used to take place in the county, ended in 1978.

Many of the carnivore records collected since 1994 came from road casualties (or, in the case of the otter, spraints). More than 500 records of badgers found dead along the county's roads were received in the last five years; despite this figure, the species is more widespread than ever before. A similar number of foxes were also reported; many of them were recorded on the dual carriageways of southern Essex.

Perhaps the most exciting news involving the carnivores previously lost to Essex is that in 1982–83, polecats were re-introduced at several sites in central and south-west Hertfordshire. During this period, 26–30 animals were released, and their descendants have been regularly reported in subsequent years (M. Clark, pers. comm.). The polecat has been expanding its range since the 1920s, spreading from its former strongholds in Wales and the English border counties. This expansion has seen recent records from Northamptonshire and Leicestershire, but the presence of this species in a neighbouring county suggests that the recolonisation of Essex may occur early in the next century.

The seals (pinnipeds) are a very distinctive group, closely related to the carnivores that they descended from around 25 million years ago. Two species, the grey seal and the common seal, occur in Essex and are increasing in numbers. A record count of 82 seals (the species were not counted separately) was made off Foulness early in 1999 (B. Dawson, pers. comm.).

Fox

Vulpes vulpes (Linn., 1758)

Status: Abundant, increasing

Equally at home in both urban and rural surroundings, the fox is widespread throughout Essex and is thought to be increasing in numbers. This versatile species has no specific habitat requirements, being found in all areas where there is suffficient food and cover. In towns, dens are sited under sheds and buildings; elsewhere they may be dug in banks or adapted from existing rabbit burrows and disused badger setts. Outside the breeding season, most foxes prefer to shelter above ground in dense cover, only resorting to earths during adverse weather conditions. The litter of four to five cubs is born in March, the young being part of a family group that stays intact until the juveniles disperse after six to twelve months. A wide variety of food has been recorded, including lagomorphs, rodents, birds, invertebrates and fruit – much of which is obtained by scavenging from gardens and garbage put out for disposal, as well as by taking advantage of mammals killed along busy roads. Although foxes may live for ten years, life expectancy is commonly around twelve months: most deaths are caused by man-induced events such as traffic accidents, shooting and trapping (Harris & Lloyd, 1991).

Historical references to the fox in Essex are often associated with hunting; in one of the earliest, King Henry III gave permission to the Abbess of Barking to hunt the fox in Havering Park in 1221 (Rackham, 1989). The destruction of foxes was also recorded in chuchwarden's accounts, an example of which comes from the parishes of All Saints and St Peter, Maldon. A bounty of one shilling per head was paid for both foxes and badgers and, during the years from 1716 to 1754, 114 foxes were killed in an area of 670ha. Not surprisingly, the species declined during this period, with no payments being made during the last four years (Fitch, 1887). During the 19th century, (a period of intensive gamekeeping) it is likely that the fox was conserved for the chase; a century that saw the eradication of the polecat and pine marten in Essex apparently gave protection to our largest carnivore. Laver (1898) described the fox as *"fortunately-common"* and devoted the whole of his account to

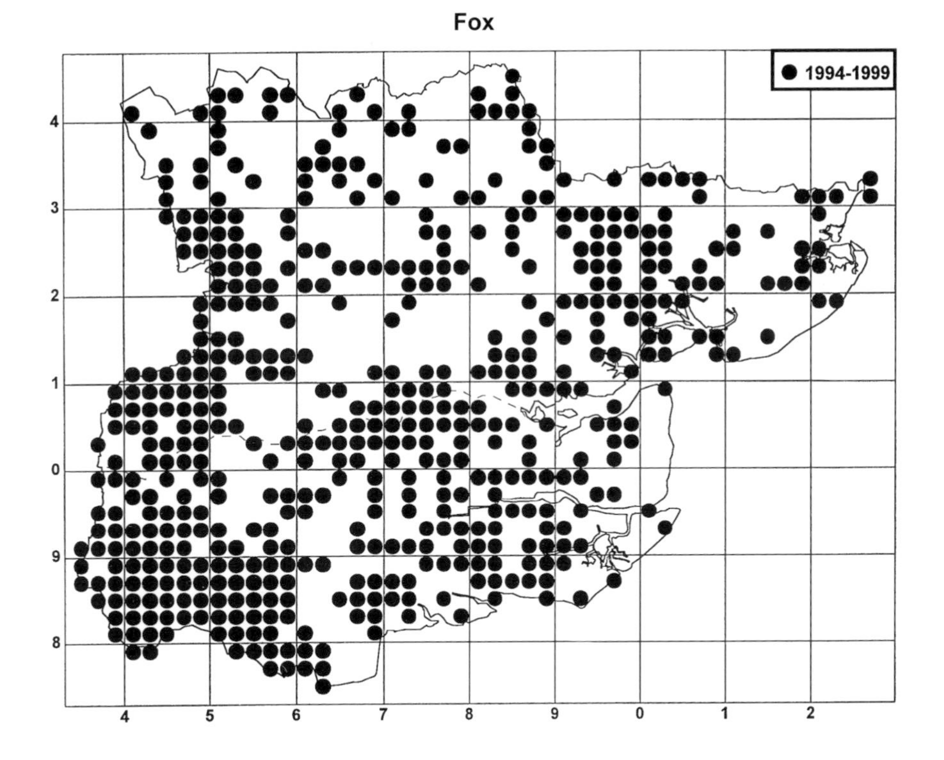

hunting stories, including one in which a fox was finally killed after covering 24 miles in three and a half hours.

The adaptability of the fox has enabled it to extend its range in Essex during the second half of the 20th century. The introduction of myxomatosis proved only a temporary setback (the increased areas of ungrazed vegetation generating a higher population of field voles that were preyed upon by foxes) and Hughes (1986) noted that from the 1970s onward, more reports of foxes were received from urban rather than rural areas. Whether this represented a change in fox distribution or a growing awareness of town wildlife is unclear; however, the trend towards an increased number of urban sightings in metropolitan Essex has continued during the present survey. Since 1994, reports have come equally from sightings of live animals and road casualties – additionally, the fox is the only species represented by olfactory records!

The current status of the fox does not seem to be affected by the present level of persecution. Of the four hunts covering the county, two (the Essex and Suffolk Hunt and the Essex Farmers Hunt) account for around 110 foxes during a season.

However, it is the increase in lamping (shooting at night) associated with pheasant-rearing that causes higher mortality. On one estate at Orsett, 60 foxes a year are killed in this way; a figure which, if typical, would mean many hundreds of foxes being destroyed each year across the county.

Today, the fox is a common sight in Essex. It thrives in a sometimes hostile countryside as well as the highly-populated urban environment. That it has been able to adapt so readily to both is worthy of our admiration.

Pine marten

Martes martes (Linn., 1758)

Status: Extinct

Today the pine marten is locally common in parts of Scotland and is slowly expanding its range. It remains rare in Wales, and in England is only to be found in Northumbria, Durham, Cumbria and north and west Yorkshire – that said, the total population (in England and Wales) may number as few as 150 animals. Sadly, recent evidence suggests that, away from the north-east, the species may be contracting and that in some localities populations may cease to be viable (Harris *et al.*, 1995).

During the 18th century, the pine marten was probably widespread in Essex. An early reference comes from Robert Smith, *"late Rat-catcher to Princess Amelia"*. In 1768 he wrote *"I knew one that used to run tame about the kitchen of the Bald-Face Stag, on Epping Forest. They have no strong disagreeable scent, like the polecat, weasel, and other stinking animals of a similar nature, but are reckoned the sweetest of the vermin kind. I caught several one winter on the aforesaid forest and sold their skins for four shillings and sixpence each, for the sake of the fur, which is exceedingly good."* Martens were apparently easy to tame and a farmer at Terling seldom had less than two although they tended to return to the woods if they managed to escape (Daniel, 1812). The same author recorded that *"the most ever met with was in the large woods near Rayleigh"* (presumably Hockley Woods). In 1810 a pine marten was shot at Terling, and the specimen kept in the possession of a local family until 1890 when it was presented to Stratford Museum.

At this time, the English population of the pine marten was declining rapidly as a result of deforestation and determined persecution by gamekeepers. Most reports from Essex refer to further destruction and, in 1822, one was shot out of a crow's nest in Waltham Woods near Chelmsford (Laver, 1898). By 1845, the species was *"occasionally found in Essex . . . and I have heard old sportsmen speak of shooting it from deserted magpies' nests"* (Lubbock, 1845). In 1881, a Colchester taxidermist told J.E. Harting (an eminent zoologist) *"that the last Marten he had seen in Essex was killed in the autumn of 1845 at Walton, near Colchester, by a keeper, who sold*

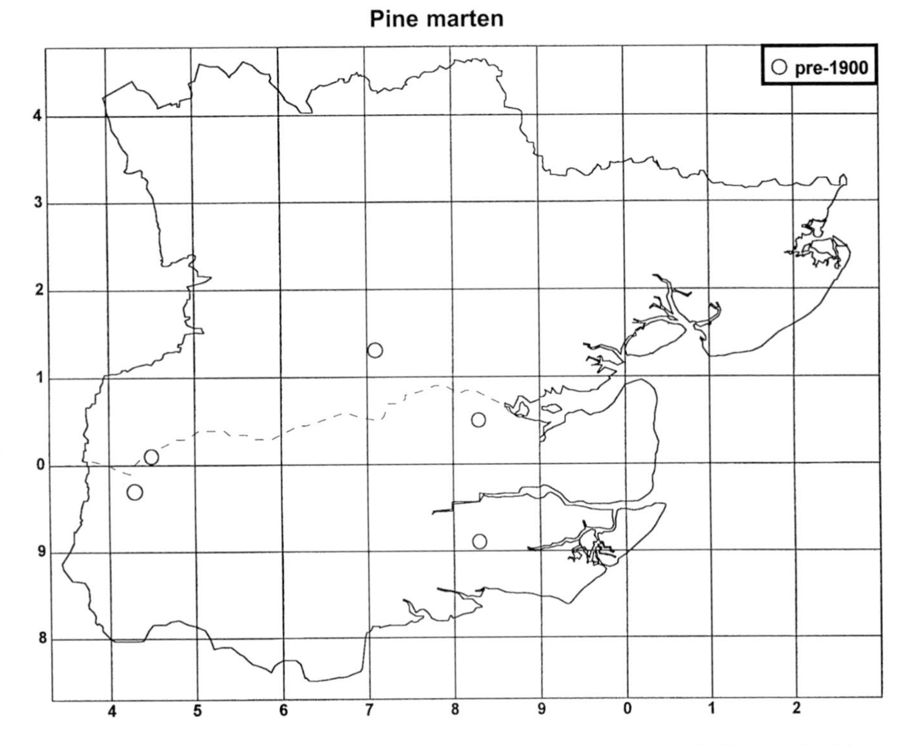

it to him for half-a-crown. He skinned and preserved it, and disposed of it to Mr. Maberley, of Colchester for ten shillings." (Harting, 1891). Another individual, that also changed hands for money was trapped at Loughton in the spring of 1853 and a few years later, pine martens were said still to occur in Hazeleigh Hall Wood, near Maldon, although a specimen was not obtained (Fitch, 1890).

An Essex specimen, said to have been killed at Chingford (date unknown) came up for auction on 10th December 1889 at Steven's Auction Rooms. Part of lot 52, a case of *"British Weasels"*, it was bought in at a reserved price for the owner, Mr. West of High Street, Gravesend. Perhaps the last confirmed record of a pine marten in Essex was of one that was seen by several observers near Ambresbury Banks in Epping Forest, on 30th July 1883 (Laver, 1898).

It is unlikely that this species will return to Essex. Where they occur, pine martens are present at low density and their low reproductive rate makes them particularly vulnerable to local extinction. Excessive persecution during the 19th century finally eradicated an animal that is now fully protected by Schedule 5 of the Wildlife and Countryside Act 1981 and is the subject of active conservation measures to ensure its continued survival.

Stoat

Mustela erminea Linn., 1758

Status: Fairly common, declining

"This rapacious, active and destructive member of a specially blood-thirsty family is very common throughout Essex. Persecution, from every quarter, seems to have little influence in diminishing its numbers." (Laver, 1898).

Today, despite continued trapping by gamekeepers, the stoat can still be found in those habitats of the county such as woodland, farmland and marshland which offer both cover and prey. The stoat is separated from the weasel by its larger size, cream-coloured under-fur and black tip to the tail. The diet consists of larger mammals such as rabbits, water voles and brown rats, many of which are caught in their burrows; the size of the stoat prevents it from entering the smaller tunnels of mice and voles. The eggs and chicks of gamebirds are also taken; however, the trapping of stoats by gamekeepers has only a temporary effect on the population as the numbers are replaced by others dispersing into the area (Tapper *et al.*, 1982). Breeding occurs during the spring when a single litter of six to twelve young is born, the number of young surviving being determined by the availability of prey.

Although the stoat has probably always been fairly common in Essex, there are very few published references of the species. Occasionally an ermine, in full winter coat, is sighted – the first report is of one shot at Roxwell (Christy, 1888) with later records of one shot by a Pest Control Officer at Layer de la Haye in January 1965, another found dead at Suckstead Green in 1967 (Chapman, 1967) and individuals seen at Halstead and Aldham in 1974. More frequently, animals still retaining some normal coloration are seen and several reports have been received from Forestry Commission staff (S. Leatherdale, pers. comm.). Of other records obtained during the present survey, the most frequently reported was the sighting of a stoat seen crossing a road. When foraging for prey, stoats use linear features such as hedgerows, stream banks and roadside verges to provide cover, moving swiftly between hunting areas along the easiest route (King, 1991a). It is at this time that

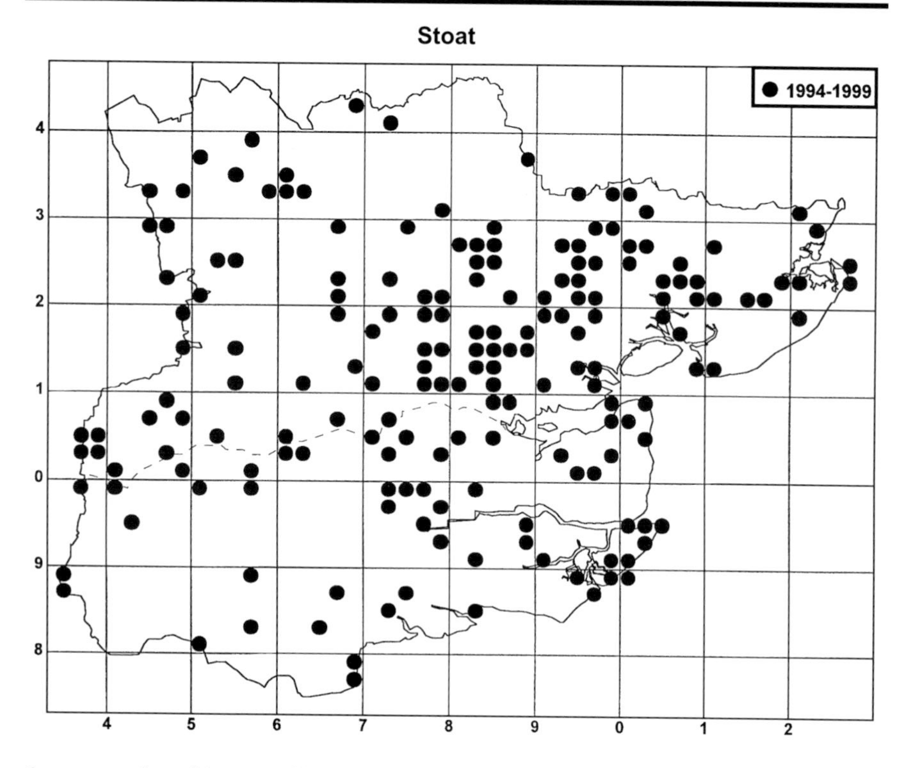

they are vulnerable to traffic and the second most common source of records was the finding of road casualties.

Nationally, the stoat population is thought to be in decline. The number of stoats killed, as recorded by the National Game Bag Census (Trout *et al.*, 1986), showed that there had been a partial recovery from the losses that followed the outbreak of myxomatosis in 1953; however the same census has demonstrated a further decline since the mid-1970s (Tapper, 1992). The reasons are unclear although the rise in the fox population will have increased the risk of predation and reduced the ability of stoat numbers to respond to the continuing increase in the rabbit population. Other prey species such as water voles and brown rats have declined and the loss of hedgerows and other linear features from the landscape has reduced the cover that stoats use when foraging for prey (Harris *et al.*, 1995).

The stoat is present throughout Essex, but probably under-recorded due to its secretive lifestyle. Persecution by gamekeepers still occurs but despite this any reduction in the local population is temporary. Although there may be fewer small carnivores in the county today than before myxomatosis, the sight of a hunting stoat is still a fairly common event in the Essex countryside.

Weasel

Mustela nivalis Linn., 1766

Status: Fairly common, declining

Weasels are found throughout the Essex countryside, in those habitats that support the small mammals that serve as prey. The weasel can be distinguished from the stoat by its smaller size and the absence of a black tip to the tail. Males average twice the weight of females and the two sexes occupy separate territories – the size of which is influenced by the season and availability of food. Small rodents form the major part of the diet – voles being particularly vulnerable to a predator that can enter their burrows – with the larger prey items such as young rabbits and rats being captured more often by the larger male animals. Gamebird chicks are also taken and occasionally nest boxes are raided when small mammal populations are low. The four to six young are born during spring and early summer and a second litter is produced during good vole years. This ability to respond to high vole numbers is unique amongst carnivores; however in poor vole years breeding may be unsuccessful leading to local extinctions of the species (King, 1991b).

Laver (1898) reported that the weasel was common despite persecution, especially on the marshes near the coast where it was often taken by the heron. Regretting the actions of gamekeepers, he described the weasel as *"another of the so-called 'vermin', and is ruthlessly destroyed whenever it is found. This, in my opinion, is a great mistake, since its prey consists chiefly of the smaller Mammals, which might otherwise become too numerous."* The collapse of the rabbit population following the introduction of myxomatosis in 1953 and the subsequent growth of ground cover in previously grazed areas led, in the late 1950s, to an increase in the numbers of small rodents available as prey for weasels. Record catches were reported at this time from keepered estates (Sumption & Flowerdew, 1985). Seear (1964) considered the weasel to be more common in Essex than the stoat. Nationally, the weasel population declined from the early 1960s to the mid-1970s as stoats recovered from the advent of myxomatosis. However, since then, there has been no obvious increase in the weasel population, during a period that has seen a further decline in the number of stoats (Harris *et al.*, 1995).

Weasel

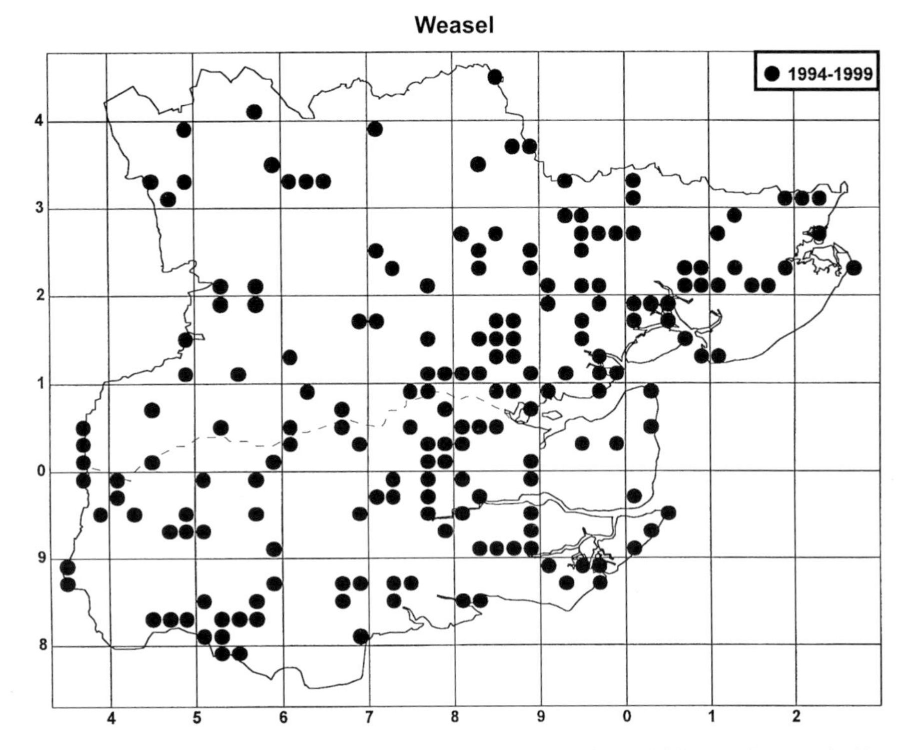

During the recording period, weasels were reported from 191 tetrads – a similar number to that of the stoat. The apparent scarcity of the species in the north-west of the county is probably due to the lack of recorders, rather than a real absence of weasels. Most sightings were of individuals seen darting across a road or hunting in the countryside, with reports of road casualties the second most frequent source of records. Mustelids are often found as road victims, their vulnerability perhaps being due to their habit of hunting along linear features such as roadside verges. A less common cause of mortality is predation by domestic cats – recorded on two occasions at Upminster and Ulting. Other threats to survival include persecution by gamekeepers, with up to 60 per year trapped on an estate near Orsett – however, local declines in the population are made up by animals dispersing from surrounding areas. Despite their ability to enter the tunnels of mice and voles, weasels are rarely caught in Longworth traps and the only recent report of one being captured in this way occurred during a teaching session on small mammals at Daws Hall Field Centre in July, 1998. Although fairly common in Essex, the future for the weasel will depend upon sympathetic management of the countryside that ensures the continuing availability of prey-rich habitats, such as hedgerows, woodland and rough grassland.

Polecat

Mustela putorius Linn., 1758

Status: Extinct

The exact date of the disappearance of the polecat from Essex is uncertain. Laver (1915) described them as *"fairly frequent up until 1830 in many parts of Essex, especially bordering the marshes"* but considered them *"extremely rare"* in 1915. Although last recorded from Epping Forest around 1880, there were occasional reports from wooded country along the Lea Valley in 1900 and Frohawk writing in 1926 considered that they were still present in marshes along the Thames in 1905.

What is certain is that persecution by gamekeepers was the major factor contributing to the demise of the polecat – it was only when predator control relaxed after the First World War that the species was able to increase in numbers and extend its range in Britain.

The spread back into England by natural means has been hastened by recent releases in Hertfordshire. These seem to have led to a firmly established and expanding population that has spread to within a few kilometres of the Essex border (M. Clark, pers. comm.).

It seems likely that the polecat will again soon be present in Essex and, since there is some evidence that they act as natural competitors with the introduced mink, this will be a doubly welcome event.

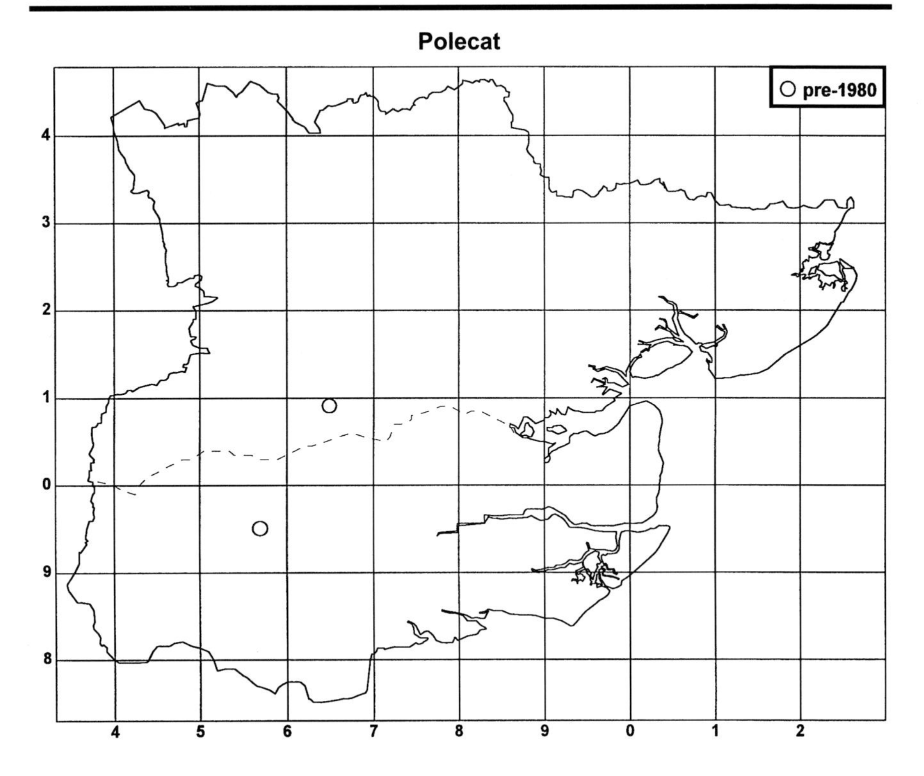
Polecat
pre-1980
4
3
2
1
0
9
8
4
5
6
7
8
9
0
1
2

Ferret

Mustela furo Linn., 1758

Status: Rare

There have been a number of reports of ferrets in recent years, although there is no evidence that a feral population has been established. Perhaps the first record of a ferret in Essex was of one that was killed by a gamekeeper in Great Waltham (Hills, 1936); although it was described at the time as a polecat, it was recorded some 30 years after the polecat was though to have become extinct in Essex. Since that date, specimens have been found dead on the road at widely scattered localities such as Wivenhoe, Birch and most recently at Epping in March 1996 and at South Woodham Ferrers and Sutton in December 1998. The only recent sighting of a live ferret occurred at Walthamstow in April 1997.

Ferrets have been found in gardens on two occasions: *"a very fine specimen was killed in a garden at Leigh in December 1969"* (Hunford, 1970), while the second, recorded at Parsons Heath in July 1978, killed a pet guinea pig. The only report involving more than one animal occurred in 1950 when several were seen near Saffron Walden. At present, ferrets are still widely kept as pets and it is likely that further escapes will be recorded.

Ferret

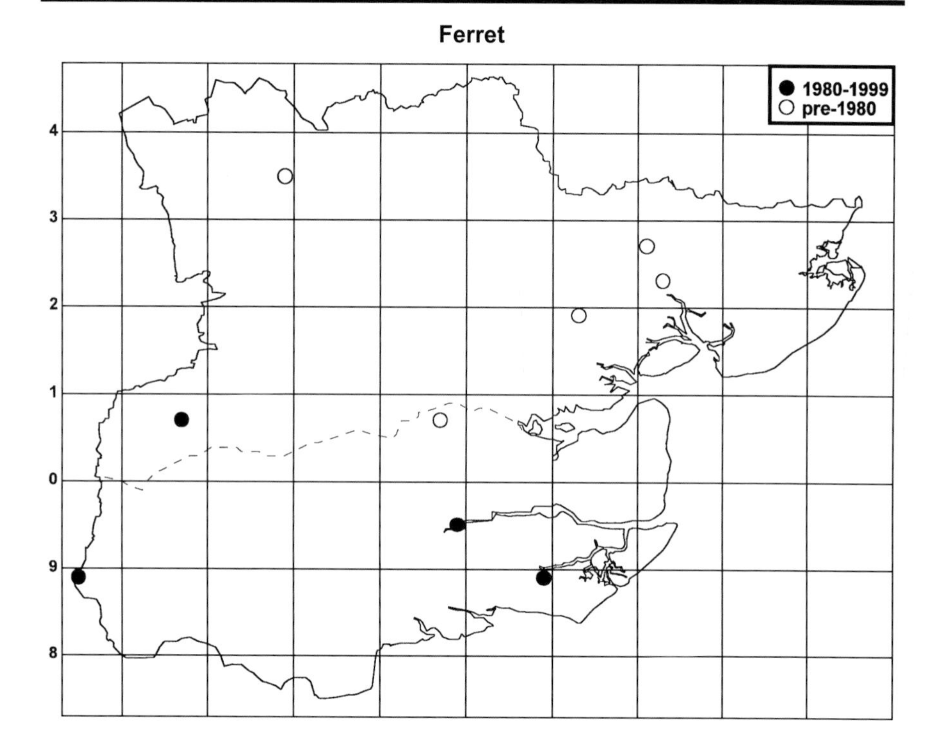

Mink

Mustela vison Schreber, 1777

Status: Scarce, increasing

"Mink are multiplying tremendously, and if there is not a concerted effort, they will reach epidemic proportions. What we need is concerted action. I am surprised that conservationists will not help because mink are decimating flora and fauna as much as road-side spraying." (*Daily Telegraph*, September 1982)

Few mammals generate such emotion and, during their short residence, mink have been blamed for the recent decline of many indigenous mammals and waterbirds. A native of North America, mink were first introduced to stock fur farms in 1929. Escapes were soon reported and breeding in the wild was first recorded in 1957, in Devon. As opportunistic feeders (eating mammals, fish, birds and invertebrates), they were quickly able to take advantage of a previously unoccupied niche and have become widely distributed throughout most of Britain (Lever, 1994).

Although occasionally found away from water, mink prefer aquatic habitats with emergent vegetation. In Essex, these are often riverine and the home range of a mink is usually between one and six kilometres. In Britain, one litter of four to six young is born in May with juveniles dispersing in August (Birks & Dunstone, 1991).

The first documented occurrence in Essex was of an individual killed at Abberton Reservoir on 25th September 1962, having itself killed seven ducks that had been trapped prior to ringing. A mink farm at Hawkwell suffered the occasional escape (and a deliberate release by an animal welfare group, with most being recaught) and one trapped near Rochford (Hunford, 1967) may well have originated from this source. At the end of the 1960s, mink were established along the River Chelmer and the Chelmer and Blackwater Navigation Canal; a sustained period of trapping by MAFF produced ten animals, with additional individuals being accounted for at Good Easter and Ford End.

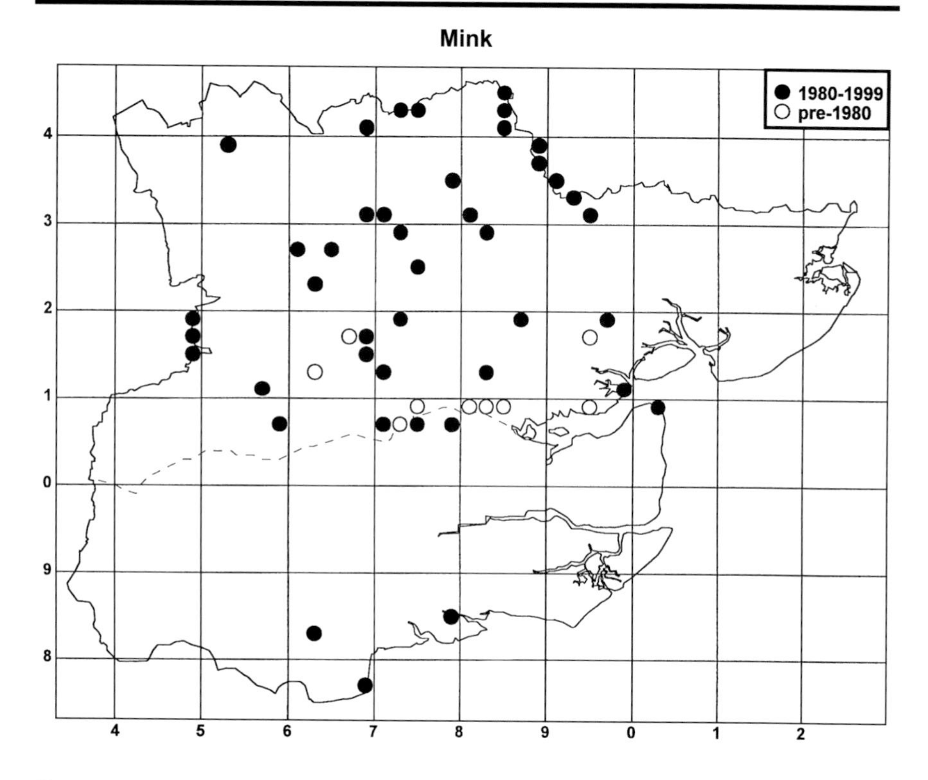

Since 1980, mink have been reported from a number of widely scattered localities without ever suggesting that they have become as common in Essex as in other counties. One was seen at Shinglehead Point, Tollesbury in January 1988 and, more recently on two occasions, at Bradwell Bird Observatory. Fortunately for coastal breeding birds in Essex, predation by mink has not yet been reported and they have still to be recorded at the wardened RSPB Reserve at Old Hall Marshes. Away from the coast, mink and otters both occur along the Stort and also on the Stour – two mink having been trapped at Lamarsh, with another killed on the road at Wormingford. Mink have been seen on three occasions at the Abberton Reservoir Visitor Centre (S. Beary, pers. comm.), with other sightings coming from Steeple Bumpstead, Benfleet Downs and the Rodings. The University of Essex otter survey and the 1998 water vole survey, conducted by the Essex Wildlife Trust and the Environment Agency, both found widely-scattered evidence of mink along many of the county's rivers – however, mink were recorded less frequently than the subjects of the surveys!

During the last twenty years, the mink has often been blamed for the decline in waterside wildlife. Although mink may have contributed to the disappearance of the water vole in some areas, it is likely that human disturbance, pollution and modern bankside management have had a greater impact. Certainly in Essex, the number of records suggests that mink have had a negligible effect and any reduction in mammalian populations must be due to other causes. After all, a hunting mink is seldom far from a warren and the rabbit is often the commonest prey item in its catholic diet (Dunstone, 1993).

The mink is becoming established in Essex and is here to stay. It seems likely that the population will increase, and with it the prospect of being made a scapegoat for any reduction in numbers of aquatic mammals and birds. The danger of such a philosophy is that it may distract attention away from the changes in the countryside that are having a more far-reaching impact on our wildlife.

Badger

Meles meles (Linn., 1785)

Status: Common

The history of the badger in Essex during the last 150 years is confusing. The population approached near-extinction at the end of the 19th century, whereas currently the badger is increasing and may be more common than at any previous time. Fortunately, this species has been the subject of greater interest than most mammals and historical changes were recorded by Victorian naturalists. More recently, the status and distribution of the badger in Essex has been reviewed in several surveys (Scott, 1960, Cowlin, 1972, Skinner *et al.*, 1991).

Today, the badger is widespread in all but the heavily urbanised south-west of the county, excavating its setts in woodland, scrub, hedgerows and along man-made embankments. They live in social groups of between two and twenty individuals, feeding mainly on earthworms; however, they also consume insects, carrion, small mammals, cereals, fruit and fungi. The litter of between one and five young is born in February, the cubs first emerging from the sett at eight weeks of age. Subsequent mortality is high with 50–65% of cubs dying in their first year (Neal & Cheesman, 1991). Although badgers rarely exceed six years in the wild, three females in Thundersley have survived beyond eleven years of age (D. Hunford, pers. comm.).

Persecution has played a prominent part in the fortunes of the badger and perhaps the earliest reference comes from the accounts of churchwardens, where payments for the destruction of 'vermin' are entered. In the parish of All Saints and St Peter, Maldon, badgers were priced at a shilling a head and, in an area of unpromising countryside, 52 badgers were killed between 1716 and 1748. Not surprisingly, the frequency of captures declined during this period as badgers became more scarce (Fitch, 1887b). In 1882, Christy, upon discovering a dead badger, wrote *"so far as I can discover, no other badger has been seen or heard of in the neighbourhood for many years, and I should have thought it to have been an extinct animal"*. Fitch

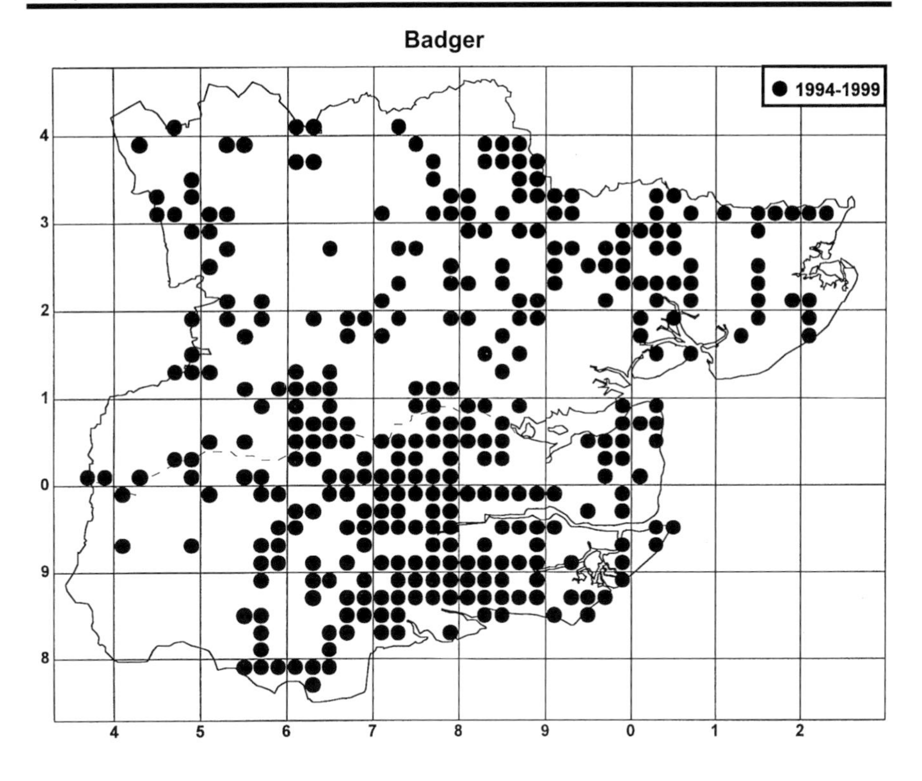

(1887) also considered that the badger was well nigh extinct in Essex and expressed his disappointment at being unable to obtain a young animal in the county. This gloom was reinforced by Laver (1898), who wrote: *"This animal, known so well to most of us by hearsay from a previous generation, has now become scarce in the county, where fifty years ago, it was very common. Clearance of woods, diminution of hedgerows, and excessive game preserving have been the most effectual causes of its decrease. The latter, as it is now practised, will, I fear, in time blot out not only the poor Badger, but every other animal which, whether useful or not, can be classed by ignorant gamekeepers or their masters under the head of 'vermin'."* The apparent scarcity of the badger at this time was such that the discovery (and usually, the subsequent destruction) of these animals was often of sufficient interest to merit inclusion in local newspapers. In 1903, the vicar of Pitsea described how he had obtained a specimen that had been shot at Mucking (Hutton, 1903).

However, in contrast to the earlier pessimism, Dent (1922) considered that *"Badgers are much commoner in the County than is generally supposed. In the south-eastern parts they are very numerous, particularly about Laindon, Grays,*

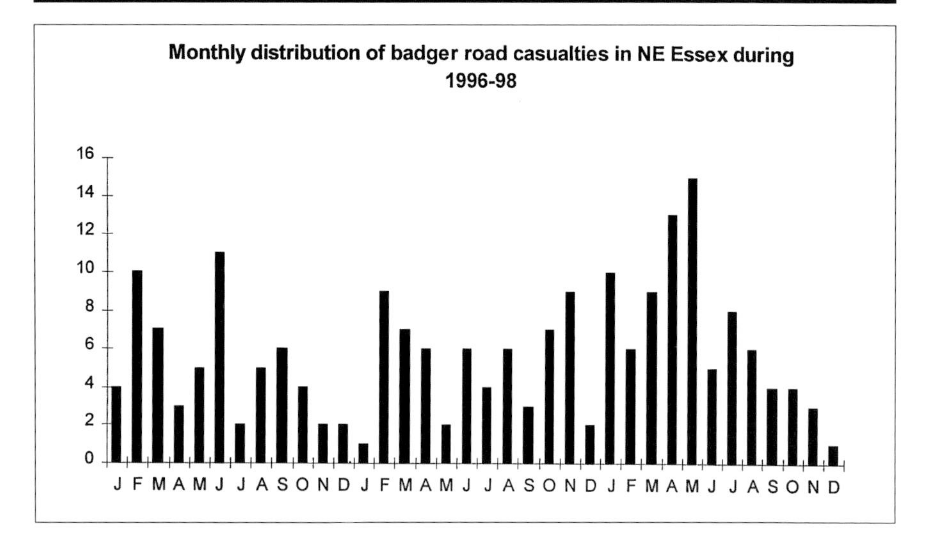

Tilbury, Dawes Heath and the surrounding country", before going on to describe several other parts of Essex where they were fairly common.

The causes of this increase, which took place within a generation, have been recently reviewed (Skinner *et al.*, 1991). It seems likely that the badger may not have been as scarce as the Victorians thought, and that Christy, who lived at Roxwell, was describing their status in an area where badgers are still scarce; the region described by Dent is still a stronghold for the county's badgers. Persecution by gamekeepers would certainly have had an effect on the population; however, this influence would have declined with the departure of keepers to the First World War. The increase in south Essex that was noted by Dent was mainly due to the creation of the plotlands, whereby land of limited agricultural value was sold off as individual housing plots to Londoners seeking a new start in the Essex countryside. Many of these plots remained undeveloped and gradually reverted to scrub and woodland. This cover, together with a surface geology favouring sett construction, proved ideal for badgers and the area is the setting for one of the most successful urban badger populations in the country.

The first county-wide survey of setts was conducted by R.A. Cowlin from 1963–71 and important baseline information was recorded on the location, size and structure of each sett, together with adjacent land use – information that was again collected during a subsequent survey between 1983–86. The results of this second survey, a mere twenty years later, showed that of the viable setts recorded by Cowlin, 36% had disappeared or become derelict and of those remaining, 14% were no longer occupied by badgers. In addition, the modal sett size was also reduced, from six holes to three, presumably an indication of a decline in numbers. Of the causes of sett loss, agricultural activity had the greatest impact and this was most prevalent in the north and south-east of the county. In the more populous south, road building and development were most likely to be implicated, although badgers gained from the protection conferred on the plotlands and Green Belt sites (Skinner *et al.*, 1991).

Road deaths are one of the major causes of mortality in Essex with some locations, such as the A12 near Brentwood and Galleywood, providing several records during the last five years. Traffic casualties are monitored by badger groups and the figures for north-east Essex show that at least 207 badgers were killed in this way during 1996-98 (data provided by North East Essex Badger Group).

A further national survey took place between October 1994 and January 1997 which showed that the British population had increased by 77%. (of which 47% was due to an increase in size of social groups and 30% to the development of new social groups.) There was also encouraging evidence that badgers were slowly expanding their range into hitherto unoccupied areas (Wilson, *et al.*, 1997). Although the results of this survey were not given at a county level, it is likely that the Essex badger population has increased during the last decade – this supposition is supported by anecdotal reports from landowners, gamekeepers and the three local badger groups. Two reasons for this success are the increased public awareness of the legal protection conferred on both badgers and their setts, as well as the reduction in persecution after the introduction of the Protection of Badgers Act 1992. The 1990s survey showed that, nationally, the digging of main setts had reduced by more than 50% from ten years earlier – a decline that was also reported by badger groups in Essex. This finding contrasts with the situation in the county during the 1980s, when several prosecutions of badger diggers took place – one resulting in a custodial sentence (D. Hunford, pers. comm.).

Today, the distribution map shows that the badger is widespread throughout most of Essex – a welcome change from Laver's time. The recent increase in numbers may also see further expansion into areas that are currently under-populated such as the north-west of the county. The success of this attractive species will be threatened in some areas however, by the proposed increase in housing development planned for many parts of Essex. It seems inevitable that conservation organisations will need to be vigilant in the future to ensure that the badger retains its present status.

Otter

Lutra lutra (Linn., 1758)

Status: Rare, increasing

After a century of fluctuating fortunes, the otter is once again to be found in Essex. Although at present it only occurs in small numbers, there is much evidence of a recolonisation from the north. This, aided by improvements in habitat management and water quality and supported by a programme of releases, gives hope that the otter will regain its status as a widespread breeding species in the county.

Otters are equally at home in freshwater systems or coastal habitats where access to freshwater is available, provided that there are adequate fish stocks and undisturbed cover for lying up during the day. Home ranges are dependent on the food supply and males may patrol a territory of up to 40km on a regular basis. When travelling along river catchments (or overland between river catchments), males can cover considerable distances, having been tracked for up to 16km in a single night. Otters are opportunistic feeders, taking mainly fish; however, crayfish, amphibians, waterfowl and occasionally rabbits and water voles have also been recorded in the diet. Breeding activity can occur throughout the year, but, the litter of generally two to three young is usually born during the summer – the period of lactation coinciding with the time of greatest food availability. The young first take to the water at three months, staying within the family group for up to a year before seeking out territories of their own. Sexual maturity is attained during the second year (Chanin, 1991).

"It is very distressing to read in the county newspapers paragraphs announcing, time after time, the shooting or trapping of otters. Why are these poor beasts so persecuted? One would think that any one with a spark of feeling for nature would cherish rather than seek to destroy such an interesting inhabitant of our streams and rivers." (Anon, 1892). Written over 100 years ago, the author then went on to include details of the destruction of nine otters that had been reported in Essex newspapers during the preceding two months. Two typical reports are as follows:

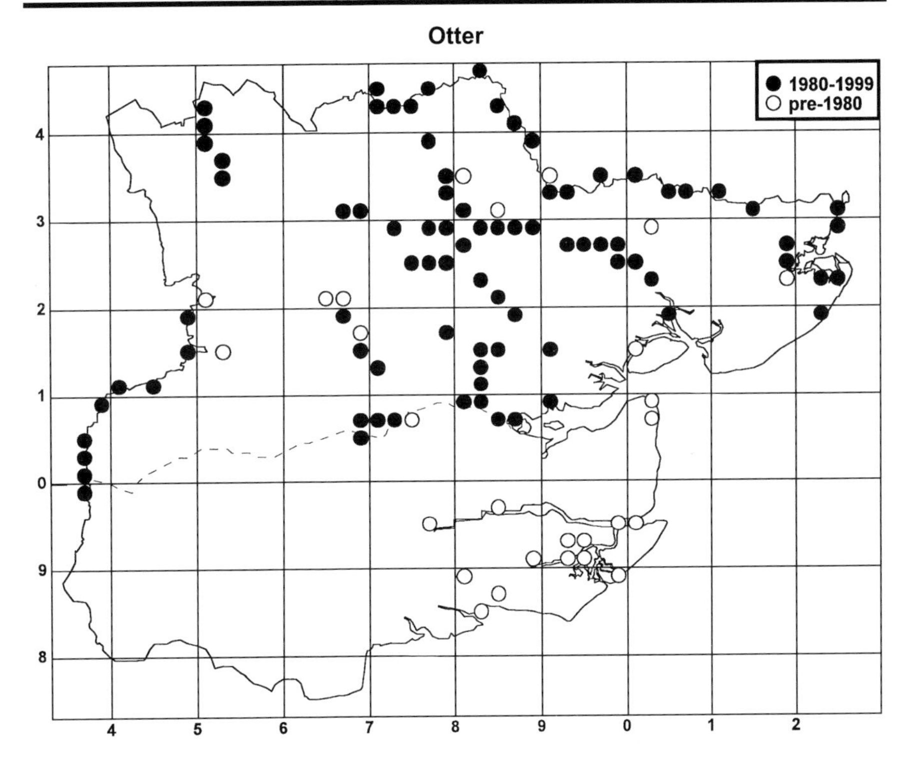

"Mr Luigi Corti, of the Cottage, Great Bentley, last week shot two otters, which were turned out of a fleet near his house." (*Essex County Chronicle*, 25th December 1891).

"On Wednesday morning, Albert Wheeler, groom to Mr Garrad Baker, observed a young otter in the river Chelmer, which runs at the foot of his master's garden. After one or two fruitless efforts, he succeeded in pinning the animal down between the tines of a stable fork, and he then killed it by a blow on the head. The otter weighed 8lbs. On the same day Mr A.T. Aldham, of Tower House, Springfield, shot two otters, weighing about 15lbs, near the spot where Wheeler killed the first otter." (*Essex Weekly News*, 19th February 1892).

Laver (1898) also regretted this *"sport"*, but thought the otter to be more common than in previous years, when extinction had seemed a possibility. In 1903 he wrote that *"most Essex rivers are now haunted by otters, and they are also to be found in the reed beds and fleets of the marshes"*.

There are few records of otters in Essex during the first half of the 20th century, but they appear to have been widespread during the 1950s and 1960s. At that time there were records from all the major rivers (except the Thames) as well as from coastal areas such as Bradwell, Wrabness and West Mersea. By 1970, the number of reports had fallen, with otters recorded from only the Chelmer and Blackwater Navigation Canal, Fingringhoe and Bradwell with the last record for this period coming from Ardleigh Reservoir in August 1974. The collapse in the population was also tracked by the county mammal recorders of the time, with 32 reports occurring during the 1960s but only four after 1970 (Hughes, 1986).

The decline witnessed in Essex was part of a disastrous reduction in the otter population that was occurring across most of the country, caused by the loss of suitable bankside habitat and, particularly in the south-east, increasing levels of organochlorine residues (notably PCBs) in the food chain. Although during the 1980s the national population was starting to show signs of recovery, in East Anglia the otter continued to decline (Chanin, 1992). Unfortunately, Essex rivers were omitted from the national survey of 1977–79, but otters were absent at sites close to the county boundary in south Suffolk (Lenton *et al.*, 1980). A second survey of England, conducted between 1984–86 included sites along the Stour, Colne, Blackwater and Chelmer but again, no evidence of otters was found (Strachan *et al.*, 1990). A further survey took place in 1991–94 and, despite the search for evidence being hindered by high water levels, two of the sites on the Stour held positive signs – the animals possibly originating from a recent release of captive-bred otters in south Suffolk. There was also further evidence at one site on the Colne from where anecdotal sightings had been reported since 1992 (C. Gibson, pers. comm.). A further 50 sites were searched on the Blackwater and Chelmer, but all proved negative as in the previous surveys (Strachan & Jefferies, 1996). The only positive record at this time was the observation of an otter, with prey, seen in the river at Goldhanger by staff of the National Rivers Authority in 1993 (J. Martin, pers. comm.).

As the recovery in the East Anglian population lagged behind other areas, a programme of restocking – using animals bred at the Otter Trust at Bungay – began in 1983. By the end of 1989, eighteen otters had been re-introduced at six sites in the region, followed by later releases that will have influenced the subsequent surveys of Essex. In October 1991, three were introduced to the River Lea with a further three released on the Stort in December of the same year. In both cases, two sisters and a male were released together – however, in February 1992, a male otter (perhaps one of the introduced animals) was found dead on a road in Bishop's Stortford. Although evidence of otters had been found in the area for several years, breeding was not proved until the tracks of an adult and cub were found at Rye Meads in 1995 (T. Hill, pers. comm.). Two further releases, in each case of two males and two females, took place on the River Glem (a tributary of the Stour) in 1995 and at Hamford Water in August 1996 (English Nature, pers. comm.).

In the autumn of 1996 scientists at the University of Essex initiated a new study, looking at the status of the otter in Essex. This project involves surveying 234 sites (covering all the river catchments in the county) over a five-year period to monitor the recolonisation of Essex by otters. An initial survey found spraints or tracks at 27% of these sites, mainly in the north of the county (S.M. Macdonald & C.F. Mason, 1996 unpublished report). Subsequent surveys have shown an expansion of range, signs having been recorded on the Chelmer and Blackwater (S.M. Macdonald & C.F. Mason, pers comm.)

The present distribution map gives cause for cautious optimism. However, expanding populations of otters can suffer set-backs (S.M. Macdonald & C.F. Mason, pers. comm.) and lone males, exploring new territory can be responsible for marking many sites along newly-colonised rivers. The presence of spraints, or tracks, does not necessarily imply the successful establishment of a breeding population.

During the last 40 years (that is, since the otter was last widespread in the county) the volume of road transport has increased considerably and traffic accidents are a major cause of otter mortality, particularly at bridges where roads pass over rivers. Sprainting sites are often chosen under bridges, and where a dry surface is unavailable, the otter will often leave the river, only to be killed on the road. Of three recent road casualties in Essex, two (at Little Chesterford and Earls Colne) could perhaps have been avoided by the provision of dry sprainting areas. One of the recommendations of the Action Plan for this species, calls for liaison between the relevant agencies so that bridges can be adapted to permit the safe movement of otters.

Another factor that will delay the return of the otter is the current management of bankside habitats. Extensive areas of cover are scarce and, with an increase in disturbance from leisure activities (particularly in the south of the county), it may be that some waterways will remain unsuitable. However, less rigorous management, together with the provision of cover through planting programmes, would help to retain those otters now present in the north of the county and make southern catchments more attractive. One former stronghold where evidence of otters has still to be found, is the coastal creeks of the Crouch and the Roach. Here, sixteen sites are being monitored and, with this new generation of otters slowly spreading southwards through Essex, it is to be hoped that the extreme south-east will be reached in the next few years.

It is apparent that through the concerted efforts of a number of conservation organisations, the otter is slowly returning to Essex. The difficult part has been done; continued monitoring, combined with sympathetic habitat management, will ensure that this flagship species can re-establish itself along our rivers.

Common seal

Phoca vitulina Linn., 1758

Status: Scarce, increasing

With a population in Essex of around 100, the common seal is one of our least numerous mammals; however, these animals are regularly observed by the increasing number of pleasure boats taking naturalists into the estuaries of the Crouch, Thames and Blackwater. The common seal can be separated from the rarer grey seal by its smaller, more rounded head, clearly defined forehead and (when seen head-on), nostrils set at a V-angle and almost joined at the base. Fish are taken in proportion to their availabilty and cephalopods, gastropods and crustaceans also form part of the diet with shrimps being favoured by young animals. Adult females first give birth at three to four years of age; the single pup, which can swim and dive from birth, being born in June or July (Bonner & Thompson, 1991).

The common seal was infrequently noted in Victorian Essex. Laver (1898) wrote: *"This Seal occurs sparingly on all parts of the Essex coast but is not seen every year. Specimens have been killed in the Stour, the Blackwater, in the mouth of the Thames, and in other places. Properly speaking, all the Seals taken on our shores can only be considered as stragglers."* He then went on to include four accounts of common seals being shot at points along the coast! Although the species was infrequently reported during the first half of the 20th century, Seear (1964) noted that the common seal was seen regularly during winter in the Colne and Blackwater.

Today the common seal has been recorded from many parts of the Essex coast. Most sightings are of single animals seen in the water, almost invariably by birdwatchers seawatching from favoured points such as Bradwell, Point Clear, Canvey Point and Southend Pier. Of the major rivers, all have produced several records with the exception of the under-watched Stour, from where only one record has been received. Occasionally common seals penetrate well upriver with sightings (usually in the autumn) from Heybridge Basin and South Woodham Ferrers. Three haul out sites are used regularly – the Pyefleet Channel, Hamford Water and Buxey Sands, off Foulness. At the two latter sites, breeding occurs during most summers.

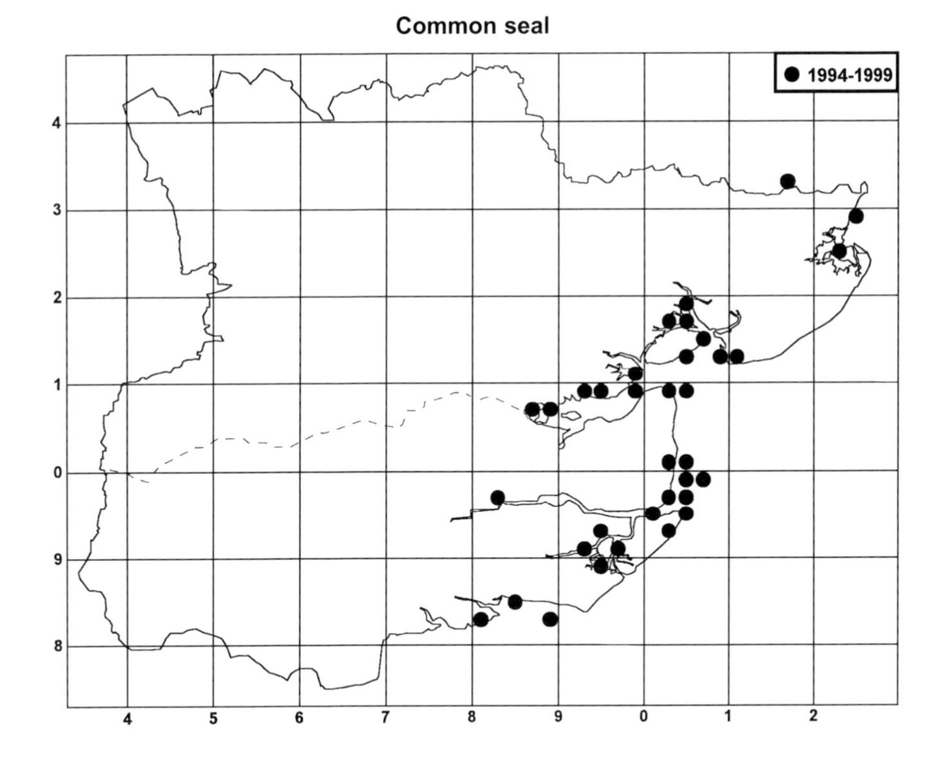

In August 1995, the Sea Mammal Research Unit conducted an aerial survey of the Essex coast as part of an ongoing survey of seal populations. In total, 78 common seals were found: 12 in Hamford Water, 3 in Pyefleet Channel, 40 off Foulness Sands and 23 on East Barrow, a sandbank 10km east of Shoeburyness (C. Duck, pers.comm.). Recent evidence that numbers off Foulness are stable came when 37 were counted from a pleasure boat in January 1998.

The status of the common seal as a breeding species in Essex may be threatened during the next decade. The phocine distemper outbreak of 1988 killed more than 18,000 common seals in the North Sea, with numbers in the Wash (presumably the origin of the Essex population) reduced by 50% and their recovery jeopardised by a proposed reclamation project (Hiby *et al.*, 1993). A more local threat is the increase in boating activity in Essex estuaries. Disturbance at breeding sites causing separation of mothers and pups may well have eliminated the species from the Isle of Wight and the Bristol Channel (Thompson, 1992) and the increasing attention that the Foulness colony receives during the summer from pleasure craft may have a detrimental effect in the future.

Grey seal

Halichoerus grypus Fabricius, 1791

Status: Rare, increasing

Grey seals are most commonly found along the rocky coasts and islets of western and northern Britain, with around 50% of the world population breeding in British waters (Arnold, 1993). This is the rarer of the two seal species to occur along the Essex coast but recent counts from natural history cruises – sixteen were counted on Buxey Sands in December 1997 – suggest that it is increasing in numbers. In contrast, Laver (1898) knew of only one record – an aged and blind individual caught in fishing nets in the River Colne in 1841.

Grey seals have been regularly recorded in the Blackwater, Crouch and Roach with additional reports from Hamford Water and the Pyefleet Channel. Although there are no reports from the Thames, an individual that achieved national prominence in *the Daily Telegraph* in 1996, by reaching as far upstream as Twickenham, may well have passed through Essex waters!

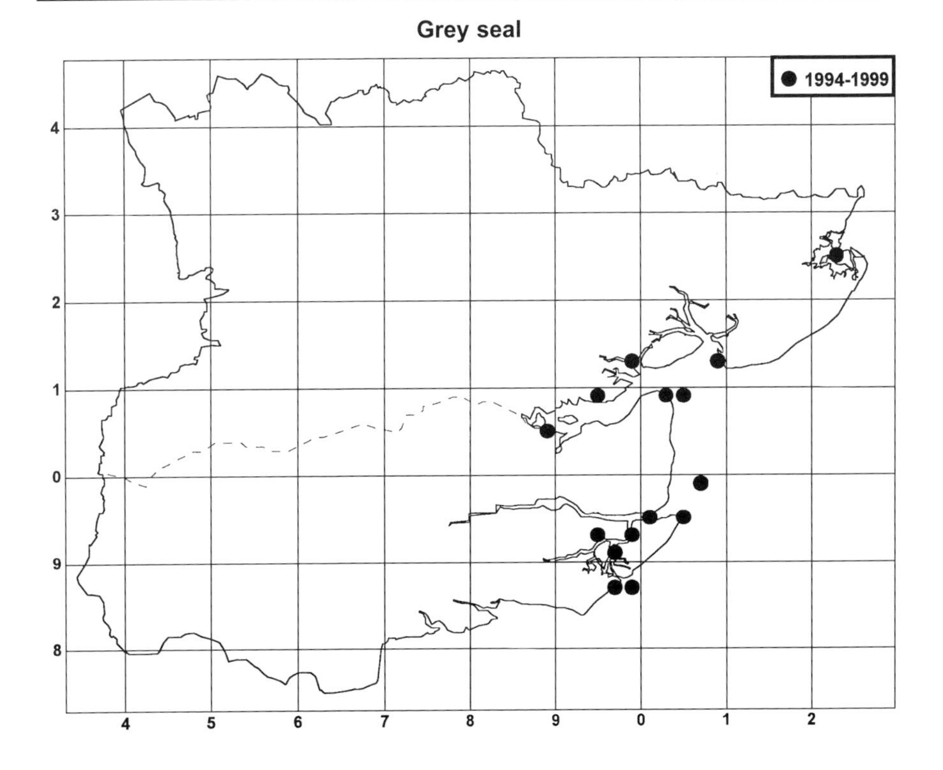
Grey seal
1994-1999
4
3
2
1
0
9
8
4
5
6
7
8
9
0
1
2

Hooded seal

Cystophora cristata (Erxleben, 1777)

Status: One record

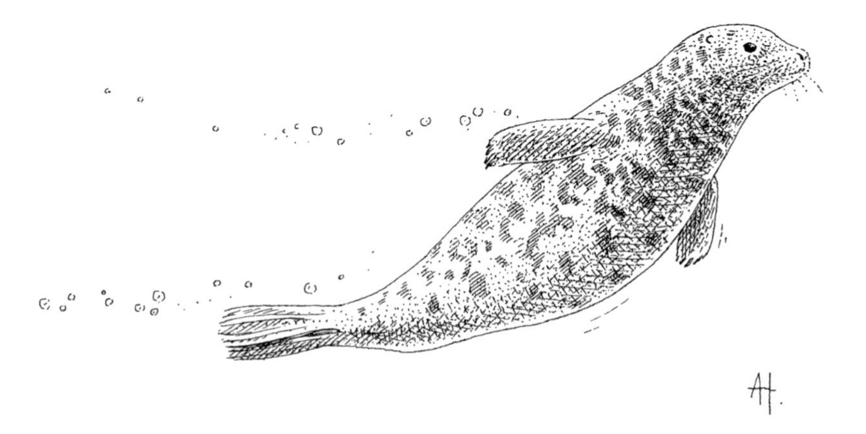

The hooded seal is to be found in the Arctic regions of the North Atlantic and occasionally occurs as a rare vagrant to British coasts, with eight records prior to 1989. Males can be identified by the presence of an inflatable hood which develops from four years of age and the presence of dark, irregular patches on the body. Females are less distinctively marked than males (Harris, 1991).

There is one Essex record of an individual included by Laver (1898). He wrote: *"Mr W.B. Clark records the capture of a specimen of this Seal, on June 29th, 1847, in the Orwell. He gives a full description of the animal, which was presented by Mr Ransome to the Ipswich Museum where it now remains. As the River Orwell empties itself into Harwich Harbour, I think we are entitled to place this Seal in our catalogue of the Essex fauna, although its normal habitation is within the Arctic circle."*

Hooded seal

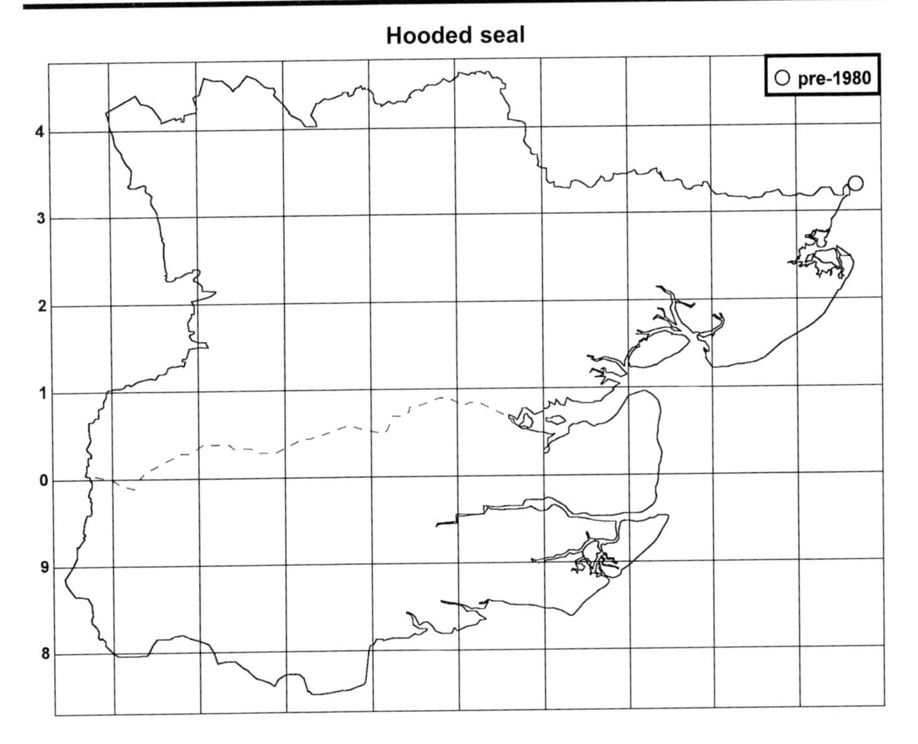

The native red and roe deer have been present in Essex since the retreat of the Ice Age. However the common species in Essex today are the introduced fallow deer and muntjac. Fallow deer have been present in Essex for more than 900 years; until recently, however, they have usually been kept in a managed deer park. The tradition of keeping animals such as deer or wild swine in parks dates from Italy during the 1st century although there is no evidence of the practice being brought to Britain during the time of the Roman Empire. The earliest reference to deer in the county comes from a will dated in 1045 that mentions a *deerhay* (usually considered to mean a hedge for either retaining or excluding deer) at Ongar Great Park. It was not until after the Norman invasion that interest in parks for deer increased; of the 35 parks listed in the Domesday Book, two were in Essex. These were the kings park at Rayleigh and Ongar Great Park, the latter retained many of the features of a deer park until it was destroyed in around 1950 (Rackham, 1989).

By 1300, deer parks were at their most popular. During the medieval period, around 100 were established in Essex – a density of one to every 40 km^2 (Cantor, 1983). Deer were also present in the royal forests, however, with hunting taking place regularly at Hatfield, Epping, Wintry, Writtle, Hainault and Kingswood. Essex deer were particularly important for the royal table, and Henry III and his court had a considerable appetite for British mammals! For example, the *Calendar of Close Rolls* records that during Christmas 1251, the king consumed 430 red deer, 200 fallow, 200 roe, 200 wild swine, 1,300 hares, 450 rabbits as well as 395 swans, 115 cranes and an unreported number of salmon and lampreys! Some of the deer may well have originated in Essex. During his 41-year reign, 228 fallow deer from Hatfield Forest were consumed, with more taken from other Essex forests.

Table 11.1 **Deer used by Henry III from Essex Forests, 1231–72 (after Rackham, 1989)**

	Bucks	*Does*	*Total*
Hatfield Forest, 1231-72			
Used by the king	38	190	228
Gifts for stocking parks	36	89	125
Gifts of carcasses etc.	84	22	106
Epping and Hainault Forests, 1234-63	567	639	1,206
Havering Park, 1234-63	428	878	1,306
Total	**1,153**	**1,818**	**2,971**

During the 16th and 17th centuries, parks became less popular and fewer new parks were created. Those that remained were often landscaped by eminent designers and it was not until the 19th century that deer returned, as ornamental animals, to enclosures in the grounds of country houses. Deer parks never regained their earlier popularity, however, and by 1892, only ten were in existence, all containing fallow deer. Other species were also present at Easton Park, Hatfield Forest, Thorndon Hall and Weald Park (Whitaker, 1892).

Table 11.2 **Deer parks in Essex in 1892 (after Whitaker, 1892)**

Park	*Grid Reference*	*Deer*	*Number in 1892*
Belhus	TQ5781	Fallow	c.100
Boreham	TL7310	Fallow	120
Easton	TL5923	Fallow	450
		Red	120
Hatfield Forest	TL5319	Fallow	300
		Red	10
Langleys	TL7013	Fallow	88
Marks Hall	TL8425	Fallow	200
Quendon	TL5131	Fallow	c.100
Thorndon Hall	TQ6191	Fallow	c.50
		Red	c.40
Weald	TQ5794	Fallow	80
		Red	70
		Sika	9
		Roe	2
Wivenhoe	TM0324	Fallow	c.100

Many of these parks were lost or fell into disrepair during both World Wars: the current distribution of fallow deer in Essex is based on the establishment of feral populations in the woodlands adjacent to these former deer parks. In 1960, a new deer park was created at St Osyth with one red deer stag and five hinds; fallow were introduced at a later date. These subsequently escaped and a small herd of fallow deer is now present in the area. Today, deer are enclosed at five sites in the county where, with the exceptions of Quendon (where deer have been kept for more than 300 years) and the Epping Forest sanctuary, they may be observed by the public.

Table 11.3 **Deer parks in Essex in 1999**

Park	*Grid Reference*	*Deer*	*Number in 1999*
Quendon	TL5131	Fallow	c.80
Epping Forest sanctuary	TQ4499	Fallow	c.100
Bedford's	TQ5192	Red	c.18
Weald	TQ5794	Fallow	c.18
Mole Hall Wildlife Park	TL5431	Fallow	c.35
		Red	c.32
		Sika	c.28
		Muntjac	c.8

The presence of sika at Weald Park at the end of the 19th century was unusual; at that time, they had occurred at fewer than ten British deer parks (Whitaker,1892). It is unknown whether they were still present in 1945 when the fences fell into disrepair, releasing the fallow deer that have since colonised the surrounding area. There were no reports of sika in the area during subsequent years, although there were several unsubstantiated reports of this species in Essex during the 1960s.

Seven deer that were considered to be sika were observed at Elmdon in February 1965, with a stag reported by a gamekeeper from Strethall in May 1966. An anecdotal account of *"Japanese"* deer near Weald Park came from a farmer in 1965 (a claim that could not be confirmed by a long-term research project that was being undertaken in the area at the time). Finally, in the Brentwood area, a sika stag was reported from Weald Park in 1970–71. Perhaps the most intriguing of these records was of a *"stag roe deer"* reported from Hatfield Forest in 1967 – the photographic evidence clearly showing a sika stag! The stag, with three does, was reported again the following year (by the same person) and the last report came from a marksman who, while culling deer in Hatfield Forest, thought that a sika deer was present (Chapman, 1977).

Four species of deer – red, roe, fallow, and muntjac – currently occur in Essex. Of these, roe, fallow and muntjac are increasing; the last two species can be readily observed (and enjoyed) by the naturalist walking in woodlands in the north and west of the county. The conditions that have allowed this increase – less disturbance in the countryside and the availability of copses and shelter belts – are still present. It seems likely that Essex deer will continue to thrive in the new millennium.

Red deer

Cervus elaphus Linn., 1758

Status: Rare

The red deer is the largest of the four species of deer occurring in Essex – the only breeding group is confined to woods in the north of the county. Historically, it was more common and was hunted by kings and queens from the time of Edward the Confessor. Laver (1898) records many anecdotes associated with the species, some of which deserve a wider readership. During the Tudor period, it is said that Henry VIII was hunting in Epping Forest at the time of the execution of Anne Boleyn; Queen Elizabeth I, meanwhile was a regular visitor to Wanstead House, home of the royal staghounds. Elsewhere in Essex, the visit of James II to New Hall, Boreham (now an independent school) to hunt red deer with the Duke of Albemarle was recounted by Sir John Bramston, of Skreens, Roxwell, in his biography. On May 3rd 1686, the king arrived at New Hall and rode to join the hunt at Bicknacre Mill with the unfortunate animal being finally killed between Brentwood and Romford. The following day, a red deer was hunted from Broomfield and Pleshey to the Rodings before being killed at Hatfield Broad Oak. Sir John reported that *"His Majestie (he says) kept pretie neere the doggs, though the ditches were broad and deep, the hedges high, and the way and feilds dirtie and deepe."* (Braybrooke, 1845). In the 18th century, Treasury Records show that the monarch's hounds killed thirteen stags in 1729, with another nine the following year. In the 19th century, the staghounds were still kept at Wanstead House and meetings were held in Hainault Forest; the annual Easter Hunt (organised by a larger-than-life character, Mr Tylney Long Pole Wellesley) being ridiculed in verse and on the stage as an

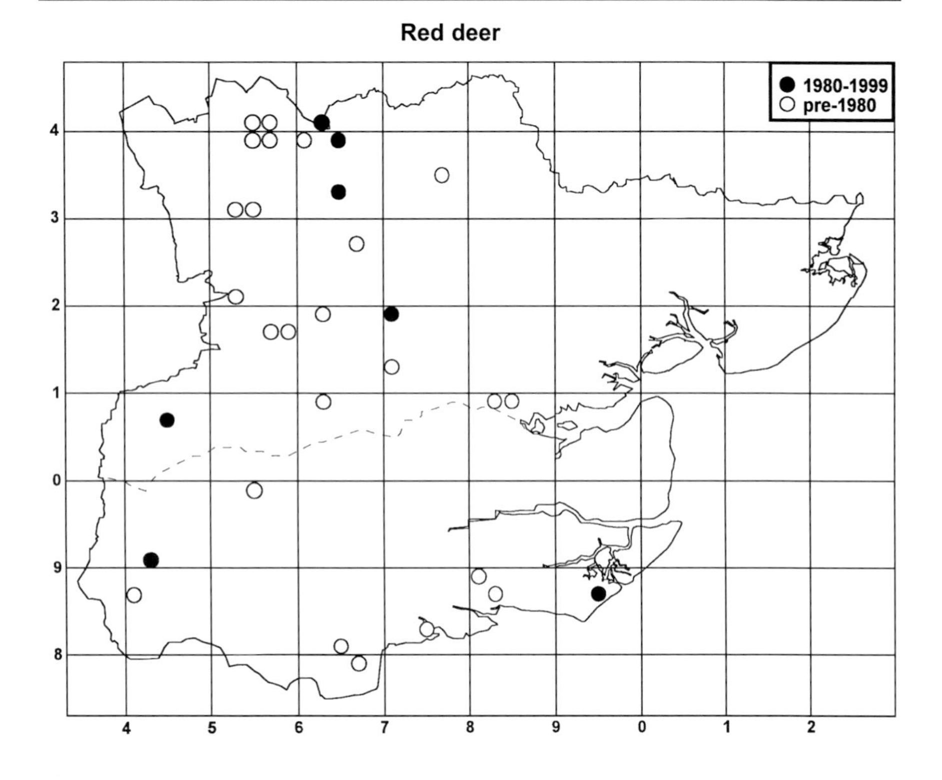

outing for East End sportsmen. After one hunt, Cary noted *"1827, Oct 20th. I met the staghounds at Hoghill House in Hainault Forest, to unharbour a stag. After drawing the coverts for a short time, a fine old stag was roused and took a turn round the Forest away for Packnall Corner, hence to Dagenham, and was taken at Plaistow. Red deer to be so near the metropolis, in their wild state, I consider as a singular circumstance."*

Clearly it was important that red deer were available to be hunted and Buxton (1897), quoting an elderly inhabitant of the forest, describes how this was achieved. *"There was a kennel at Loughton Bridge, kept by a man named Dean, and the dogs and horses for the hunt were kept there. A paddock was enclosed with high palings, and in this enclosure the deer, caught wild from the Forest, were kept, and hunted as required, but not killed....The method of taking the red-deer was by fixing a net (kept at Loughton Bridge for the purpose, and about a mile long) from the milestone in the Forest down to Monk Wood. The deer were driven up from Monk Wood into it. Two or three were then selected, and the rest, with the young ones, set at liberty. A cart for the purpose was in readiness, and the deer caught were placed in it and taken to Loughton Bridge, where they were kept in the paddock till wanted."* This sport was known as *"hunting the carted deer"*, a tradition that was continued by the Norfolk and Norwich Staghounds until 1963.

Shortly after Cary's experience, red deer were removed from Epping Forest and taken to Windsor after their numbers had been reduced by poachers and neighbouring farmers had complained about the damage done to crops. Those that were overlooked were taken by poachers and the final stag was hunted and killed at West Ham. In 1858 (Whitehead, 1964), a six year old stag was released in the forest to be hunted by City of London aldermen; the head is now displayed in the Guildhall. Later, in around 1880, three red deer were re-introduced to the forest but *"they proved to be so mischievous"* that they were destroyed soon afterwards (Buxton, 1897). In 1887, Flower recorded the presence of five red deer near Hatfield Broad Oak, the animals apparently being the progeny of a single hind that had escaped the hunt in 1875. Another hind that had escaped the hounds was present at Theydon Bois in 1911 (Buxton, 1915) but this was the last confirmed sighting in Essex for over 50 years.

Interest in Essex deer was renewed in the early 1960s, in time to record the reappearance of red deer and the status of the other three species. The results of a survey were published (Chapman, 1977) and the following records first documented at that time. During September 1964, two young red deer stags were seen in Skreens Wood, Roxwell and one, a yearling, was shot. The other was present in the area until April 1965. In July 1965, two stags were seen by a forestry worker in Grassall's Wood, Great Yeldham and by 1970 a small herd had taken up residence in Great Bendysh Wood and Little Bendysh Wood on the Essex/Suffolk border. The sight of a lactating female in these woods in June 1975 confirmed that breeding was occurring and deer from this group were also seen in neighbouring woods at Ashdon and Hempstead. In 1976, several red deer thought to be part of the same herd were seen feeding on potatoes in a field by Lubberhedges Wood, Stebbing and in April of that year, a Forestry Commission census counted at least 26 red deer in north-west Essex. Today, the present population – thought to number around 50 individuals - is still centred on the same woods.

Young stags are inclined to wander, presumably seeking new territories (Matthews, 1960) and records from elsewhere in Essex have invariably been of one or two male animals. In March 1967, a stag was reported by a gamekeeper at Garnetts Wood, Great Dunmow and tracks were found at High Roding, also during March. What may have been the same animal was seen amongst fallow deer on Woolard's Ash Farm at Hatfield Broad Oak, also in early 1967, with a hind reported from Hatfield Forest during the same winter. Two stags (perhaps including the Dunmow individual) were shot at Harps Farm, Great Hallingbury in September 1969. A stag was present at Church Wood, Navestock in July 1971 and another, presumably from the main herd, was seen at Prior's Wood, Widdington in September 1971 and observed again at Debden in February 1972.

Two stags (or perhaps one wide-ranging animal) were present in south Essex between November 1968 and March 1970. Tracks were first seen in Belfairs Wood and the stag was sighted on several subsequent occasions up to April 1969. Later, in September 1969, a red deer stag was observed in a field of cattle at Orsett and also at Linford gravel pits during the same weekend. It passed the winter in the West Tilbury area before being shot in March 1970 after its antlers became entangled with a metal chair frame. In October 1976, just 8km away, a stag was captured by an RSPCA inspector at an oil refinery at Coryton and released in Epping Forest. It was seen in the area for three months before being killed by a car on the A11 between the Wake Arms and Epping.

During recent years, the farming of red deer has made it difficult to verify the origin of some animals observed in the wild – for example, two young stags of similar age, seen by a gamekeeper at Thorrington in September 1995, were considered to have escaped from such a farm. In early 1999, only one registered farm (at Layer Marney) is breeding red deer although in previous years (with higher prices for venison) others were present. Reliable reports of a young stag came from Epping Long Green in July 1994 and what was probably the same animal was shot by a Forest Ranger after having been hit by a car at the southern end of the M11 motorway in October of the same year. Another recent wanderer was a mature stag that was present in the Foulness/Thorpe Bay area for a year from 1996. This individual generated considerable interest with headlines in the local papers until it was found dead on the tideline. The most recent record is of two young stags present near Great Leighs during November 1997 (P. Fontaine, pers. comm.).

With records from just seven tetrads in the last twenty years, the red deer is one of our rarest and most localised mammals. The captive herd of seventeen to twenty animals (including two stags), kept in two linked paddocks in Bedfords Park, Havering, offers the best opportunity to observe this species in Essex. Apart from the occasional wandering animal, the status and distribution of red deer has remained unchanged for thirty years. At a time when fallow are thriving and muntjac are extending their range, it will be of interest to see if red deer can become further established in the county during the next few years.

Fallow deer

Dama dama (Linn., 1758)

Status: Fairly common, increasing

Fallow deer were present in Britain before becoming extinct during the last Ice Age but the Normans re-introduced them into Britain for hunting during the 11th century. The keeping of deer in parks, where they were confined by a fence or 'pale', became commonplace amongst landowners such that, in medieval Essex, around 100 parks were established, incorporating available woodland or wasteland; with wild fallow deer also present in the forests of the county (Cantor, 1983). By the 18th century, the number of deer parks had declined and those that remained were as enclosures in the landscaped grounds of country mansions. In 1892, only ten were in existence and it is from escaped animals from these parks that the current population of fallow deer in the county is descended.

The fallow deer in Epping Forest have been present for several hundred years, a document from 1495 distinguishing between these and the red deer that were also present at the time (Chapman & Chapman, 1975). Black fallow deer, the variant now associated with the forest, were known to be present in Britain from at least 1465; some, received by James I from the King of Denmark in around 1612, are known to have been released into Epping Forest (Harting, 1887). Buxton (1897) considered the Epping deer to be unique, as the last representatives of the ancient deer in England – a smaller animal with less palmate antlers than those preserved in parks. However, by 1860, the forest population had decreased (due to being hunted two or three times per week and the north-eastern spread of London) to just ten individuals. In 1870, the management of the forest passed to the Corporation of London, for which a high priority was the protection of the remaining deer. The success of this project was such that the annual deer census of 1897 recorded around 200 fallow deer (Anon, 1898) and the species has thrived during the 20th

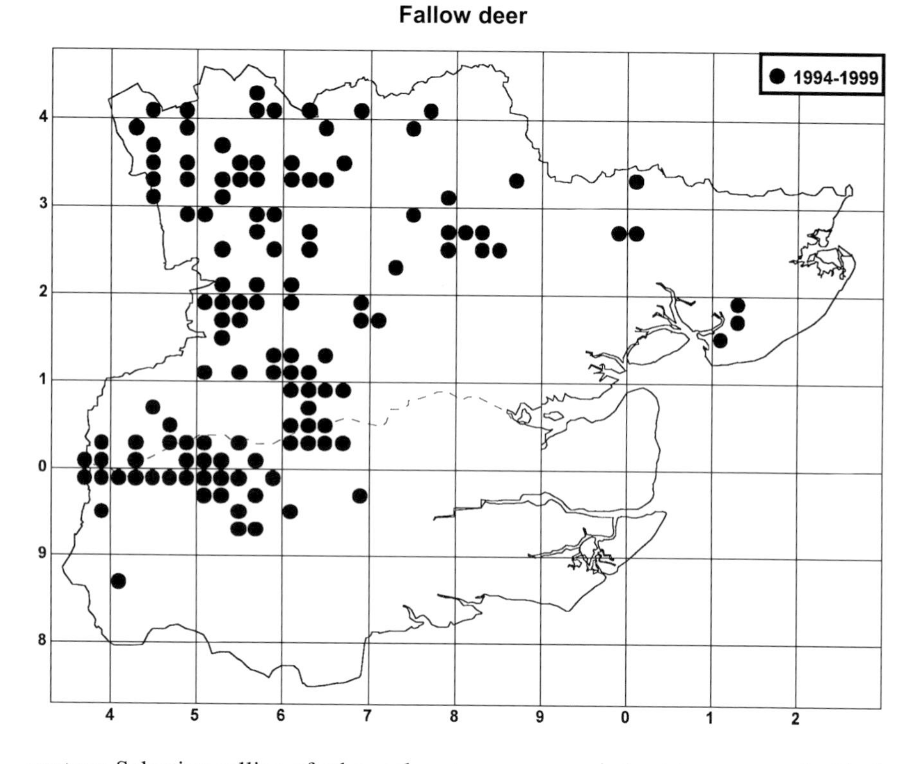

century. Selective culling of other colour types was carried out to preserve the black variety and to further ensure their survival, a 44ha sanctuary was created at Theydon Bois in 1962. At first, deer leaps were provided to allow passage to and from the forest, but these were later closed to prevent the deer becoming victims of the increasing volume of road traffic. By 1978, this enclosed herd comprised more than 100 animals – any surplus was culled rather than released back into the forest (Corke, 1979). Today, the population is maintained at around 100 animals with the deer confined within the sanctuary although Forest deer are now able to enter via a deer leap. Those of the black variety are encouraged as a source of new genetic material.

The construction of the M25 motorway has also had a significant impact on the Forest deer, restricting free movement between the forest and the buffer lands to the north. However, there are four possible crossing points at Woodredon Bridge, Copped Hall Bridge, Crown Hill road underpass and the Selvage 'deer' tunnel and a recent study showed that regular dispersal occurred via Woodredon Bridge (Dunn & Cousins, 1997). As the population in the buffer lands has increased (488, of all colour variants, were counted in March 1996), numbers in the Forest have declined

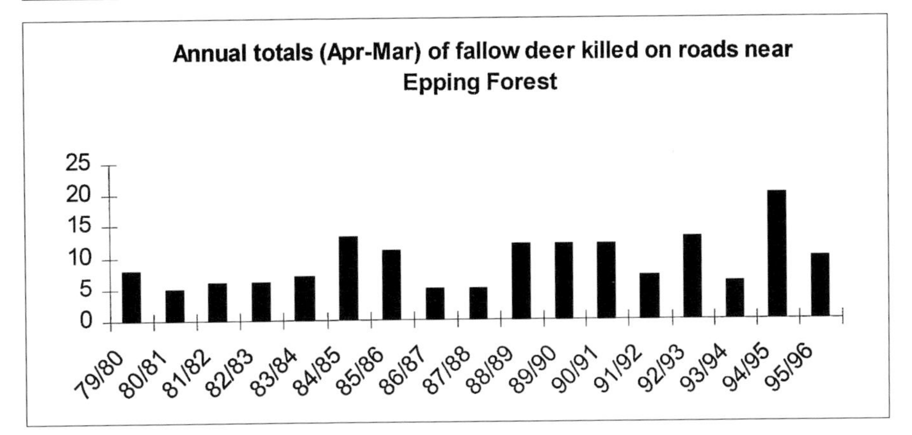

with road accidents being a major cause of mortality. At present, there are around 40 fallow deer remaining in the section of Epping Forest to the south of the M25 with, on average, nine killed per year in road accidents (A. Samuels, pers. comm.). Recent attempts to reduce this figure have included speed restrictions and the narrowing of roads in the High Beech area and the installation of 'sleeping policemen' and reflectors on other Forest roads.

Today, fallow deer prefer mature woodland for lying up and breeding, emerging onto grassy rides and agricultural land to feed. The single fawn is born in June, suckled for up to nine months and may live for over ten years. A century ago, fallow deer were present in Epping Forest and ornamental parks. Today, the descendants of park deer are more populous than ever before and numbers are controlled at several sites to minimise damage to crops and woodlands. In contrast to the muntjac, fallow deer have been reluctant to cross the A12; the herds are still concentrated in the north and west of the county, just as they were during the previous survey of 30 years ago. Occasionally, individuals wander from their normal range and a buck, present in Highwoods Country Park at Colchester for two weeks during the winter of 1996, was unfortunately shot and skinned by poachers.

Of deer occurring in Essex, fallow are the most likely to be seen by the casual observer. Up to 100 are seen regularly in fields at South Weald close to junction 28 of the M25. The public footpaths of Great Bendysh Wood, Radwinter, Shardlows Wood, Gosfield and the Marks Hall estate are perhaps the best locations in the county for the naturalist in search of fallow deer. In addition, a small herd of up to nineteen animals have been maintained in a five acre paddock in Weald Park since 1987, providing ideal viewing opportunities for families and photographers alike. The future for fallow deer in Essex will depend upon the tolerance of farmers and landowners; it is likely that the population will require a continuing degree of control to contain the level of damage they cause to the countryside.

Roe deer *Capreolus capreolus* (Linn., 1758)

Status: Scarce, increasing

Roe deer were present in Essex until medieval times when they became extinct; they are now slowly recolonising the county from Suffolk. Roe can be found in both coniferous and deciduous woodland, where they feed on the buds and shoots of trees, ivy, ferns and particularly brambles, also emerging at dusk and dawn to forage on adjacent agricultural land. The rut occurs from mid-July until the end of August, with implantation delayed until mid-winter. The young (often twins) are born during the following May or June. Females give birth for the first time at fourteen months and annually thereafter, with a life expectancy of up to eight years. If seen clearly, roe deer are readily identifiable by their small size, upright stance, distinctive black nose with white chin and bounding gait when disturbed (Staines & Ratcliffe, 1991).

Roe deer were introduced to Epping Forest from Dorset (descendants of introduced animals) in February 1884: two bucks and four does were snared in long nets, transported from Dorset overnight in a covered deer-van and released in the forest the following day (Buxton, 1897). There was a further introduction of eight more animals and the species thrived for several years, with numbers peaking at 43 in 1899. They later declined and died out by the mid 1920s (Whitehead, 1964).

In the late 19th century, roe deer of German origin were released near Thetford, Suffolk and their descendants have spread south towards Essex. They were first recorded in the county in July 1965, reliably reported by a warrener with the Forestry Commission, from Grassall's Wood, Great Yeldham (Beale, 1974). Further sightings, by experienced Forestry Commission staff, were made near Debden in 1968 and Pounce Wood, Saffron Walden in May 1970. In 1975, additional individuals were seen in Little Bendysh Wood in May, and a buck was present in Great Bendysh Wood in August (Chapman, 1977).

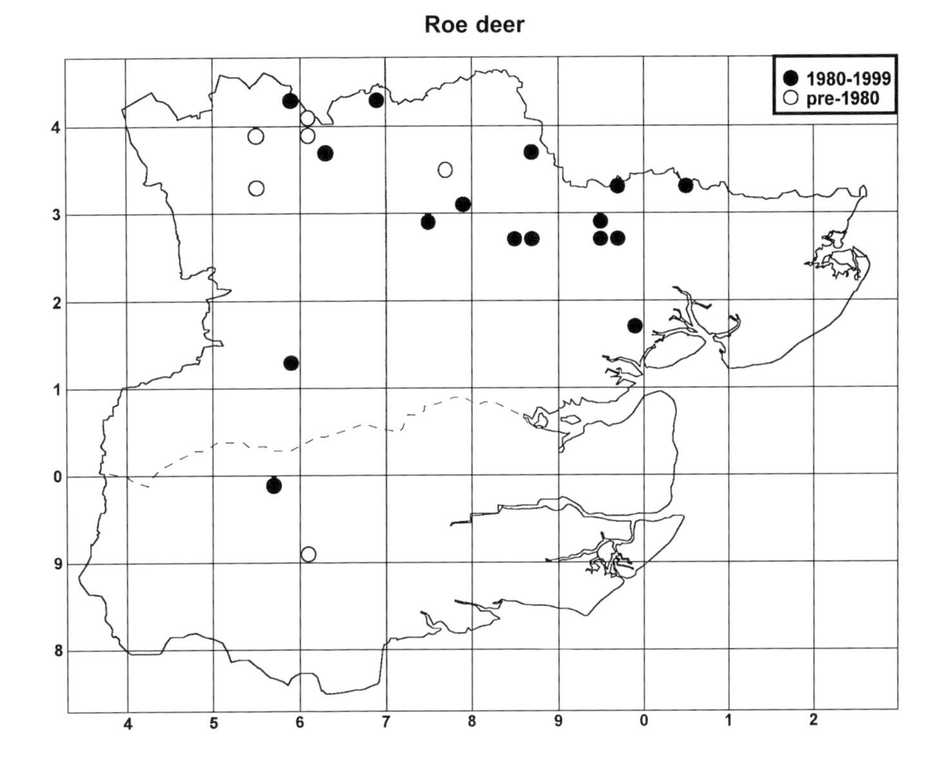

Although roe deer have been present in north Essex since around 1963, (Chapman, 1977) they are rarely seen. During the present survey, roe were recorded from Great Bendysh Wood – still the best location to see four species of deer in Essex - and Hempstead Wood, with up to three being regularly seen near Loshes Meadow Nature Reserve, at Great Henny. On one occasion during the summer of 1996, two were seen in a plantation at Abberton Reservoir and, in the winter of 1997, one was watched on several occasions at Iron Latch Nature Reserve, near Colchester; the same individual may also have been recorded from West Bergholt and Great Horkesley. Two reports were received of road casualties – one was found on the A12 on the Essex/Suffolk border in June 1997 (J. Martin, pers. comm.) with a second at Kelvedon Hatch in November 1997 (P. Fontaine, pers. comm.). A small resident population is present in the Colne Valley, with occasional records from Chalkney Wood, Broakes Wood and the Marks Hall Estate.

Although widespread in East Anglia, the roe deer has yet to successfully colonise the county. It is hoped that this attractive species will be able to make further inroads into the Essex countryside during the next century.

Muntjac

Muntiacus reevesi (Ogilby, 1839)

Status: Fairly common, increasing

The muntjac is a native of south-east China and Taiwan; it was first liberated in this country by the Duke of Bedford at the beginning of the 20th century in the woodlands adjacent to Woburn Park, Bedfordshire. Since then, following many other releases and escapes, they have colonised much of England (Chapman *et al.*, 1994). They are our smallest deer, standing only 50cm at the shoulder; favouring habitats such as woodland with ground cover, coppice, spinneys, plantations and mature gardens. Brambles are important, making up 30–40% of the diet throughout the year; ivy, ferns, fungi, leaves, nuts, fruit and grasses are also consumed. There is no clear breeding season: females give birth after seven months of gestation and usually conceive again a few days later (Chapman, 1991).

Although muntjac would have reached Essex from the west, the earliest records were from the east of the county. The first report was of an individual shot near Colchester in 1941 (Waller, 1954), followed soon afterwards by a second killed at Easthorpe (Whitehead, 1964). Four years later, a male was killed on the road near Gosfield but it was not until 1958 before the first resident population was reported by the gamekeeper at Coptford Hall, Margaretting (Chapman, 1977). In the succeeding years, there was an increasing number of reports of wandering individuals (invariably male), with sightings from Basildon, West Ham, Stebbing and Chelmsford where one was captured on a housing estate in July, 1966. By the mid-1970s, muntjac had been found in many Essex woods and the current survey has confirmed that they are now widespread throughout the county. Most records are of sightings of single animals, but there have been several cases of road kills, deer heard barking and the characteristic 3cm slots have been found in a number of woodlands during the winter. The A13 and A127 have not proved to be barriers:

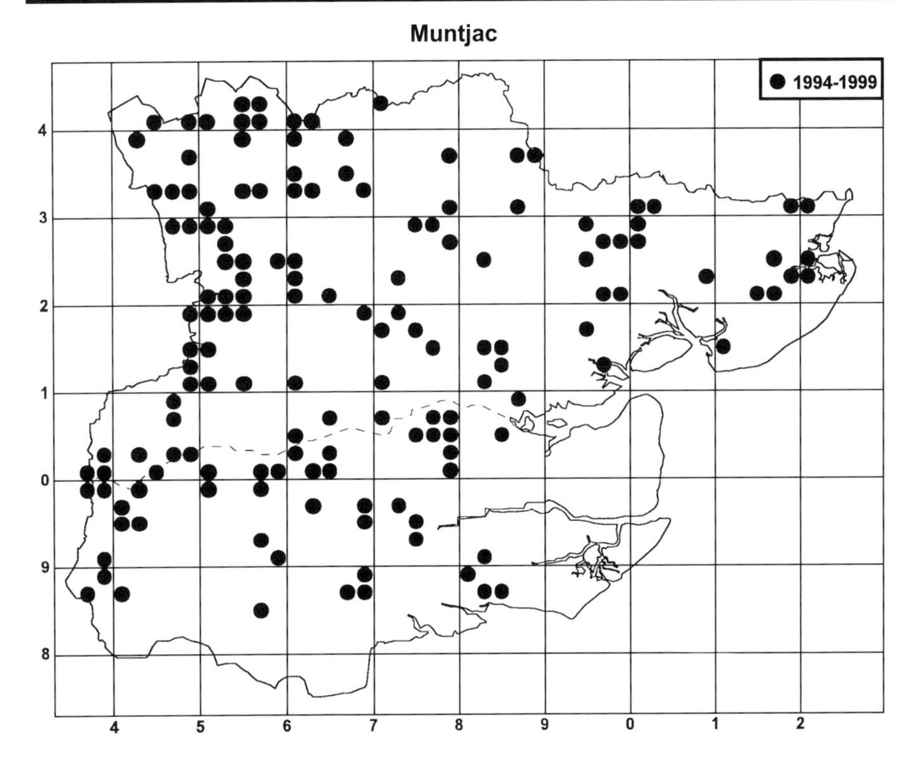

muntjac are breeding in the Langdon Hills and were reported by Essex Wildlife Trust wardens at both Cranham Marsh and Pound Wood Reserves. Muntjac were first seen regularly in Belfairs Nature Reserve, Leigh in 1996, and a wandering individual was recorded from Chalkwell Park in the urban outskirts of Southend in 1995.

The successful colonisation of Essex has proved a mixed blessing. The sight of deer in the countryside brings pleasure to many but the presence of muntjac on a nature reserve can be detrimental to woodland management. A recent study (Cooke, 1994) showed that muntjac damage to primroses at some sites could be as high as 50% and that for bluebells and orchids, it could exceed 90%. An additional problem that may occur in the future, in those north-east Essex woodlands where the white admiral butterfly is present, is of muntjac browsing honeysuckle, which may reduce the availability of this plant as an egg-laying site (Pollard & Cooke, 1994).

The last twenty years has seen the muntjac continue its spread across the county. Where suitable habitat is present, so is the muntjac; only the arable areas inside the sea walls of the Dengie and south Essex, with their absence of woodland and copses, remain unconquered.

Several of the mammals that have been recorded in Essex during the 20th century have become established as a result of deliberate introduction (grey squirrel, muntjac) or accidental escape from captivity (mink, coypu). Another species, the ferret, has been regularly reported as an escape and could potentially survive in the county, the population being sustained by the plentiful supply of rabbits.

The following species have all occurred in Essex and are included because they have been the subject of successful introductions elsewhere, or, in the case of the beaver and wild boar, were formerly a native species.

Beaver *Castor* spp

The European beaver (*C. fiber*) was formerly a member of our native fauna, finally becoming extinct in Scotland during the 16th century. It has recently been successfully re-introduced into thirteen European states and there is a wide level of support for its re-establishment in Scotland. However, it is the Canadian beaver (*C. canadensis*) that is most commonly encountered in British zoos and successful captive colonies have also been maintained on a number of private estates (Hills, 1991).

On 1st January 1984, a male beaver of unknown origin, was captured on Latimer Common near Harlow by the RSPCA and subsequently transferred to Camperdown Wildlife Park (S. Baker, pers. comm.).

Fat dormouse *Glis glis*

This species was introduced to England at Tring Park, Hertfordshire in 1902 and has slowly expanded its range to cover most of the Chilterns. The only Essex record is of two that escaped from captivity at High Beech, Epping in November 1968 (Hughes, 1986).

Raccoon *Procyon lotor*

The raccoon is a native of North and Central America that was brought to Europe to stock fur farms after the Second World War. Following escapes in Germany and eastern Russia, it has now spread to France and the Netherlands. In Britain, the raccoon is commonly kept in collections and of the twenty, widely-scattered records, one is of an animal that avoided recapture for four years.

There is one Essex record of an individual caught in a snare on Lord Petre's estate at Ingatestone on 1st November 1969 and later taken to Colchester Zoo (Hughes, 1986).

Egyptian mongoose *Herpestes ichneumon*

The Egyptian mongoose has been introduced to southern Spain and Portugal, where it occupies both rocky and cultivated habitats feeding on a variety of mammals, birds and rodents. In 1956, the *Halstead Gazette* recorded that an individual, first reported as a pine marten, was killed near Greenstead Green (Hughes, 1986).

Wild boar *Sus scrofa*

Wild boar, although still widespread in Europe, were hunted to extinction in England during the late 17th century. However, as the population declined, so small numbers were maintained in semi-captivity and wild boar survived in Essex in this way during medieval times. The de Veres (Earls of Oxford) preserved Chalkney Woods as a swine-park until at least 1500, although the population was destroyed soon after as a result of the damage that escaped animals caused to neighbouring land (Laver, 1898).

During the 19th century, wild boar were introduced to a number of private estates in the United Kingdom and in 1820, two were reported in woodland to the south of Colchester (Hills, 1991). There are no further Essex records until the last decade of the 20th century when boar were again being kept (with local authority permission under the Dangerous Wild Animals Act 1976) to service the restaurant trade.

On 18th January 1990, an incident was reported in *Horse and Hound* in which a wild boar attacked two foxhounds during a hunt at Woodham Walter. The boar, *"black with four inch tusks"* had apparently escaped five weeks earlier and had been living in nearby woods (S. Baker, pers. comm.). In 1996, there were several records thought to have arisen from a group of boar that escaped whilst being used to clear an area of woodland. An adult was in collision with a car at Wickham Bishops; there were anecdotal reports from the Dengie and, at the RSPB reserve at Old Hall Marshes, two that took up residence in January 1996, were shot a few weeks later to prevent possible disturbance to ground-nesting birds.

At the same site, a third animal, thought to be the surviving offspring of a litter born to the earlier invaders, was still present on the reserve, two years later (C. Tyas, pers. comm.) Based on the photograph (Plate 20), S Baker (pers. comm.) believes this is not a pure-bred wild boar but a cross with some domestic pig blood in its veins. Although a large animal and present on a well-wardened reserve, this individual is seldom seen and illustrates how easily this species could remain undetected, even in a county such as Essex. During the autumn of 1997, a wild boar was killed in a traffic accident at West Hanningfield and the most recent record was of one sighted in woodland near Stock in November 1997 (P. McKenna, pers. comm.). Elsewhere, a small feral population has become established in Kent and, more recently, there have been similar reports from other southern counties.

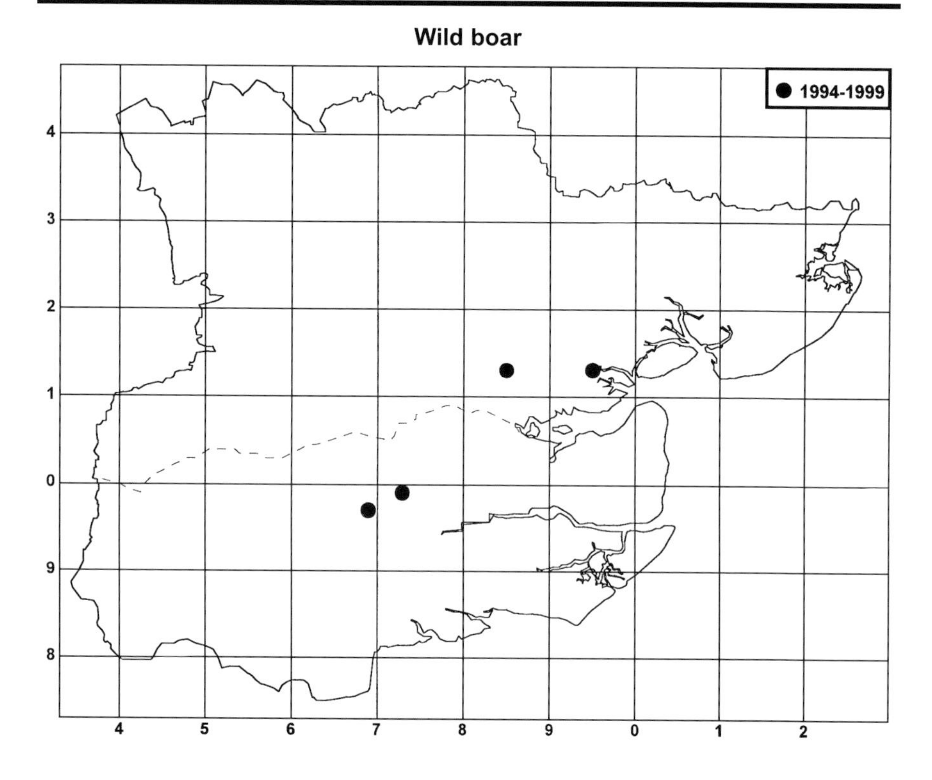

Wallaby

Macropus sp.

Feral colonies of red-necked wallabies (*M. rufogriseus*) have occasionally become established in Britain. However, the best known of these, in the Peak District, has recently died out after 50 years as a result of harsh weather and increased mortality from traffic accidents. In April 1993, a wallaby escaped from a private collection at Weald Park but was sighted by a motorist and later recaptured (S. Baker, pers. comm.).

These plans were prepared by the Essex Biodiversity Action Plan Steering Group and published in March 1999. They are reproduced here by their permission.

A number of abbreviations are used in the following pages:

ASCOBANS	Agreement on the Conservation of Small Cetaceans of the Baltic and North Seas
BASC	British Association for Shooting and Conservation
BCT	Bat Conservation Trust
CITES	Convention on International Trade in Endangered Species
DDE	breakdown product of dichlor-diphenyl-trichlor-ethane (DDT)
DoETR	Department of Environment, Transport and the Regions
EA	Environment Agency
EBG	Essex Bat Group
EC	European Community
ECC	Essex County Council
EFC	Essex Field Club
ELMS	Existing Land Management Schemes
EN	English Nature
ESA	Environmentally Sensitive Area
EWT	Essex Wildlife Trust
FA	Forestry Authority
FE	Forest Enterprise
FRCA	Farming and Rural Conservation Agency
IUCN	International Union for the Conservation of Nature
JNCC	Joint Nature Conservation Committee
LA	Local Authority
LA21	Local Agenda 21
LEAP	Local Environment Agency Plan
MAFF	Ministry of Agriculture, Fisheries and Food
NFU	National Farmers Union
PCBs	polychlorinated biphenyls
PPG 9	Planning Policy Guidance 9
RSNC	Royal Society for Nature Conservation
SAC	Special Area of Conservation
SINC	Site of Importance for Nature Conservation
SSSI	Site of Special Scientific Interest
TGCT	The Game Conservancy Trust
VWT	Vincent Wildlife Trust
WCA	Wildlife and Countryside Act
WCMC	World Conservation Monitoring Centre
WWF	World Wildlife Fund

Pipistrelle bats *Pipistrellus pipistrellus*

1 Current status in the UK

1.1 Pipistrelle bats are small bats (head and body up to 45mm) with variable brown/grey coloration. They roost in a variety of modern buildings and structures including churches, modern houses, bridges and walls. They forage in many habitat types including woodlands, urban areas such as parks and gardens, lakes, ponds and wet/marshy areas.

1.2 In the UK, pipistrelle bats are the most abundant bat species and the species most likely to come into contact with humans. However, the National Bat Colony Survey suggests a decline of 70% between 1978 and 1993. The UK pre-breeding population estimate stands at about 2 million. The problems of estimating population trends have been compounded by the recent discovery that there are two distinct species of pipistrelle bat in the UK.

1.3 Bats use high frequency echo-location calls to detect their insect prey whilst flying. The two species of pipistrelle can be distinguished by monitoring these calls with a bat detector – one species uses calls around 46kHz, the other 55kHz.

1.4 The pipistrelle is listed in Appendix III of the Bern Convention, Annex IV of the EC Habitats Directive, and Appendix II of the Bonn Convention. It is also included under the Agreement on the Conservation of Bats in Europe. It is protected under schedule 2 of the Conservation (Natural Habitats) Regulations 1994 and schedules 5 and 6 of the WCA (1981) and schedules 5 and 6 of the Wildlife (Northern Ireland) Order (1985).

2 Current status in Essex

2.1 Mirroring the national distribution, pipistrelles are the most abundant bat species in the county. Both species of pipistrelle are present in Essex, although survey work is at an early stage. The 46kHz type has been recorded from 42 10km squares (all districts) and the 55kHz type from 23 10km squares (10 districts).

2.2 Where colonies have been counted over successive years, a decline has been seen e.g. in Maldon a colony declined from over 1,041 bats in 1990 to 440 in 1998; at Little Baddow the decline was from 656 bats in 1988 to 264 in 1995. However, in South Woodham Ferrers and Bicknacre, colony size has remained relatively unchanged over several years.

3 Current factors causing loss or decline

3.1 Reduction in insect prey abundance due to high intensity farming practices and inappropriate riparian management.

3.2 Loss of insect-rich feeding habitat such as wetlands and hedgerows.

3.3 Loss and disruption of flightline features (linear landscape elements) such as hedgerows.

3.4 Loss of roost sites in buildings and trees due to cavity wall insulation, use of UPVC barge-boarding and soffits and clearance of dead trees.

3.5 Disturbance and destruction of maternity roosts due to building work and conflict with householders.

4 Current action

4.1 The National Bat Colony Survey is monitoring several colonies in Essex.

4.2 Essex Bat Group continues to provide support to EN in an advisory capacity and in surveying, monitoring and educational activities.

4.3 Field work is being undertaken to record distribution of the two pipistrelle species in Essex.

4.4 Licensed bat workers carry out advisory visits to householders to discuss management for bats.

5 Action plan objectives and proposed targets

5.1 Maintain existing populations and distribution of pipistrelles.

6 Proposed action with lead agencies

6.1 Policy and legislation

6.1.1 Encourage water quality levels which will help support populations of aquatic insects on which pipistrelles feed. (ACTION: EA, EWT, EBG)

6.1.2 Ensure the needs of this species are considered in incentive schemes designed for the management of suitable pipistrelle habitats. (ACTION: FWAG, NFU, EWT, EN)

6.2 Site safeguard and management

6.2.1 Encourage favourable management of land adjacent to known roost sites to support foraging by juvenile pipistrelles. (ACTION: EN, EWT, NFU)

6.3 Species management and protection

6.3.1 See action 6.6.2 below

6.4 Advisory

6.4.1 Ensure landowners are aware of the presence and legal status of pipistrelle bats and that advice is available on appropriate methods of management for conservation of their roosts and foraging habitats. (ACTION: EBG, BCT, FWAG)

6.5 Future research and monitoring

6.5.1 Undertake fieldwork to record distribution of both species. (ACTION: EBG)

6.5.2 To continue to monitor summer maternity roosts. (ACTION: EBG)

6.5.3 Pass information gathered during survey and monitoring of this species to BCT and Robert Stebbings Consultancy so that it can be incorporated in a national database and contribute to the maintenance of an up-to-date Red List. (ACTION: EBG)

6.6 Communications and publicity

6.6.1 To maintain programmes of roost visiting, general education and publicity. (ACTION: EN, EBG, BCT)

6.6.2 Continue to inform the public about the harmlessness of bats and encourage householders not to 'evict' them from house roosts. (ACTION: EBG, EN, EWT)

Brown hare *Lepus europaeus*

1 Current status in the UK

1.1 The brown hare is one of two species of hare that occurs in the British Isles, the other being the native mountain hare. The brown hare is considered a common and widespread farmland species in Britain and was probably introduced by the Romans from mainland Europe. In Europe this species inhabits the open steppe and has colonised farmland. In Britain it is abundant in arable areas with cereal farming, although woods and hedgerows can provide cover and resting areas.

1.2 It is widespread over the whole of Britain except the north-west and western Highlands. Although it was formerly considered as abundant, the brown hare seems to have undergone a decline in numbers since the 1960s. Population estimates now vary between 817,500 and 1,250,000. Numbers have remained relatively constant for the last ten years. Similar population changes have taken place over the rest of Europe.

1.3 This species does not have any specific protection under EU or English law. However, together with all wild mammals, cruelty to the brown hare is prohibited under The Wild Mammals (Protection) Act 1996.

2 Current status in Essex

2.1 This species has always been locally common in Essex and a general increase in numbers was seen after the onset of myxomatosis in the rabbit population. Results from the last national hare survey and other county records show that hares are present in all the districts of Essex. Numbers or estimates of breeding pairs are not available at present.

3 Current factors causing loss or decline

3.1 Loss of habitat diversity in the agricultural landscape.

3.2 Changes in planting and cropping regimes, such as a move from hay to silage and reduction in over-wintering stubbles.

3.3 Some deaths from poisoning where pesticides (e.g. paraquat) are used heavily.

3.4 Illegal hare coursing.

3.5 Road casualties can be important cause of mortality in some areas.

4 Current action

4.1 JNCC commissioned a survey from Bristol University in 1991/92. The current distribution map for the species is based on these data.

4.2 A survey covering the whole country has been initiated by Bristol University and the Mammal Society. This was started in 1997/8 and is being added to in 1998/9. This includes survey squares in Essex, the results of which are awaited.

4.3 The population in the county is also monitored by the numbers seen or shot during hunting.

4.4 Essex, Cambridgeshire, Hertfordshire and Bedfordshire police worked together on 'Operation Tortoise' to combat illegal hare coursing around the borders of these counties. This also involved participation from local landowners and resulted in a big decline in coursing in north-west Essex.

4.4 Some habitat is managed and benefits hares under the ESA, Countryside Stewardship and Pilot Arable Stewardship schemes run by MAFF.

4.5 Compilation of an Essex Mammal Atlas by the Essex Field Club.

5 Action plan objectives and proposed targets

5.1 Maintain the current numbers of breeding hares in Essex.

5.2 Reduce the amount of illegal hare coursing and review the situation regarding legal coursing with dogs.

6 Proposed actions with lead agencies

6.1 Policy and legislation

6.1.1 Encourage the uptake of agri-environmental schemes such as Countryside Stewardship and Arable Stewardship (in the pilot areas) and consider the needs of brown hares when implementing subsequent changes in land management. As well as increasing food availability and cover after ploughing and harvesting, such schemes can result in a reduction in the amount of herbicides and pesticides: this will in turn reduce deaths from incidental poisoning. (ACTION: FWAG, FRCA, NFU, EN)

6.1.2 Encourage the uptake of the new flexible set-aside scheme instead of rotational set-aside; habitats are therefore left in place for longer, providing a more stable environment for this and other species. (ACTION: NFU, FWAG, EN)

6.2 Site safeguard and management

6.2.1 Target areas where the population is seen to be low and/or declining for inclusion in agri-environmental schemes as above. (ACTION: FWAG, FRCA, NFU, EN, EWT)

6.2.2. Monitor the effect of ELMS on hare populations. (ACTION: FRCA, farmers through NFU)

6.3 Species management and protection

6.3.1 Consider repeating Operation Tortoise in other parts of the county which have seen a recent increase in illegal hare coursing. (ACTION: Essex police, NFU)

6.3.2 Co-ordinate data collection from shooting records and feed in more closely to any county monitoring scheme. (ACTION: BASC, FWAG, EFC, EWT)

6.3.3 As a last resort consider translocating individuals from areas of high populations (e.g. Foulness) to areas with low and/or declining populations. This can only be done after investigations into available habitat and reasons for loss and decline in these areas. (ACTION: EN, EWT, EFC)

6.4 Advisory

6.4.1 Distribute widely any management advisory booklet compiled by JNCC, together with advice tailored to the county. (ACTION:EN, FWAG, NFU)

6.5 Future research and monitoring

6.5.1 Input into new national hare survey and any subsequent surveys. (ACTION: EWT, FWAG, EN)

6.5.2 Set up a programme to continue to monitor the numbers of the hare in the county. This is to continue after the current national survey and link with the Atlas of Mammals in Essex. (BASC, EFC, EN, EWT, FWAG, NFU)

6.5.3 Research into the effect of shooting on the Essex population. (ACTION: TGCT, FRCA, FWAG, NFU)

6.5.4 Research into the effects of legal and illegal hare coursing on the Essex population. (ACTION: FRCA, FWAG, NFU, TGCT)

6.6 Communications and publicity

6.6.1 Use the brown hare, with other farmland species, to highlight the impact of modern agricultural practices on biodiversity in the county. (ACTION: FWAG, NFU, EN, EWT)

6.6.2 Encourage local public surveys to raise the profile of this species. (ACTION: Las, LA21 groups, EWT, EN)

Water vole *Arvicola terrestris*

1 Current status in the UK

1.1 The water vole (or water rat) is the largest of the British voles with a head and body measuring around 20cm. Due to its size and semi-aquatic lifestyle it is often confused with the brown rat when swimming, but the two can be distinguished quite easily as rats have more prominent ears, pointed snout and hairless tails.

1.2 Water voles inhabit the banks of slow-flowing rivers, streams and ditches as well as non-flowing water features such as lakes, ponds and dykes. Their presence can be determined by searching for their burrows at and above the water level, together with characteristic piles of droppings (latrines) and feeding remains.

1.3 Previously a common and frequently seen species throughout the United Kingdom, the water vole has declined in distribution and numbers in recent years. A recent survey of water voles showed that populations had seriously declined, with 67% of those sites in the UK previously recorded as occupied in 1939 having no water voles recorded in 1989–90. Most of this is thought to have occurred in recent years and it is estimated that losses will have reached 94% by the year 2000.

1.4 In 1998 the water vole received limited protection under the quinquennial review of the Wildlife and Countryside Act (1981) under schedule 5 section 9(4). It is now an offence to damage or destroy or obstruct access to any structure or place which water voles use for shelter or protection and/or disturb water voles while they are using such a place.

2 Current status in Essex

2.1 The survey of 1989–90, carried out by the Vincent Wildlife Trust showed that East Anglia was one of the least-affected areas of water vole decline, with 60–80% of sites still being occupied.

2.2 More recent records (1997) from the RSNC national water vole survey indicate that water voles are still present on most of the main river catchments in all districts in Essex, although population numbers are thought to have declined at some sites.

3 Current factors causing loss or decline

3.1 Habitat loss: loss of suitable bankside habitats as a result of engineering, bankside development, over-zealous vegetation clearance and general decline of habitat condition have all contributed.

3.2 Population fragmentation: increasingly, populations are being fragmented by human interference, from new roads to canalisation, development, and loss of suitable inter-connecting river corridor habitat and the presence of mink.

3.3 Water level fluctuations: water voles need steady water levels in channels to make their tunnel entrances secure. Recent years have seen significant water level fluctuations in many rivers as a result of droughts. As a consequence, flooding of chambers and increased predation can occur (see also below).

3.4 Predation: the spread of feral mink (*Mustela vison*) throughout the UK has increased predation levels on water voles.

3.5 Pollution: contamination of freshwater environments by pesticides, heavy metals, DDE, PCBs and organic pollution from slurry and sewage may have contributed to the decline of water voles in certain river catchments; however, water voles have been recorded as thriving on some polluted watercourses in some areas.

3.6 Poisoning: indirect poisoning of water voles by non-specific rodenticides targeted at brown rats can be a localised problem.

4 Current action

4.1 A handbook providing advice on habitat management and conservation of water voles is being produced nationally by EN and EA. There is currently a section regarding water voles in the EN species conservation handbook.

4.2 A water vole and mink survey of main rivers and some non-main river sites in Essex has been completed (1998) – the results became available in 1999.

4.3 A national re-survey of 2,970 sites in the UK originally surveyed in 1989–90 UK survey is being carried out in 1997–98 by the Vincent Wildlife Trust.

4.4 A national survey of water vole sightings by volunteers, carried out by the RSNC during 1997, has produced many results in Essex. These results will be collated and will be available in 1999.

4.5 Distribution of mink in Essex is being included in the county otter survey being carried out by Essex University.

4.6 Compilation of county Mammal Atlas including water vole records is being carried out by EFC.

5 Action plan objectives and proposed targets

5.1 Endeavour to halt the decline of water voles in Essex by the year 2000.

5.2 Restore viable populations of water voles to those river catchments in the county that have lost them by the year 2010.

5.3 Improve riverine and other habitats for water voles throughout the county based on current research regarding their habitat requirements.

5.4 Monitor and record populations of water voles and mink in selected river catchment areas in the county.

6 Proposed action with lead agencies

6.1 Policy and legislation

6.1.1 Seek prioritisation of river corridor habitats in agri-environment schemes applicable to Essex – Countryside Stewardship, Essex Coast ESA and Arable Stewardship. (ACTION: NFU, FWAG, EN, MAFF)

6.1.2 Include specific mention of water vole habitat management in all LEAPs and water level management plans. (ACTION: EA)

6.1.3 Include water voles, as a protected species, in development plan policies. (ACTION: ECC, LAs)

6.2 Site safeguard and management

6.2.1 Identify prime water vole populations on county river sections and safeguard from adverse river management works. (ACTION: EA)

6.2.2 Identify river sections suitable for water level/bankside management for recolonisation of water voles. (ACTION: EA)

6.2.3 Target adjacent landowners for uptake of ELMS. (ACTION: EA, EN, EWT, FRCA)

6.3 Species management and protection

6.3.1 Carry out county-wide survey of water voles before 1999. (ACTION: EA, EWT, FWAG)

6.3.2 Carry on with county-wide survey of mink in Essex. Consider controlling mink to prevent the spread into currently mink-free areas. (ACTION: University of Essex, EA, EN)

6.4 Advisory

6.4.1 Distribute widely management advisory booklet compiled by EN/EA (available 1998) to all relevant partners and riparian controllers. (ACTION: EA, EN)

6.4.2 Promote water vole-friendly management of aquatic sites by water authorities and statutory organisations. (ACTION: EA, Water Authorities, EN)

6.4.3 Promote better awareness of water voles and their requirements amongst private landowners and managers. (ACTION: EA, EWT, FWAG, NFU, angling clubs)

6.5 Future research and monitoring

6.5.1 Research into viable methods of mink control. (ACTION: EA, EN)

6.5.2 Lobby for national research on the inter-relationship (if any) of freshwater pollutants and water vole populations. (ACTION: EA, EN)

6.5.3 Monitor the effect of rat-trapping and the use of rodenticides on water vole populations. (ACTION: EA, EN, EWT)

6.5.4 Communications and publicity

6.5.5 Use the water vole, with other freshwater species, as an indicator of good water quality/riverine habitat in Essex waterways. (ACTION: EA, EN, EWT)

6.5.6 Publicise the risk of rodenticides to water voles and promote careful use of such chemicals near water courses. (ACTION: EA, EN, FWAG, NFU)

Common dormouse *Muscardinus avellanarius*

1 Current status in the UK

1.1 The dormouse with its characteristic furry tail and orange-brown fur is a nocturnal, arboreal rodent which inhabits mixed broadleaved woodland, hedgerows and orchards. In the United Kingdom, the dormouse is mainly restricted to England, with only a few known populations in Wales. In England it has become extinct in up to 7 counties (half its former range) in the last 100 years. The species is mainly absent in the north, with only a few populations in Cumbria and Northumberland, and although dormice are still widespread in southern counties, they are patchily distributed. Population densities are much lower than other small mammals, and less than ten adults per hectare are present even in good habitats.

1.2 The dormouse is listed on Appendix 3 of the Bonn Convention and Annex IVa of the EC Habitats Directive. It is protected under Schedule 2 of the Conservation (Natural Habitats etc) Regulations, 1994 (Regulation 38) and Schedule 5 of the WCA 1981.

2 Current status in Essex

2.1 There are currently a few scattered records for Essex, mainly based around nestbox monitoring programmes and 'nut hunts'. This distribution is spread over several districts. There are many locations of potential habitat which have not been surveyed, for example Epping and Hatfield Forests, and it is thought that the current distribution is one which is based on under recording.

3 Current factors causing loss and decline

3.1 Loss of broadleaved ancient woodland, which provides the optimum habitat for dormice when managed in a suitable way; also the loss of hedgerows, which can provide suitable habitat and corridors between woodland.

3.2 Changes in woodland management have also reduced the number of suitable sites for dormice. Coppicing has greatly declined over the last 50 years, resulting in taller trees shading out the shrub layer and leaving fewer interconnected runways for dormice. However, if coppicing is carried out in large adjacent blocks, large areas of possibly suitable woodland will be unusable by dormice for approximately five years. Coppicing that takes place on a short rotation (ten years) also effectively reduces suitable habitat since shrubs do not reach fruiting age.

3.3 Woodland management in plantation forests does not provide good dormouse habitat, consisting of few species, tall straight trees and little or no understorey.

3.4 Fragmentation of suitable habitats can leave small, isolated, non-viable populations. The lower threshold limit for woodland has been calculated as 20ha, where short gaps of as little as 100m can be an effective isolating barrier. This applies within a woodland as well as between woodlands.

3.5 Warfarin put out to control grey squirrels may cause a problem locally, whereas large grey squirrel populations may reduce the amount of available hazel nuts.

4 Current action

4.1 National ecological research has led to practical proposals for conservation management. A national nestbox scheme has been established aimed at collating data on breeding and population density. Twenty sites in Essex are being monitored by the EWT, but this is mainly for presence or absence at the current time.

4.2 In 1992, the dormouse was added to English Nature's Species Recovery Programme. Grants from this scheme have been utilised in Essex to erect and check nestboxes all over the county.

4.3 The Great Nut Hunt in 1993 took place in many woods in Essex, but there were only seven positively-confirmed results. Unconfirmed results were used to identify possible locations for boxes, several of which have since been identified as dormouse sites.

4.4 Dormice occur in some known (and possibly many as-yet unknown) sites which have no protection as nature reserves or SSSIs. These sites may have value as links or corridors, especially where habitats are fragmented and below optimum size. PPG 9 requires local planning authorities to have regard for such habitats, as well as the presence of a protected species being a material consideration.

4.5 Management of derelict hazel coppice is covered by FA grant through the Woodland Grant Scheme, via the supplementary Woodland Improvement Grants.

5 Action plan objectives and proposed targets

5.1 Maintain current known dormouse populations in Essex and provide scope for enhancement in suitable areas.

5.2 Survey woodlands and other suitable sites (e.g. old orchards), especially those in areas of the county with few records, to extend current knowledge of their distribution.

6 Proposed action with lead agencies

6.1 Policy and legislation

6.1.1 Seek to ensure that PPG 9 guidance issued by the DoE is taken into account by Highways Authorities and Local Authorities. Target – 1998 onwards. (ACTION: DoE, Las, ECC, EN)

6.1.2 Push for designation, statutory or non-statutory, of sites which support dormice and currently have no protection. Target – next CWS review and ongoing. (ACTION: EN, EWT)

6.2 Site safeguard and management

6.2.1 Provide advice to land managers on appropriate management for dormice using EN Dormouse Species Recovery Plan booklet – targeted after 'nut hunts' have identified new locations. Target – 1998 onwards. (ACTION: EN, EWT)

6.2.2 Encourage land owners to use grant-aid and incentive schemes (such as Woodland Grant Schemes) to help them manage suitable habitat appropriately. Target – ongoing. (ACTION: FA, EN, MAFF, FWAG)

6.2.3 Prioritise identified dormouse sites to target both the management of existing populations and WGS/CS to reconnect habitat on adjacent land (hedges and woodland). This is a long-term aim beginning in 1998, but planned for the next 50 years. (ACTION: EWT, FA, FWAG, LAs, MAFF, Thames Chase)

6.3 Species management and protection

6.3.1 Continue to monitor the progress of dormouse introductions in other counties, including the requirements for woodland size and type. This could only take place in large reserves where the habitat is suitable; it is certain there are no dormice present; and that the resources are available to sustain the project. Target – ongoing. (ACTION: EN, EWT)

6.4 Advisory

6.4.1 Distribute any new national publications. Target – ongoing. (ACTION: EN, EWT)

6.4.2 Develop training for dormouse conservation for landowners, managers and wardens. Target – two county training sessions by end of year 2000. (ACTION: FA, MAFF, EN, EWT)

6.4.3 Ensure that any new information on habitat management and ecology is passed on to landowners, managers and wardens. Target – ongoing and through training sessions. (ACTION: FA, MAFF, EN, EWT)

6.5 Future research and monitoring

6.5.1 Continue research into dormouse ecology in Essex, such as nesting materials and habitat preferences and feed this into national research. Target – ongoing. (ACTION: EN, EWT)

6.5.2 Continue to analyse and disseminate research findings and modify forestry practices as appropriate. Target – ongoing. (ACTION: EN, EWT, FA)

6.5.3 Continue and expand the established Dormouse Nestbox Monitoring Scheme in Essex, both within EWT Reserves and other sites, aiming to refine distribution data by further sampling. Target – four new sites by end of year 2000. (ACTION: EWT)

6.5.4 Support and expand repeat surveys based on Great Nut Hunt to provide data on county distribution. Target LNRs, non-statutory nature reserves and LA land. Target – 1998 and 2/3 yearly intervals. (ACTION: EN, EWT, LAs)

6.6 Communications and publicity

6.6.1 Continue to make the public aware of this species and its role as a key indicator of good woodland and hedgerow management during talks, presentations and in publications. Target – ongoing. (ACTION: EN, EWT, FA, Las)

6.6.2 Use the dormouse as a flagship species to explain the value of coppicing in woodlands. Target – 1998 onwards. (ACTION: EN, EWT, LA,s FE)

Harbour porpoise *Phocoena phocoena*

1 Current status in the UK

1.1 The harbour porpoise is the only species of true porpoise found in European waters. It is the smallest British cetacean, never reaching more than two metres in length. It has a dark grey back and is paler below, a small round body and small head with no beak. The dorsal fin is triangular and placed in the middle of the back. Porpoises are most often seen in small groups or individually within ten kilometres of the shore. They can be observed in all months, but there is a seasonal peak between July and October.

1.2 There is some evidence of a decline in numbers of harbour porpoise in United Kingdom waters since the 1940s, especially in the southern North Sea and English Channel. The conservation status of the species around the whole UK coast is unknown, but the recent SCANS survey of small cetaceans in the North Sea, Channel and Celtic Sea indicated that the population in those waters was approximately 350,000.

1.3 The harbour porpoise is listed on Appendix II of CITES, Appendix III of the Bern Convention and Annex II and IV of the EC Habitats Directive. It is also on Appendix 2 of the Bonn Convention and is covered by the terms of the Agreement on the Conservation of Small Cetaceans of the Baltic and North Seas (ASCOBANS), a regional agreement under the Bonn Convention. It is protected under Schedule 5 of the WCA 1981.

2 Current status in Essex

2.1 At the present time the status of this species off the Essex and East Anglian coast is uncertain. Casual remarks suggest that they were common off the coast about 50 years ago. The majority of local records are old and mainly refer to dead individuals. No map for the distribution of this species was included in the Essex Mammal Atlas of 1986, although some cetaceans were included. It is probably still found off the coast in small numbers.

3 Current factors causing loss or decline

3.1 These are not clear at the present time, but could include: Incidental capture and drowning in fishing nets.

3.2 Environmental contaminants – toxic substances at sea, marine debris, disease, noise disturbance and physical disturbance from large amounts of marine traffic.

3.3 Environmental change – effects of fishing and possibly climate change.

4 Current action

4.1 No known action is being undertaken in Essex, with the exception of occasional sightings. No survey has been undertaken close to the East Anglian coast in recent years.

4.2 Distribution studies have been undertaken by JNCC since 1980. The Sea Mammal Research Unit co-ordinated the international SCANS survey (which included the North Sea) in 1994.

4.3 Conservation management and research action is being undertaken and planned under ASCOBANS, but it is not thought that any is planned for this region.

5 Action plan objectives and proposed targets

5.1 Determine size and distribution of harbour porpoise population in coastal waters around Essex and East Anglia.

5.2 Set up an East Anglian coastal network to monitor any porpoises present and co-ordinate data received from casual sightings.

5.3 Revise plan if there are porpoises present close to the Essex coast.

6 Proposed action with lead agencies

6.1 Future research and monitoring

6.1.1 Carry out a comprehensive survey of the waters off the Essex coast (and if possible the rest of the East Anglian coast) for coastal mammal species. (ACTION: EWT, Sea Watch, Whale and Dolphin Conservation Society)

6.1.2 Set up a coastal recording network to report all sightings. (ACTION: EA, EN. Essex and Kent Fisheries, EWT)

6.1.3 Ensure that all casualties are sent for post-mortem and tissue studies. (ACTION: EA, EN, EWT, LAs)

6.2 Communications and publicity

6.2.1 Highlight the fact that there are native species of cetacean off the Essex coast and that they are part of the natural heritage and not just present in exotic waters. (ACTION: EN, EWT, Whale and Dolphin Conservation Society)

6.2.2 Initiate a scheme for the public to report any sightings of both live and stranded individuals. (ACTION: EN, EWT)

Until some research has taken place, other action for this species cannot really be determined. If they are found still to be present off the coast, the following actions are likely:

6.3 Policy and legislation

6.3.1 Introduce agreed codes of conduct to reduce disturbance from acoustic sources and physical pressures. (ACTION: JNCC, EN)

6.4 Site safeguard and management

6.4.1 Introduce speed limits and no-go areas to ensure the safe passage of the species (ACTION: EN, LAs)

6.4.2 No further action is required with regard to marine protection as practically all of the Essex coast has SAC designation for other reasons.

6.5 Species management and protection

6.5.1 Work with fishers with the aim of reducing and avoiding by-catches in active and pasive fishing gear, and to dispose of discarded gear safely. (ACTION: MAFF, JNCC)

6.5.2 Introduce a code of practice to reduce disturbance by other marine craft (speedboats etc). (ACTION: EA, EN, LAs)

6.6 Advisory

6.6.1 Disseminate best practice from any future national research.

6.6.2 Provide and advisory service to accompany any codes of best practice. (ACTION: EA, EN, LAs)

Otter *Lutra lutra*

1 Current status in the UK

1.1 The otter is a large, semi-aquatic member of the stoat and weasel (mustelid) family. It can be distinguished from other mustelids and aquatic rodents by its large size and flattened head. It occurs in rivers, streams, lakes, marshes and coastal habitats. Otters are opportunistic hunters that will take a wide range of prey depending on the habitat, but most feed mainly on fish.

1.2 The otter is a top predator in the river ecosystem and as such it occurs at a naturally low density. Its sensitivity to river management and water quality makes it a valuable indicator of the health of riverine ecosystems.

1.3 Despite the decline of the 30 years from 1960, the UK as a whole supports a significant population of otters in a European context.

1.4 The otter is listed on Appendix I of CITES, Appendix II of the Bern Convention and Annexes II and IV of the Habitats Directive. It is protected under Schedule 5 of the WCA 1981 and Schedule 2 of the Conservation (Natural Habitats etc) Regulations, 1994 (Regulation 38). The European subspecies is also listed as globally threatened on the IUCN/WCMC Red Data List.

2 Current status in Essex

2.1 The otter was widespread in Essex until the early 1960s, but a rapid decline throughout the decade culminated in its disappearance from the county in the mid-70s and 80s. This decline was the result of a number of factors, of which the most significant is likely to have been bioaccumulating organochlorines, especially PCBs.

2.2 Surveys in 1996 and 1997 by the University of Essex for the WWF have found the otter to be present on a significant number of rivers in Essex, particularly in the north and east. These include the Colne, Stour, Blackwater, lower Chelmer, Stort, Lee and Cam. The increase in the population locally is at least in part due to a re-introduction project in East Anglia. In Essex, small groups were released into Hamford Water and the rivers Stort and Stour. The current optimistic situation should be tempered by the fact that several years of population consolidation will be needed before the future of the otter in Essex is more secure.

3 Current factors causing loss or decline

3.1 Water quality: as long as a river is virtually free of bioaccumulating contaminants and has a sufficiently good water quality to enable it to support fish, it can support otters. In Essex, perhaps only the Mardyke system is currently incapable of supporting otters on the grounds of water quality. However, if they do establish themselves on the rivers of the south-east of the county, these populations are only ever likely to be marginal. Individual populations are vulnerable to isolated pollution incidents.

3.2 Low rainfall and over abstraction: low flow and its attendant problems for water quality may have posed problems for the spread of the otter in Essex.

3.3 Loss of habitat: intensification of riparian management has led to loss of habitat for otters, in particular the loss of breeding and resting sites.

3.4 Insufficient food: associated with low water quality, leading to a reduction in fish stocks. Currently only a problem in the Mardyke catchment.

3.5 Accidental death: road traffic accidents are probably the biggest single threat to the re-establishment of a thriving otter population in Essex. Otters are reluctant to pass under bridges that do not provide opportunities for sprainting. Therefore, they cross roads and are vulnerable to traffic accidents. Road building, and the density of traffic on roads, has increased enormously since the end of the 1950s when otters were last common in the county.

3.6 Drowning in fish/eel traps continues to pose a threat to otters in some regions.

4 Current action

4.1 Releases of captive-bred otters have taken place on a piecemeal basis since the early 1990s, but the documentation of this activity is incomplete. The national Framework Document on otters produced by the JNCC is opposed to the release of captive-bred otters and this approach is reflected in the EWT's approach to re-introduction programmes for the species.

4.2 A survey of the Essex river catchments is being carried out by S.M. MacDonald and C.F Mason and has funding from WWF until 2001. This involves surveying for evidence of otter (spraints) every spring and autumn at fixed points along rivers.

4.3 The River Colne Countryside Project is, in partnership with relevant bodies and funded by EA, pioneering a scheme to build fauna passages under major road bridges on the Colne in the hope of reducing the potential for otters to be involved in traffic accidents.

5 Action plan objectives and proposed targets

5.1 Encourage the expansion of the otter population to all major catchments and coastal habitats in Essex by 2010.

5.2 Reduce the danger posed by road traffic through the provision of safe road crossings at appropriate bridge locations.

5.3 Encourage otter-sensitive riparian land management in Essex.

5.4 All rivers in the county to be fisheries target classes (see EA Leap plans)by 2010.

5.5 Encourage the introduction of new fisheries legislation to make the fitting of otter guards compulsory on all fyke nets used in waters likely to support otter populations.

6 Proposed actions with lead agencies

6.1 Policy and legislation

6.1.1 Review abstraction guidelines in order to maintain flows sufficient to maintain high ecosystem classification in all Essex rivers. (ACTION: EA)

6.1.2 Ensure all wetland or riparian sites found to be regularly used by otters are designated as SINCs and recognised and protected in Local Plans. (ACTION: EN, EWT, LAs)

6.2 Site safeguard and management

6.2.1 Include action for otters in all LEAPs. (ACTION: EA)

6.2.2 Promote the take-up of agri-environment schemes to encourage appropriately managed riparian habitat. (ACTION: EA, EN, FRCA, FWAG, LAs)

6.2.3 Ensure that all new bridges have fauna passages or provide opportunities for sprainting under them. (ACTION: EA, ECC, LAs)

6.2.4 Identify and then improve those existing bridges on roads six metres wide or over (including pavements) that are not found to be 'otter-friendly'. (ACTION: EA, ECC, LAs, University of Essex)

6.2.5 Ensure, where possible, that the rate of flow in main rivers remains high enough to prevent a reduction in water quality. (ACTION, EA)

6.2.6 Ensure that the level of fish stocks in main rivers remain adequate to support otters. (ACTION: EA)

6.3 Species management and protection

6.3.1 Review the need for current and future local release practices of otters; this should be done in the light of the national Framework Document policies on release schemes and the natural recolonisation of local river systems. (ACTION: EA, EN, EWT, Otter Trust, University of Essex)

6.3.2 Promote the creation of a selected small number of ponds (stocked with fish) close to rivers. (ACTION: EA, EN, EWT, FWAG, LAs)

6.3.3 Seek to establish an Essex Otter Forum to co-ordinate conservation, information exchange, publicity and research. (ACTION: EA)

6.4 Advisory

6.4.1 Ensure that landowners are aware of the legal status of otters and that advice is available on appropriate management of their habitat. (ACTION: EA, EN, EWT, LAs)

6.4.2 Ensure that the Highway Authority, Highways Agency and EA are aware of the needs of otters in relation to bridges. (ACTION: EA, ECC, EN, Highways Agency)

6.5 Future research and monitoring

6.5.1 Survey all existing bridges for their 'otter-friendliness'. (ACTION: EA, EWT, LAs, University of Essex)

6.5.2 Continuation of the present research beyond 2001. (ACTION: University of Essex and potential funding partners, EA, EN, WWF – current funding body)

6.5.3 Monitor the rate of flow in rivers with a view to controlling abstraction rates to support flow rate. (ACTION: EA)

6.5.4 Ensure that the level of fish stocks in main rivers remains adequate to support otters. (ACTION: EA)

6.6 Communications and publicity

6.6.1 A careful programme of publicity, exercising discretion, needs to accompany any attempts to conserve the otter in Essex. It is premature at this time to promote as a success story the return of the otter to the county. (ACTION: EA, EN, EWT, LAs, University of Essex)

6.6.2 Promotion to landowners highlighting positive management actions which would benefit otters. (ACTION: EA, EN, EWT, FRCA, FWAG, LAs, NFU)

6.6.3 Promote monitoring of otter population by providing opportunities for local people to report any sightings (with careful checking to avoid inaccurate attribution). (ACTION: EWT, Local Biological Records Centres)

References

Alibhai, S.K. & Gipps, J.H.W. (1991) The bank vole. In Corbet G.B. & Harris S. (eds)

Anon. (1892) Destruction of Otters in Essex. *Essex Naturalist* **6:** 41–42

Anon. (1898) Number of deer in Epping Forest. *Essex Naturalist* **10:** 292

Anon. (1900) Stranding of a common rorqual whale in the Thames at North Woolwich. *Essex Naturalist* **11:** 190–181

Arnold, H.R. (1993) *Atlas of mammals in Britain*. HMSO, London

Barnes, R.F.W. & Tapper, S.C. (1986) Consequences of the myxomatosis epidemic in Britain's rabbit (*Oryctolagus cuniculus* L.) population on the number of brown hares (*Lepus europaeus* Pallas). *Mammal Review* **16:** 111–116

Barratt, E., Deauville, R., Burland, T.M., Bruford, M.W., Jones, G., Racey, P.A. & Wayne, R.K. (1997) DNA answers the call of pipistrelle bat species. *Nature* **387:** 138–139

Barrett-Hamilton, G.E.H. & Hinton, M.A.C. (1910–21) *A History of British Mammals*. Gurney and Jackson, London

Beale, P. (1974) The wild deer of north and north west Essex. In: *Nature in North East Essex* **1973:** 21–23

Bell, T. (1874) *A History of British Quadrupeds, including the Cetacea.* 2nd edition London

Bentley, E.W. (1959) The distribution and status of *Rattus rattus* L. in the United Kingdom in 1951 and 1956. *Journal of Animal Ecology* **28:** 299–308

Berrow, S.D. & Rogan, E. (1997) Review of cetaceans stranded on the Irish coast, 1901–95. *Mammal Review* **27**: 51–76

Berry, R.J. (1991) The ecology of an island population of the house mouse. *Journal of Animal Ecology* **37:** 445–470

Berry, R.J. (1991) The house mouse. In Corbet, G.B. & Harris, S. (eds)

Birks, J.D.S. & Dunstone, N. (1991) The mink. In Corbet, G.B. & Harris, S. (eds)

Bonner, W.N. & Thompson, P.M. (1991) The common seal. In Corbet G.B. & Harris S. (eds)

Braybrooke, Lord ed.(1845) *Autobiography of Sir John Bramston.* Camden Society, London

Bright, P.W., Mitchell, P. & Morris, P.A. (1994) Dormouse Distribution: Survey Techniques, Insular Ecology and Selection of Sites for Conservation. *Journal of Applied Ecology* **31:** 329–339

Bright, P.W. & Morris, P.A. (1996) Why are Dormice rare? A case study in conservation biology. *Mammal Review* **26:** 157–187

Bright, P.W., Morris, P.A. & Mitchell-Jones, A.J. (1996) A new survey of the Dormouse *Muscardinus avellanarius* in Britain, 1993–4. *Mammal Review* **26:** 189–195

Brockie, R.E. (1960) Road mortality of the hedgehog (*Erinaceus europaeus* L) in New Zealand. *Proceedings of the Zoological Society of London* **134:** 505–508

Burtsal, K.F. (1950) An Occurrence of Leisler's Bat in Essex. *Essex Naturalist* **22:** 19–20

Buxton, E.N. (1897) *Epping Forest.* (4th Edition) Edward Stanford. London

Buxton, E.N. (1915) Red deer at large in Epping Forest. *Essex Naturalist* **18:** 87–88

Cary, J (1796) *Survey of the Country Fifteen Miles round London.* London

Cantor, L. (1983) *The Medieval Parks of England: A Gazetteer.* Loughborough University of Technology

Chanin, P. (1991) The otter. In Corbet G.B. & Harris S. (eds).

Chapman, D.I. (1967) The Occurrence of a White Stoat, *Mustela erminea* L., in Essex. *Essex Naturalist* **32:** 64–65

Chapman, D.I. (1977) *Deer of Essex.* Essex Field Club, London

Chapman, D.I. & Chapman, N. (1975) *Fallow Deer, their History, Distribution and Biology*. Terence Dalton, Lavenham

Chapman, D.I. & Hammond, P.M. (1962) A preliminary report on investigations in the deneholes of Hangman's Wood, Grays, Essex. *Essex Naturalist* **31:** 1–15

Chapman, N.G. (1991) The chinese muntjac. In Corbet G.B. & Harris S. (eds).

Chapman, N., Harris, S. & Stanford, A. (1994) Reeves' Muntjac *Muntiacus reevesi* in Britain: their history, spread, habitat selection and the role of human intervention in accelerating their dispersal. *Mammal Review* **24**: 113–160

Christy, M (1887) Notes on bats found in the Grays deneholes. *Essex Naturalist* **1:** 259

Christy, M. (1906) Whale at Mersea in 1299. *Essex Naturalist* **14:** 135–136

Christy, R.W. (1888) Ermine shot at Roxwell. *Essex Naturalist* **2:** 20

Churchfield, S. (1990) *The Natural History of Shrews.* Christopher Helm. London

Churchfield, S. (1991a) The common shrew. In Corbet G.B. & Harris S. (eds)

Churchfield, S. (1991b) The pygmy shrew. In Corbet G.B. & Harris S. (eds)

Cole, W. (1905) Occurrence of deWinton's Mouse in Essex. *Essex Naturalist* **13**: 294–295

Cole , W. (1906) Hairy-armed Bat in Essex. *Essex Naturalist* **14:** 165

Cooke, A. (1994) In Massey M. and Welch R.C. (eds). *Monks Wood National Nature Reserve: The Experience of 40 years, 1953–1993, Symposium Proceedings* English Nature, Peterborough

Corbet, G.B. & Harris, S. (eds) (1991) *The Handbook of British Mammals* 3rd edition Blackwell Scientific Publications

Corke, D. (1965) Notes on Essex Mammals, 1963–64. *Essex Naturalist* **31:** 273–277

Corke, D. (1974) The comparative ecology of the two British species of the genus *Apodemus* (Rodentia, Muridae). Ph.D thesis, University of London

Corke, D. (1979) The Mammals of Epping Forest. In Corke D. (ed.) *The Wildlife of Epping Forest.* Essex Field Club, London

Corke, D & Harris, S. (1972) The small mammals of Essex. *Essex Naturalist* **33:** 32–59

Cowan, D.P. (1991) The rabbit. In Corbet G.B. & Harris S. (eds)

Cowlin, R.A. (1972) The distribution of the Badger in Essex. *Essex Naturalist* **33:** 1–8

Crouch, W. (1888) Notes on the Whale, Rudolphi's Rorqual (*Balaenoptera borealis* Lesson), and record of a male specimen stranded at Tilbury, Essex, and of a female stranded in the Humber. *Essex Naturalist* **2:** 41–46

Crouch, W. (1891) On a female specimen of the common rorqual (*Balaenoptera musculus*), captured near Burnham. *Essex Naturalist* **5:** 124–128

Dale, S. (1732) *The History and Antiquities of Harwich and Dovercourt.* London

Daniel, W.B. (1812) *Rural Sports.* London

Dent, G. (1907) Occurrence of the Serotine Bat (*Vesperugo serotinus*) in Essex. *Essex Naturalist* **15:** 96

Dent, G. (1922) Badgers in Essex. *Essex Naturalist* **20:** 108

de Winton W.E. (1894) On a neglected species of British field mouse, *Mus flavicollis*, Melchior. *Zoologist* 3rd series. **18:** 441–445

Dobson, J. (1985) Bats in deneholes. In Dobson, J. (ed.) *Essex Bat Group Report* 1985: 8–9

Dobson, J. (1985) Serotine feeding on ground. In Dobson, J. (ed.) *Essex Bat Group Report* 1985: 13

Dobson, J. (1994) Parti-coloured bat. In Dobson, J. (ed.) *Essex Bat Group Report* 1994: 12

Dobson, J. (1997) Bats and Timber Treatment. In Dobson, J. (ed.) *Essex Bat Group Report* 1997: 5–6

Doubleday, H. (1843) The Bats of Epping Forest. *Zoologist* 1843: 6

Dunn, M. & Cousins, S.H. (1997) Fallow Deer in the Epping Forest region: an analysis of the influences on their distribution and the consequences for forest management. *Essex Naturalist* (New Series) **14:** 89–114

Dunstone, N. (1993) *The mink.* T. & A.D. Poyser, London

Ellis, V (1995) Straying whale is saved from a grim end. *Harwich and Manningtree Standard* June 9th 1995

Essex County Council, (1996) *Essex Trends. The statistical profile of Essex and its communities – 1996.* Essex County Council

Evans, P.G.H. (1987) *The Natural History of Whales and Dolphins.* Christopher Helm, London

Evans, P.G.H. (1991) Chapter 9, Whales, Dolphins and Porpoises: Order Cetacea. In Corbet G.B. & Harris S. (eds).

Evans, P.G.H. (1995) Whales, Dolphins and Porpoises. In Barme S.H., Robson C.F., Kaznowska S.S. and Doody J.P. (eds). *Coasts and Seas of the United Kingdom. Region 7.* JNCC, Peterborough

Fisher, J. (1950) The Black Rat, *Rattus rattus* (L.) in London. *London Naturalist* **29:** 136

Fitch, E.A. (1887a) The Badger. *Essex Naturalist* **1:** 114

Fitch, E.A. (1887b) Badgers formerly at Maldon. *Essex Naturalist* **1:** 186

Fitch, E.A. (1890) Rats and Mice in Essex. *Essex Naturalist* **4:** 121–124

Fitch, E.A. (1890) The Marten in Essex. *Essex Naturalist* **4:** 153

Fitch, E.A. (1891) Another rorqual in the Crouch river. *Essex Naturalist* **5:** 134

Fitch, E.A. (1900) The Lesser Rorqual in the Essex Blackwater. *Zoologist* 4th series **4:**517-518

Fitter, R.S.R. (1949) A Check-List of the Mammals, Reptiles and Amphibia of the London Area, 1900–1949. *London Naturalist* **28:** 98–115

Fitter, R.S.R. (1960) Further records of Mammals, Reptiles and Amphibians in the London Area. *London Naturalist* **39:** 18–21

Flower, W.H. (1886) On a Specimen of a Whale, Rudolphi's Rorqual (*Balaenoptera borealis*, Lesson, – *Sibbaldius laticeps*, Gray) lately taken in the River Crouch,

Essex. *Transactions of the Essex Field Club* **4:** 111–115

Flower, W.H. (1887) A herd of red-deer from a single hind. *Zoologist* 3rd series **2:** 344–345

Fraser, F.C. (1974) *Report on cetacea stranded on the British coasts from 1948 to 1966,* No.14. London: British Museum (Natural History)

Fuller, T. (1662) *History of the Worthies of England.* London

Gipps, J.H.W. & Alibhai, S.K. (1991) The field vole. In Corbet G.B. & Harris S. (eds)

Gorman, M.L. & Stone, R.D. (1990) *The Natural History of Moles.* Christopher Helm, London

Greenaway, F. & Hutson, A.M. (1990) *A Field Guide to British Bats*. Bruce Coleman Books, Uxbridge

Groupe Mammalogique Normand. (1988) *Les Mammifères Sauvages de Normandie*. Groupe Mammalogique Normand

Gurnell, J. (1981) Woodland rodents and tree seed supplies. In Chapman J.A. and Pursley D. eds. *The worldwide furbearer conference proceedings.* Donnelly, Virginia, USA

Gurnell, J. (1991) The grey squirrel. In Corbet G.B. & Harris S. (eds)

Harris, S (1973/74) The history and distribution of squirrels in Essex. *Essex Naturalist* **33:** 64–78

Harris, S. & Lloyd, H.G. (1991) The fox. In Corbet, G.B. & Harris, S. (eds)

Harris, S., Morris, P., Wray, S. & Yalden, D. (1995) *A review of British mammals.* JNCC, Peterborough

Harris, S. & Trout, R.C. (1991) The harvest mouse. In Corbet G.B. & Harris S. (eds)

Harting, J.E. (1887) The deer of Epping Forest. *Essex Naturalist* **1:** 46–62

Harting, J.E. (1891) The Marten (Martes sylvatica) in Essex. *Zoologist* 3rd series **15:** 456

Harting, J.E. (1906) Whale at Mersey in 1299. *Essex Naturalist* **14:** 149–152

Heathcote, P. & Heathcote, P. (1994) *The Bats of Kent.* Kent Field Club, Faversham

Hiby, L., Duck, C. & Thompson, D. (1993) Seal stocks in Great Britain: surveys conducted in 1991. *NERC news*, **24:** 30–31

Hills, A (1936) Polecat at Great Waltham. *Essex Naturalist* **25:** 105

Hills, D (1991) Ephemeral Introductions and Escapes. In Corbet G.B. & Harris S. (eds)

Holinshed, R. (1586) *Chronicles* iii: 1315

Holley, A.J.F. & Greenwood, P.J. (1984) The myth of the mad March hare. *Nature* **30:** 549–50

Howes, C.A. (1979) The noctule bat *Nyctalus noctula* in Yorkshire. *Naturalist* **20:** 107–110

Hughes, F. (1986) *A Provisional Atlas of the Mammals of Essex.* Essex Biological Records Centres Publication No. 5. Stratford: Passmore Edwards Museum

Hunford, D.A.J. (1967) Mammal Section Report. *South Essex Naturalist* 1966: 65–66

Hunford, D.A.J. (1970) Mammal Section Report. *South Essex Naturalist* 1969: 58–61

Hunford, D.A.J. (1976) Mammal Report for 1974 and 1975. *South Essex Naturalist* 1975: 40

Hutchings, M.R. & Harris, S. (1996) *The current status of the brown hare (Lepus europaeus) in Britain* JNCC, Peterborough

Hutton, A.B. (1903a) Serotine Bat at Laindon Hills. *Essex Naturalist* **13:** 203

Hutton, A.B. (1903b) Badgers at Mucking. *Essex Naturalist* **13:** 203

Johnston, F.J. (1938) The Grey Squirrel in Epping Forest. *London Naturalist* 1937: 94–99

King, C.M. (1991a) The stoat. In Corbet G.B. & Harris S. (eds)

King, C.M. (1991b) The weasel. In Corbet G.B. & Harris S. (eds)

Laver, H. (1889) The white-beaked dolphin (*Delphinus albirostris*) in the River Colne. *Essex Naturalist* **3:** 169–170

Laver, H. (1898) *The Mammals, Fishes and Reptiles of Essex.* Essex Field Club Special Memoirs No 3

Laver, H. (1903) Mammalia in *Victoria County History of Essex.* **1:** 254–259

Laver, H. (1915) The Distribution of the Polecat (*Mustela putorius*) and the Yellow-necked Mouse (*Mus flavicollis*) in Essex. *Zoologist* 4th Series **19:** 151

Lenton, E.J., Chanin, P.R.F. & Jefferies, D.J. (1980) *Otter survey of England 1977–79.* Nature Conservancy Council, London

Lever, C. (1994) *Naturalized Animals.* T & A.D. Poyser, London

Lloyd, H.G. (1962) The distribution of squirrels in England and Wales, (1959). *Journal of Animal Ecology* **31:** 157–165

Lloyd, H.G. (1970) Variation and adaptation in reproductive performance. *Symposia of the Zoological Society of London* **26:** 165–188

Love R.A. (1998) The analysis of barn owl pellets from the Dengie Hundred, Essex. *The Essex Bird Report* 1996: 125–131

Lubbock, R. (1845) *Observations on the Fauna of Norfolk.* Norwich

Lucas, A. (1997) *Mammals in Carmarthenshire.* Andrew Lucas, Wales

Macdonald, D. (1995) *European Mammals: Evolution and Behaviour.* HarperCollins. London

Mallorie, H.C. & Flowerdew, J.R. (1994) Woodland small mammal ecology in Britain: a preliminary review of the Mammal Society survey of wood mice *Apodemus sylvaticus* and bank voles *Clethrionomys glareolus*, 1982–1987. *Mammal Review* **24:** 1–15

Marsh, A. (1999) *The national yellow-necked mouse survey.* Mammals Society, London.

Matthews, L.H. (1960) *British Mammals* 2nd edition. Collins, London

Mellanby, K. (1971) *The mole.* Collins. London

Middleton, A.D. (1930) The Ecology of the American Grey Squirrel (*Sciurus carolinensis* Gmelin) in the British Isles. *Proceedings of the Zoological Society of London* 1930: 809–843

Middleton, A.D. (1931) *The Grey Squirrel.* Sidgwick and Jackson, London

Middleton, A.D. (1932) The grey squirrel (*Sciurus carolinensis*) in the British Isles, 1930–1932. *Journal of Animal Ecology* **1:** 166–167

Mitchell-Jones, A (1990) The March noctules. *Batchat* **14**: 8–11

Morris, P.A. (1983) *Hedgehogs.* Whittet Books, London

Morris, P.A. (1993) *A Red Data Book for British Mammal,* Mammal Society, London

Morris, P.A., Bright, P.W. & Woods, D. (1990) Use of nestboxes by the Dormouse (*Muscardinus avellanarius*). *Biological Conservation* **51:** 1–13

Neal, E.G. & Cheeseman, C.L. (1991) The badger. In Corbet G.B. & Harris S. (eds)

Newman, E. (1896) The Bats of Epping Forest. *Essex Naturalist* **9:** 134–138

Newman, E. (1874) *The Field.* March 14th 1874: 263

Newton, E.T. (1884) Notes on the bones found in the deneholes in Hangman's Wood. *Essex Naturalist* **1:** 257–259

Oakeley, S.F. & Jones, G. (1998) Habitat around maternity roosts of the 55kHz phonic type of pipistrelle bat (*Pipistrellus pipistrellus*). *Journal of Zoology, London* **245**: 222–228

Owen, C. (1960) The coypu. *Essex Naturalist* **30:** 279

Parsons, B.T. & Middleton, A.D. (1937) The distribution of the grey squirrel (*Sciurus carolinensis*) in Great Britain in 1937. *Journal of Animal Ecology* **6:** 286–290

Pernetta, J.C. (1977) Population ecology of British shrews in grassland. *Acta theriologica* **22:** 279–296

Perrow, M.R., Peet, N.B. & Jowitt, A.J.D. (1992) The small mammals of drainage ditches – the influence of structure. *Transactions of the Suffolk Naturalists Society* **28:** 3–9

Pollard, E. & Cooke, A.S. (1994) Impact of muntjac deer *Muntiacus reevesi* on egg-laying sites of the white admiral butterfly *Ladoga camilla* in a Cambridgeshire wood. *Biological Conservation* **70:** 189–191

Pourreau, J. (1988) Le mesoplodon de Sowerby. In *Les Mammifères sauvages de Normandie* Groupe Mammalogique Normand

Racey, P.A. (1991) The parti-coloured bat. In Corbet G. B. & Harris S. (eds)

Rackham, J. (1979) *Rattus rattus*: the introduction of the black rat into Britain. *Antiquity* **53:** 112–120

Rackham, O. (1986) *The History of the Countryside*. Weidenfeld and Nicholson, London

Rackham, O. (1989) *The Last Forest.* J.M. Dent, London

Ritchie, J. (1927) A long flight – the European parti-coloured bat (*Vespertilio murinus*) in Scotland. *Scottish Naturalist* **1927:** 101–103

Robinson, M & Stebbings, R.E. (1993) Food of the serotine bat, *Eptesicus serotinus* – is faecal analysis a valid qualitative and quantitative technique? *Journal of Zoology* **231:** 239–248

Robinson, M. & Stebbings, R.E. (1994) Changing land – use in south Cambridgeshire: its effect on serotine bats. *Nature in Cambridgeshire* **36:** 62–69

Roer, H. (1995) 60 years of bat-banding in Europe – results and tasks for future research. *Myotis* **32/33:** 251–261

Ross, J. & Sanders, M.F. (1984) The development of genetic resistance to myxomatosis in wild rabbits inBritain. *Journal of Hygiene, Cambridge* **92: 255–261**

Seear, M. (1964) Notes on the Mammals of Essex. *Essex Naturalist* **31:** 176–187

Scott, D.R. (1960) The Badger in Essex. *Essex Naturalist* **30:** 272–275

Scott, D.R. (1969) Notes on Essex Mammals, 1967–68. *Essex Naturalist* **32:** 236–239

Sheail, J. (1971) *Rabbits and their history*. David & Charles, Newton Abbot

Sheldrick, M.C. (1989) Stranded whale records for the entire British coastline, 1967–1986. *Investigations on Cetacea*, **22:** 298–329

Shillito J.F. (1963) Field observations on the water shrew, *Neomys fodiens. Proceedings of the Zoological Society of London* **140:** 320-322

Shorten, M. (1946) A survey of the distribution of the American grey squirrel (*Sciurus carolinensis*) and the British red squirrel (*Sciurus vulgaris leucorus*) in England and Wales in 1944–5. *Journal of Animal Ecology* **15:** 82–92

Skinner, C., Skinner, P. & Harris, S. (1991) The past history and recent decline of Badgers *Meles meles* in Essex: an analysis of some of the contributory factors. *Mammal Review* **21:** 67–80

Smith, R. (1768) *Universal Directory for taking alive and destroying Rats and all other Kinds of four-footed and winged Vermin*

Spooner, B.M. and Bowdrey, J.P. (eds) (1988) *Hadleigh Great Wood The Wildlife and History of Belfairs Nature Reserve*. South Essex Natural History Society

Staines, B.W. & Ratcliffe, P.R. (1991) The roe deer. In Corbet G.B. & Harris S. (eds)

Stansfield, G. (1966) Parti-coloured bat (*Vespertilio murinus* L.) from a North Sea drilling rig. *Journal of Zoology* **150:** 491–492

Stebbings, R.E. (1988*) Conservation of European bats*. Christopher Helm, London

Stone, R.D. & Gorman, M.L. (1991) The mole. In Corbet G.B. & Harris S. (eds)

Strachan, R., Birks, J.D.S., Chanin, P.R.F. & Jefferies, D.J. (1990) *Otter survey of England 1991–1994* Nature Conservancy Council, Peterborough

Strachan, R. & Jefferies, D.J. (1993) *The Water Vole (Arvicola terrestris) in Britain 1989–90: its distribution and changing status.* Vincent Wildlife Trust, London

Strachan, R. & Jefferies, D.J. (1996) *Otter survey of England 1991–1994* Vincent Wildlife Trust, London

Stubbs, F.J. (1923) Remarks on the Squirrels of Epping Forest. *Essex Naturalist* **20:** 205

Sumption, K.J. & Flowerdew, J.R. (1985) The ecological effects of the decline in rabbits (*Oryctolagus cuniculus* L.) due to myxomatosis. *Mammal Review* **15:** 151–186

Tapper, S.C. *et al.* (1982) Effects of mammalian predators on partridge populations. *Mammal Review* **12:** 159–167

Tapper, S.C. (1992) *Game heritage – an ecological review from shooting and gamekeeping records.* Game Conservancy, Fordingbridge

Tapper, S.C. & Parsons, N (1984) The changing status of the brown hare (*Lepus capensis* L.) in Britain. *Mammal Review* **14:** 57–70

Taylor, K.D., Fenn, M.G. & MacDonald, D.W. (1991) The brown rat. In Corbet G.B. & Harris S. (eds)

Taylor, K.D. (1991) The ship rat. In Corbet G.B. & Harris S. (eds)

Thompson, G.L. (1999) *Essex Water Vole Survey 1998.* Environment Agency & Essex Wildlife Trust

Thompson, H.V. (1956) The origin and spread of myxomatosis, with particular reference to Great Britain. *Terre et la Vie* **103:** 137–151

Thompson, H.V. (1968) British wild mink. *Annals of Applied Biology* **81:** 345–349

Thompson, P.M. (1992) The conservation of marine mammals in Scottish waters. *Proceedings of the Royal Society of Edinburgh* **100B:** 123–140

Trout, R.C., Tapper, S.C. & Harradine, J. (1986) Recent trends in the rabbit population in Britain. *Mammal Review* **16:** 117–123

Tucker, D.G. (1948) "Other vertebrates" in Report on the Survey of the Ludgate Plain Area, 1946–7. *London Naturalist* **27:** 73

Twigg, G. (1984) *The Black Death.* Batsford, London

Twigg, G. (1992) The Black Rat *Rattus rattus* in the United Kingdom in 1989. *Mammal Review* **22:** 33–42

Veale, E.M. (1957) The rabbit in England. *Agricultural History Review* **5:** 85–90

Waller, A. (1954) Deer from Asia – in Essex. *The Field* **203:** 78

Watt, H.B. (1923) On the American Grey Squirrel (*Sciurus carolinensis*) in the British Isles. *Essex Naturalist* **20:** 189–204

Watts, C.H.S. (1968) The food eaten by wood mice *Apodemus sylvaticus* and bank voles *Clethrionomys glareolus* in Wytham Woods, Berkshire. *Journal of Animal Ecology* **161:** 25–41

Wheeler, A.C. (1958) Squirrels in Essex. *Essex Countryside* **7:** 28–29

Wheeler, A.C. & May, A. (1992) The Status and Distribution of the Mole in Epping Forest. *The London Naturalist* **71:** 151–155

Whitaker, J. (1892) *A Descriptive List of the Deer-Parks and Paddocks of England.* Ballantyne, Hanson and Co., London

White, G. (1789) *The Natural History and Antiquities of Selbourne, in the County of Southampton.* London (Letter XXVI, dated 8.12.1769)

Whitehead, G.K. (1964) *The Deer of Great Britain and Ireland: An Account of their History, Status and Distribution.* Routledge and Kegan Paul, London

Whitten, A.J. (1990) *Recovery: a Proposed Programme for Britain's Protected Species.* Nature Conservancy Council, Peterborough

Wilson, G., Harris, S. & McLaren, G. (1997) *Changes in the British Badger Population, 1988 to 1997.* People's Trust for Endangered Species, London

Wilson, P.R. (1979) White-beaked dolphin (*Lagenorhyncus albirostris*). *South Essex Naturalist* **1978:** 11

Winter, P. (1983) Mammals and Reptiles of Fingringhoe Ranges. *Nature in North East Essex* **1982:** 98–101

Yalden, D.W. (1977) Small mammals and the archaeologist. *Bulletin of the Peakland Archaeological Society* **30:** 18–25

Yalden, D.W. (1999) *The history of British mammals.* T. & A.D. Poyser, London

Index

The page references are to the main sections concerned with each species. The figures in **bold** are the plate numbers of colour illustrations

Lopinga Books

Lopinga Books specialises in publishing books in association with natural history societies and wildlife conservation trusts.

The Mammals of Essex is the second book in the *Nature of Essex* series. It is published in association with, and in aid of the work of, the Essex Field Club and the Essex Wildlife Trust. These organisations will share a royalty on every copy of the book sold.

The Butterflies of Essex by David Corke

The first book in the *Nature of Essex* Series, *The Butterflies of Essex* was published in association with the Essex Wildlife Trust and the local branch of Butterfly Conservation.

"This thoroughly researched and well produced book provides a useful documentation on the state of butterflies in Essex as well as adding considerably to our knowledge and understanding of butterflies in general." (Atropus, January 1999)

"This is really a superb book, presented in an attractive coloured cover by Gordon Beningfield. Both textually and typographically it is a joy to possess and read." (Bulletin of the Amateur Entomologists' Society, October 1998)

Lopinga Books publications are available through bookshops or direct from:

Lopinga Books
Tye Green House
Wimbish, Saffron Walden
Essex CB10 2XE

e-mail: Lopinga@aol.com
☎ 01 799 599 376

The Essex Field Club

- The Club was founded in 1880 and is the oldest natural history society in Essex.
- It holds field meetings and indoor talks throughout the county to which members and visitors are welcomed. There are about 50 meetings each year, many of which are organised by the Club's Botany, Bird, Fungus, Geology and Mammal groups.
- Club recorders maintain records and organise surveys of 24 groups of plants and animals plus geology. Recorders encourage members to help with this survey work and will help with identifications.
- Club survey work (like the mammal survey on which this book is based) provide the information essential for wildlife and environmental conservation in the County.
- *The Essex Naturalist*, published annually, contains high-quality articles on Essex natural history, geology and prehistoric archaeology plus reports from the Club recorders.
- A quarterly *Newsletter* keeps members in touch with Club activities.
- Details of the Essex Field Club are available from:

Essex Field Club
Department of Life Sciences
University of East London
Romford Road, Stratford
London E15 4LZ

The Essex Wildlife Trust

- The Essex Wildlife Trust is one of the largest of the 46 county wildlife trusts which work together throughout the British Isles as *The Wildlife Trusts*.
- In Essex there are more than 15,500 members who enable the Trust to conduct campaigns for wildlife conservation.
- The Trust protects over 6,500 acres of land on 90 nature reserves.
- Four conservation visitor centres are open (Abberton, Fingringhoe, Langdon, Thorndon Park) and a fifth (at Hanningfield reservoir) will open late in 1999.
- Members receive *Essex Wildlife* and *Natural World* magazines keeping them in touch with conservation work in Essex and throughout the United Kingdom.
- Local groups arrange meetings and activities in all parts of Essex (including those parts of London close to Essex).
- Many members enjoy taking part in work parties to help manage the nature reserves or in other voluntary work with the Trust.
- Information about the Trust is available from:

> Essex Wildlife Trust
> Fingringhoe Wick Nature Reserve
> Fingringhoe, Colchester
> Essex, CO5 7DN
>
> ☎ 01 206 729 678